FUNDAMENTALS OF
Physiology

EVERYDAY HANDBOOKS

FUNDAMENTALS OF
PHYSIOLOGY

REVISED EDITION ·

Elbert Tokay, Ph.D.

Professor of Biology
Vassar College

BARNES & NOBLE, INC. • NEW YORK

PUBLISHERS • BOOKSELLERS • FOUNDED 1873

PRINTED IN THE UNITED STATES OF AMERICA

Preface to the Revised Edition

SINCE THE WRITING of the first edition, the pace of scientific research has been tremendously accelerated, as much in physiology and other biological sciences as in the physical sciences. The increased volume of scientific data and discoveries does not invalidate or overthrow all of our previous concepts and interpretations, however; much of our basic knowledge of anatomy and physiology can still be well applied. On the other hand, there are numerous findings, both large and small, that promote better understanding of this complex topic. In some cases the findings are "revolutionary" in their impact; in other cases they increase the depth of our knowledge, make more precise what was heretofore vague or less precise, and provide the background for different interpretations and speculations.

All of the book has been carefully scanned. Many corrections and additions of new material have been made. There has been much rewriting for different emphasis and organization in an attempt to make the subject matter consistent with up-to-date information and opinion.

The most extensive and notable changes are as follows: new material on the cell (Chapter II); inclusion of material on nucleic acids (DNA and RNA) and their roles in genetics, and in cell multiplication and function (Chapters II, XIV, and XV); new material on blood cells and their formation, blood clotting and transfusions, and control of blood pressure and flow (Chapter IV); reworking of the section on control of breathing (Chapter V); new material on the formation of urine and maintenance of the composition of the blood (Chapter VII); new material on the mechanism of muscular activity, including chemical changes related to this activity (Chapter IX); new material on and explanation of the nerve impulse (Chapter X); complete rewriting and updating of the sections on reflex action and on the functions of spinal cord and brain, including higher mental functions (Chapter X); new material on hormones (Chapter XI) and vitamins (Chapter XIII); new material on and explanation of the chemical activities of cells (Chapter XIV); a new discussion of the genetic code and the passing

on of hereditary information (Chapter XV); new material on sleep
(Chapter XIX); and new material on antibodies and the chemical
treatment of disease (Chapter XXI).

I wish to thank the publishers for affording me the opportunity
for large-scale revision of this book.

October, 1966   E. T.

Preface to the First Edition

THE STUDY of the human body is naturally a subject of the greatest interest to all of us. *Fundamentals of Physiology* aims to give the reader a clear picture of the structure of the body and a clear understanding of the way in which the various bodily systems and organs work.

So far as possible the book progresses from the simpler to the more complex topics. It is therefore particularly desirable that the chapters should be read in order from the beginning to the end, even though the reader may have a special interest in one or another aspect of the subject. The sequence is important because certain chapters can be understood best in the light of information given in earlier chapters; all scientific and technical terms are carefully defined in non-technical language when they are first introduced, and will therefore be readily understood when used later.

The first three chapters provide the background for the book as a whole. Chapter I discusses the meaning, aims, and principles of physiology, and gives a brief introductory account of the main functions and activities of the body, which the later chapters consider fully. Chapter II presents such facts of elementary biology, chemistry, and physics as the reader needs in the study of physiology. Chapter III gives a working outline of the structure and organization of the body as a whole.

Chapters IV through XII constitute the main descriptive part of the book, each chapter dealing with one of the major systems of the body: The Circulatory System (the blood, the heart, the blood vessels—veins and arteries—and the lymphatic system); The Respiratory System (the lungs, the mechanism of breathing); The Digestive System (the stomach, the intestines; other abdominal organs); The Excretory System (the kidneys); The Skeleton (bones and bone structure); The Muscular System (kinds of muscle and action of muscles); The Nervous System (the brain, the spinal cord, nerve fibers, nerve impulses, the senses); The Endocrine System (the glands of internal secretion: thyroid, adrenal, pancreas, pituitary); The Reproductive System (the male sex organs; the female sex organs).

The following chapters (XIII through XXII) are devoted to special topics in physiology of wide importance and interest, such as:

vitamins, minerals, proteins, carbohydrates, fats, diets); ...ism (the body's rate of disposal of foodstuffs, liberation of energy); Growth (the development and repair of body cells); Body Temperature (heat production and heat loss); Movement; Exercise (moderate exercise, strenuous exercise, effects of training); Fatigue, Rest, and Sleep; Coordination of Bodily Functions; Protection against Disease; The Health of the Body.

Throughout the book emphasis is placed on the normal physiology of the average individual. However, abnormal physiological conditions are mentioned when they occur frequently, or when reference to them aids in explaining the normal function or structure. *Fundamentals of Physiology* is concerned primarily with the working of the healthy body.

In the selection and presentation of the material in this book, I have undoubtedly been influenced by the teaching and writing of many physiologists, especially those under whom it has been my privilege to work and study. To them all I should like to express my sincere appreciation.

The illustrations have been prepared especially for this book by Mr. Tanner M. Clark, of the Vassar College faculty. The lettering on the illustrations is the work of another artist. I am extremely grateful to Mr. Clark, not only for his excellent drawings, but also for his valuable contribution to the ideas and designs which are the basis of the drawings. I wish to thank the University of Chicago Press for permission to include ten illustrations redrawn from Carlson & Johnson's *The Machinery of the Body;* and to thank Erpi Classroom Films, Inc. for permission to redraw one of the views from their film, *The Heart and Circulation.* I am also particularly indebted to Dr. Ruth E. Conklin, who graciously consented to read the manuscript and whose suggestions have been most constructive and valuable.

I can only hint at the thanks due my wife, whose assistance in the checking, correcting, writing and rewriting of the manuscript has truly made this book possible.

E. T.

Contents

CHAPTER I

The Subject Matter of Physiology

HAVE YOU ever asked yourself, "What goes on inside me" or "Why am I hungry" or "Why can't I hold my breath over long periods"? If you have, your curiosity is much the same as that which, over the centuries, has prompted men to delve into the mysteries of the body's functions. Until the 18th century, however, little satisfaction of this curiosity was possible. Scientific progress in general was retarded by the reverent acceptance of precepts handed down by ancient authorities. And the scientific method of investigation itself, based on observation of natural phenomena and deductions therefrom was considered blasphemous, and its advocates were subject to bitter persecution.

For about two hundred and fifty years, and especially during the last hundred years, the attitude towards science and attitudes within science itself have been liberalized. With their newly-found social security, all sciences, including the science of physiology, have made tremendous advances. Today, then, much of the veil of mystery that had for so long obscured the workings of the body has been lifted. Although it is true that many questions still remain unanswered, and others have not yet even been asked, it is possible to arrange and interpret facts that have been accumulated in a fashion that enables us to understand many of the things that make us "tick."

The science of biology involves the organized study of all living things. It is made up of a number of daughter-sciences, each of which covers a smaller section of the large field. For example, *anatomy* is concerned with the *structure* of living things; *embryology*, with their *development* from egg to adult. *Physiology* has as its purpose the observation of the *activities* of living things and their parts, and—more important—the explanation of how these activities occur.

Thus, the physiologist must not be satisfied to discover only that a certain activity occurs or is useful to an organism; he must probe more deeply and endeavor to bring to light the *mechanism* behind the activity. Some may question the importance of the latter aspect of the physiologist's job. But when we stop to consider that a prime objective of physiology is the eventual understanding of the body, an understanding that will enable us to prevent or correct flaws in its operation, we can dismiss such an objection.

A physiologist would not be doing his job well if, for instance, he reported that we are able to see because we have eyes; he must investigate how the structures in the eyeball, their nervous connections, and that section of the brain responsible for vision translate light rays into a meaningful image. Only when enough of this knowledge has been obtained can we correct or prevent disturbances of vision. In some cases we can do this now. Eventually it may even be possible to learn how we can improve vision.

The ultimate aim of the physiologist is to uncover the orderly processes which enable men to live and adapt themselves to their environment. It is necessary, therefore, for him to experiment with living things in most cases. Since it is true that in a great many instances experiments on human beings are not feasible or are too dangerous, experiments on dogs, cats, guinea pigs, rabbits, rats, and other animals have been substituted. We owe an eternal debt of gratitude to these humble creatures. Many of our medical treatments have been possible only because of preliminary experimentation on animals. While using these animals, the physiologist is careful not to cause them pain. The use of anesthetics, which eliminate consciousness of pain but allow most other life processes to proceed, makes this possible.

Of course, the physiologist must always keep in mind the possible application to man of his discoveries in lower animals. The ever-increasing number of such applications completely justifies this use of animals. For example, in the past medical men had observed cretinous children (children who we now know are suffering from decreased activity of the thyroid gland) but could do nothing to alleviate their condition if iodine feeding proved ineffective. About the turn of this century, however, it was found that if the thyroid gland were removed from a young dog the animal would develop symptoms quite similar to those of the cretin. In following up these experiments other scientists discovered that feeding thyroid gland or an extract from the gland to such a dog relieved the symptoms and allowed normal development. When the same treatment was subsequently applied to cretinous children, a similar cure was effected.

It is well to keep in mind, however, that not every physiological study, or other scientific study, can become immediately useful in a practical sense. There is often a considerable lag between discovery and application for use. Furthermore, many apparently isolated or impractical scientific facts may be correlated in such a way as to attain practicality or may point the way to other studies of tremendous importance. We can be confident that in the long run most scientific knowledge will prove as valuable as it has in the past.

Another point to recognize is that physiologists believe all the phenomena of life can eventually be explained in terms of physical and chemical processes. This belief may never come to pass for every manifestation of life, but recent events have indicated that such a belief furnishes a better working hypothesis than the theory that life and its processes are "vital" phenomena whose ultimate foundations are beyond the scope of man's understanding.

THE BODY AS A WHOLE

Man, like a machine, needs energy in order to act; he needs energy in order to live, since life always implies action of one sort or another. The energy displayed in various activities of the body is of different kinds—mechanical (as in muscular contraction), electrical (as in nervous impulses), chemical (as in the digestion of food), and heat (as a by-product of various chemical reactions). What is the source of these energies?

Ultimately all forms of and all of the body's energy can be traced to the "burning" of various substances within the body in the presence of oxygen. This burning is similar in some respects to the burning of wood, oil, or coal in which, as you may know, the combination of any one of these fuels with the oxygen of the air is required. This chemical combination of another substance with oxygen is known as *oxidation*.

The substances that the body oxidizes are the breakdown products of the food ingested. Cells must be provided with nourishment and oxygen. We all realize that living in our complex society involves more than merely eating or breathing. Nevertheless it is true (and perhaps so obvious to some people that it is overlooked) that nothing can be done unless men's basic needs are adequately supplied. The object of this book is to acquaint you with these needs in terms of what occurs in the body, how the various parts work together to produce a healthy and physically integrated human being. Let us now take a brief glance at the major activities of the body, remembering that we shall cover the same ground more thoroughly in succeeding chapters. For ready reference, Fig. 1 shows an outline of the body with important internal organs exposed and labeled.

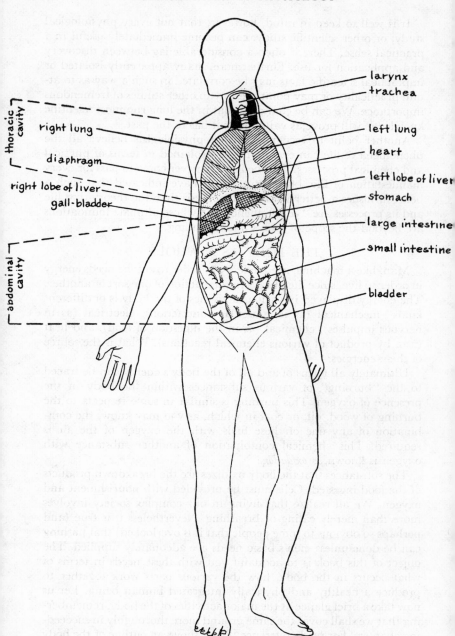

FIG. 1—Diagram showing some of the principal internal organs of the body.

THE SYSTEMS OF THE BODY

All living things are composed of microscopic compartments, *cells*, which serve as the units of both structure and function. Cells of like nature grouped together for a common purpose form *tissues* (muscular, nervous, etc.); various tissues may be gathered into a larger structural unit, an *organ*, which has a specific function (stomach, eye, kidney, etc.); organs whose combined functions fulfill larger needs compose a *system* (circulatory, digestive, excretory, etc.); and, finally, the unified collection of all these parts is the *organism* (man, dog, fish, tree, fly, etc.). All organisms that are many-celled carry on their numerous activities by the principle of division of labor, certain of their parts being specialized for particular uses.

The Digestive System. The food we eat is generally too complex to be immediately available to the cells of the body. As we saw, the fuels of the body are the breakdown products of the food eaten. The function of the digestive system is, therefore, to convert complex food to smaller, chemically simpler substances. When food is swallowed, it passes from the *mouth* into the *pharynx* and then into the *esophagus* or gullet, a muscular tube which transports it to the *stomach*. In the stomach food is churned, broken into smaller particles, and mixed with digestive juices which begin its conversion to simpler substances. The semiliquid, partially digested food is pushed into the *small intestine*, a long, very much coiled tube in which its digestion is finally completed by the action of other digestive juices. The simple products thus produced pass from the cavity of the intestine into the blood stream. From the small intestine the undigested, still somewhat fluid residue proceeds to the *large intestine* where water is absorbed from it. Now in a more solid form it is propelled into the *rectum* for temporary storage until excreted through the *anus*.

The organs mentioned above are all parts of the *digestive tract* or *alimentary canal*, which is fundamentally one long tube from mouth to anus. Other organs—the *salivary glands*, *liver* and *pancreas*—are included in the digestive system, although not anatomical parts of the digestive tract, because they contribute digestive secretions important in aiding the conversion of food to usable materials.

The Circulatory System. The simple products of digestion which pass out of the small intestine into the blood stream must be conveyed to cells all over the body. This is accomplished by the various parts of the circulatory system. We may think of it as a closed system of tubes into which a pump is sealed. Leading from the *heart* are large blood vessels, *arteries*, which progressively subdivide into smaller and smaller vessels. The smallest of these, microscopic in size, are the *capillaries*. Capillaries, much as streams uniting to form rivers, join with one another to form larger vessels which in turn unite with others of their size. The vessels resulting from these unions are the *veins* which lead back toward the heart. The heart is continually pumping blood around this circuit, arteries to capillaries to veins and back to the heart. But how do the nutrient materials travelling within this closed system reach the body cells? From the capillaries these materials together with water "leak out." This watery solution is called *tissue fluid* because it bathes most of the tissue cells in the body. From this fluid, nutrient materials enter the cell. Some tissue fluid returns directly to the blood through the capillary walls while the rest passes into other small tubes, the *lymph vessels*. These merge with one another, larger and larger vessels being formed, and the largest empty into veins. The *lymphatic system* is, then, an accessory part of the circulatory system.

The Respiratory System. Now the cells have received the nutrients they need. But they also require oxygen to change some of these nutrients into a form in which they can release life-giving energy. Air, including oxygen, is sucked into the *pharynx* through either the *nasal* (nose) or *oral* (mouth) cavity and from there into the *trachea* or "windpipe." The trachea subdivides into two tubes, the *bronchi*, each supplying one lung. Air passes down these tubes and through their branching passageways until it reaches tiny *air-sacs* in the lung tissue which are the termini of the smallest bronchial subdivisions. Oxygen in the air-sacs diffuses through their thin walls and those of adjacent capillaries into the blood, while carbon dioxide in the blood diffuses into the air-sacs. Once in the blood, oxygen combines with the *hemoglobin* (the pigment that colors blood red) of the red blood cells and is carried to all parts of the body. In the capillaries of the body tissues oxygen is released by the hemoglobin, passes into the tissue fluid and from there into the cells.

What is the mechanism of inspiration (breathing in)? In order that air may be sucked into the lungs, the chest cavity must be expanded. This is accomplished by the contraction and consequent fall of the *diaphragm* (a muscular partition between the chest and abdominal cavities) and the upward and outward movement of the ribs. The lungs then expand and air is sucked in. Expiration (breathing out) is generally a passive process, the relaxation of the diaphragm and the muscles which caused the rib movements decreasing the volume of the chest cavity and the lungs partially deflating because of their own elasticity.

The Excretory System. With cells in possession of both simple nutrients and oxygen, oxidations occur. There are also many other kinds of chemical reactions that occur in cells, either simultaneously with oxidation or in the absence of oxygen. The energy released by all the reactions is used for many purposes. Part of the energy is used in furthering the chemical work of the cell. In general two types of chemical reactions are proceeding in all cells. One type involves the splitting of large, complex substances to smaller, simple ones. This type (of which oxidation itself is an example) is responsible for the energy produced by cells. The second kind is the building up of complex substances from simple ones and is the basis for the growth or repair of tissues. Not all of the simpler substances produced by splitting reactions are useful to cells; furthermore, even useful substances may be produced in excess of cellular demands. Such waste products, if allowed to accumulate, would impair efficiency or actually harm the body. Most of them diffuse out of the cells in which they are produced into the tissue fluid and then into the blood. The greater part of them, together with water, are filtered from the blood as it passes through the *kidneys*. These wastes in watery solution, after pursuing a tortuous trail through the kidney tubules, make up the urine which is transported from the kidney in the tubular *ureter* to the *urinary bladder*. After temporary storage in the bladder, urine exits from the body by way of another tube, the *urethra*.

The *renal* (kidney) system is the main excretory pathway, but some wastes leave the body by different routes. The lungs, for instance, may be said to excrete carbon dioxide and water (as vapor) in the expired air. The sweat glands in the skin also aid in the excretion of water and salts.

Muscles and Glands. Muscles and glands are the organs which do most of the obvious work of the body, moving parts of the body and secreting essential chemical substances which perform certain necessary functions. The contraction or shortening of muscles is responsible for the movements of our legs, arms, trunk, jaws, etc. Such muscles are attached to parts of the skeleton and bring about movement by pulling a bone into a new position. This kind of muscle is capable of very rapid action. There are other slower-acting muscles which provide for movements of our internal organs. These include heart muscle, muscle in the walls of the digestive tract and in the walls of various tubular structures, such as blood vessels, glandular ducts, bronchi, the ureter, etc. In general these muscles bring about the constriction or dilation of some passageway. Thus they influence such processes as the flow of blood to an organ, flow of air into the lungs and passage of food through the alimentary canal.

In the course of muscular activity heat is produced. Not all the energy produced during muscular activity and recovery is converted into useful work; in fact, the greater portion is given off as heat. In a machine this might be pure waste. In the body it is extremely useful in maintaining the body temperature.

The glands of the body are the chemical workshops that manufacture certain substances essential for the proper functioning of the various organs and for their activities. We have already mentioned the large digestive glands. Smaller glands in the walls of the stomach and small intestine secrete other digestive juices which help to break down the ingested food. Mucous glands secrete mucus which lubricates the linings of many cavities and organs.

Thus far we have become acquainted with some major activities of organs more directly concerned with the maintenance of vital energy. If the other organs and systems are not concerned directly with energy production, what are their roles in the bodily economy? They are fully as important for life as those already discussed. As we shall see, any one system is intimately interrelated with and dependent upon all other systems. The body is a unified whole; isolating its various divisions is a practice whose sole purpose is to expedite investigation and discussion of specific activities. If we think of the organs of the systems outlined above as the machinery by which various activities are carried out, then the nervous and endocrine systems can be considered as the engineers who direct the activities of the machines—stop them, start them, decide which are to be called into activity and at what rate they are to work.

The Nervous System and the Sense Organs. By means of its ramifications the nervous system extends into every part of the body. It can be divided roughly into two sections: the *central nervous system* comprising the *brain* and *spinal cord*, and the *peripheral* (away from the center) *nervous system* consisting of the *nerves* which radiate from the brain and spinal cord to outlying parts of the body. Nerves consist of bundles of fibers along which messages, the *nerve impulses*, are flashed to and from the central nervous system. Many of the nerve fibers leaving the central nervous system end in skeletal muscles and relay impulses to them which cause them to contract. Other fibers extend to muscle in internal organs and to some glands. Impulses in these fibers can initiate or inhibit, accelerate or retard muscular and glandular activities in these regions.

Still other nerve fibers conduct impulses into the central nervous system from various *sense organs* or *receptors*. These latter are structures especially sensitive to certain changes in the environment. We possess receptors for light rays, sound waves, the odor or taste of chemicals, for touch, pressure, pain, heat, cold, and a number of other kinds of environmental change. These sense organs may be located not only on or near the surface of the body but also in the internal organs and in muscles, tendons, and joints. When impulses travel from a receptor to the central nervous system, their information is interpreted in one or more centers; if action is the necessary response, a center relays impulses over outgoing nerve fibers and muscles or glands are stimulated to perform the action. This procedure is the basis of all nervous function and is called *reflex action*.

The brain is the seat of the highest nervous function. Here, in its highest levels, the nervous processes give rise to learning, memory, and ideation; here, too, are the centers for the emotions. With respect to these functions and the nervous influence upon other systems, we can agree that coördination and integration are the prime functions of the nervous system—the control of other organs in such a way as to insure their harmonious coöperation and the welding of all organs and activities into a unified whole, the organism.

The nervous system, then, is responsible in large measure for the close interrelation of organs and systems which is so essential for the proper distribution and control of energy.

The Endocrine System. Not a system in the sense of the systems already discussed, the endocrine "system" is a convenient category into which certain glands are grouped. Some important organs and glands (the liver, for example) discharge their secretions through ducts. The *endocrine glands* (glands of internal secretion) have no ducts and discharge their secretions directly into the blood stream; the wide distribution of these secretions, *hormones*, by the blood enables them to control activities and regions far from their site of production. In general, the endocrine glands, by means of their hormones, coördinate and control bodily activities at a much slower rate than the nervous system. While nervous activity adapts the body to rapid changes in its environment, these glands tend to promote long-term adjustments.

Some glands secrete more than one hormone. All glands are more or less interrelated, affecting and being affected by the activities of one another. Chief among them is the "master" or *pituitary gland* whose hormones control, among other things, growth and the secretions of most of the other endocrine organs. The *thyroid gland* controls the rate of oxidation in all cells of the body. The *parathyroid glands* regulate the amount of "active" calcium in the blood. The *adrenal glands* regulate the amount of other important minerals in the blood. The pituitary, adrenal, and thyroid glands, and the endocrine portion of the *pancreas* all contribute to the control of the amount of sugar oxidized or stored in the body. The *sex glands* or *gonads*, although endocrine structures, will be considered as part of the reproductive system.

Either hyperfunction (increased secretion of hormone) or hypofunction (decreased secretion) of any endocrine gland may lead to serious disturbances and, in some cases, death. For example, hypofunction of the pancreas brings on sugar diabetes; hypo- or hyper-function of the thyroid gland may result in different types of goiter.

The Reproductive System. While the other systems of the body are exclusively concerned with the preservation of life in the individual, this system is responsible also for the perpetuation of the species. Hormones of the pituitary gland are believed to bring on puberty by controlling the growth of the sex glands and the reproductive cells. The *sperm cells* of the male are produced in the *testes*, the *egg cells* of the female in the *ovaries*. When, following copulation, a sperm cell units with an egg cell, the *fertilized egg cell* resulting is the first stage in the life of a new individual.

Once puberty is reached, the hormones of the gonads (testes or ovaries) determine the secondary sex characteristics (distribution of hair, pitch of the voice, etc.). Regulation of sexual phenomena in the sexually mature man or woman is a function of both pituitary and gonadal hormones. This is especially true of women, in whom these two sets of hormones control the sequence of events in the menstrual cycle and during pregnancy.

CHAPTER II

Living Matter

PERHAPS five hundred or more million years ago, life first appeared on earth. We are beginning to see possible ways in which life may have begun; however it did, the first living things were probably gelatinous specks differing significantly from the non-living material about them. The offspring of these things evolved into the multitude of plants and animals that either have populated or now populate the earth. Man was a late arrival, his earliest traces indicating that he has existed for only two to fourteen million years (estimates vary).

THE CELL

As already noted, all animals and plants are made up of micro-scopic compartments, *cells*, which serve as units of both structure and

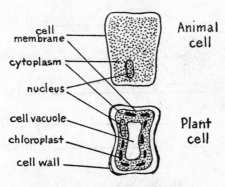

FIG. 2—Animal and plant cells.

function. The name *protoplasm* ("first form") has been given to the substance of which cells are composed.

It has been known since the nineteenth century that the protoplasm of cells is differentiated into a number of parts. All cells have a boundary layer, the *cell membrane*, separating their constituents from the medium surrounding them. Most plant cells, as distinguished from those of animals, have in addition a thick *cell wall* whose rigidity enables them to resist external forces which would change their shape. Most cells, excepting a number of more primitive ones, possess a *nucleus* (Fig. 2) and some have more than one nucleus. The remainder of the contents of a cell (protoplasm minus the nucleus) is called *cytoplasm*.

Also long recognized is the fact that behind the functioning of every living thing lies a highly organized structure. Research during the past twenty-five years has dramatically revealed to us that the preceding statement is true not only for the gross structure of organisms but equally for the interior of a cell. By means of the great resolving power of the *electron microscope* we see intricacies hitherto only suspected at best—membranes extending throughout the cytoplasm, and a variety of complexly structured little bodies (*inclusions*) of differing shapes and sizes. What is becoming quite evident, although we cannot as yet completely correlate our new knowledge of structure with function, is that each part of a cell serves only its own particular functions and that the structure of each part is peculiarly apt for its functions.

THE PROPERTIES OF LIVING MATTER

Protoplasm is unique in that it possesses a certain group of properties with which no combination of non-living substances is endowed.

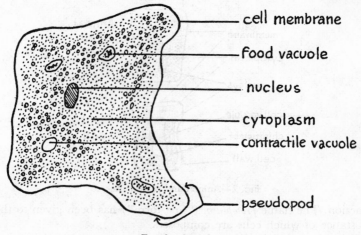

FIG. 3—Amoeba.

To determine the essential differences, let us observe the activities of a simple animal, *Amoeba*. If we place a drop of pond water on a glass slide and focus the lenses of a microscope on it, we can often see a granular, one-celled animal (see Fig. 3). What distinguishes this bit of life from its non-living environment?

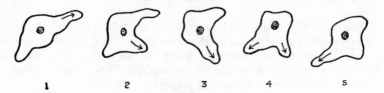

FIG. 4—Successive stages in the movement of Amoeba.

First of all, Amoeba moves (see Fig. 4). One part of its cell membrane bulges out and its granular cytoplasm flows into the bulge. The extension so formed is known as a "false foot" or *pseudopod*. (We shall meet with *amoeboid movement* again as the type of locomotion peculiar to certain white blood cells.) We can illustrate in a number of ways that Amoeba's movements are not aimless, but are reactions to *stimuli* or changes in the environment. If we put a droplet of some harmful chemical in the water, Amoeba moves away from it; if we place food for Amoeba, some plant cells or a droplet of plant cell extract, in the water, Amoeba works its way toward this more pleasant disturbance; if we poke Amoeba with a fine glass rod, it flees the rod. Thus, Amoeba responds to a stimulus—in other words, it possesses *irritability*—and can *adapt* itself to its ever-changing surroundings.

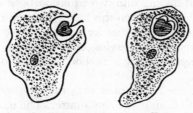

FIG. 5—Amoeba "eats" another one-celled animal.

On further observation Amoeba can be seen to "*eat*" plant cells or other kinds of one-celled animals (see Fig. 5). Note that it encircles the food particle with pseudopods and that a little clear space separates the particle from the surrounding cytoplasm. The little globule of fluid containing the food particle is a *food or digestive vacuole*. While Amoeba pursues its search for more food, within the food vacuole the outline of the particle becomes less and less distinct as it disintegrates. *Digestion* is occurring. Meanwhile the food vacuole drifts through the cytoplasm, digested substances diffusing out to the various parts of the cell. In other words, Amoeba gradually *absorbs* the products of digestion. Later, the vacuole reaches the surface of Amoeba, the cell membrane opens and the undigested residue is left in Amoeba's wake.

Amoeba, like man, needs energy for its activities and depends upon oxidative processes to produce energy. It must, therefore, *respire* —take in oxygen and give off carbon dioxide. We cannot see this happen, but we can show that Amoeba will die if not enough oxygen or if too much carbon dioxide is present.

As Amoeba continues to feed, it *grows*. We can establish this by measuring its dimensions from time to time. The digested food substances are transformed into new living matter.

We know that one portion of the fuel is broken down to supply energy for growth and activity and that waste products are formed in these reactions. These waste products probably diffuse through the cell membrane to the outside. But also note that water diffuses into Amoeba in greater quantities than can be used. The excess water enters the spherical, clear, contractile vacuole—this structure seems to pulsate, swell larger with each pulse, and then suddenly disappear. This vacuole alternately "grows" and "explodes" its contents to the outside. Amoeba can, then, be said to *excrete* waste products and excess water.

Finally, when Amoeba has grown considerably, a series of events occur which culminate in its splitting into two daughter cells. During this process complicated changes take place in the nucleus and the nuclear material divides into two equal portions which move to opposite poles of the cell. When this has been completed, the cytoplasm also halves. The two Amoebas formed are perfect likenesses of their parent, fully capable of carrying on the life processes of Amoebas. Thus Amoeba *reproduces*, by a method common to most cells capable of reproducing.

We have become acquainted with many properties by which we distinguish living from non-living matter. The most characteristic of all, however, we have not as yet mentioned by name. This is *metabolism*, the ability to break down ingested substances into simpler materials and energy, and at the same time to construct from these simpler materials new, complex substances which constitute protoplasm. Amoeba, and all living things, can *metabolize* in this manner. All living things are capable of metabolism, ingestion, digestion, absorption, respiration, excretion, adaptation, growth, and reproduction. Of these functions, metabolism is the most distinctive property and the base from which the others stem.

THE CONSTITUENTS OF LIVING MATTER

Scientific knowledge is constantly increasing; in fact, it is accumulating at an accelerating tempo. This increase in information steadily accentuates the interdependence and interconnections between individual sciences. It is not surprising, then, that the physiologist must draw upon the data and tools of many sciences, biological and physical. Physiology is dependent upon anatomy and other biological sciences. It also relies on chemistry and physics for explanations of the chemical changes and physical phenomena in terms of which we eventually hope to be able to understand all of the body's activities.

For the moment, let us focus upon the chemistry of the cell. But to understand it, we must first become acquainted with some basic chemical concepts.

Some Chemical Definitions. *Chemistry* is the science that describes the composition of substances, their properties and transformations.

Elements are the simplest chemical substances that cannot be broken down further without losing their chemical identity. Altogether, one hundred or more chemical elements are known. Elements can combine with one another chemically; a chemical combination of two or more elements is called a *compound*. This is to be distinguished from a *mixture*, in which case substances are intermingled but not chemically combined. Pure table salt is a compound of the elements sodium and chlorine; pure water, a compound of hydrogen and oxygen. When table salt is dissolved in water, the resulting substance is a mixture of the two compounds.

The smallest particle of an element that retains the chemical identity of the element is an *atom*. Hydrogen atoms differ characteristically from oxygen atoms, oxygen from sodium, etc. Rather than write out words like *hydrogen* and *oxygen*, chemists use symbols— oxygen is O, hydrogen, H. Some atomic symbols are taken from the Latin names for elements. Sodium, *natrium* in Latin, is represented by Na, for example.

Much as elements consist of atoms, compounds consist of *molecules* —the smallest particle of a compound which retains its chemical individuality. Thus, when one atom of sodium (Na) and one atom of chlorine (Cl) unite, one molecule of sodium chloride (NaCl) is formed. The molecular formula of water is H_2O, representing the union of two atoms of hydrogen with one of oxygen. Some molecules are the result of the union of many atoms; a molecule of cane sugar is composed of 12 carbon (C), 22 hydrogen (H), and 11 oxygen (O) atoms and has the formula, $C_{12}H_{22}O_{11}$.

To indicate interactions between molecules or atoms, another shorthand device is used. The reaction of an atom of sodium with an atom of chlorine to form sodium chloride is written:

$$Na + Cl \rightarrow NaCl$$

A more complex example is the formation of glucose (dextrose) from water and carbon dioxide, a reaction which occurs in green plants under the influence of sunlight and chlorophyll:

$$6\ H_2O + 6\ CO_2 \rightarrow C_6H_{12}O_6 + 6\ O_2$$

Note that in these *equations* there are the same number of atoms on each side of the arrows.

The chemical constituents of protoplasm, the substance so fundamental in physiology, are intermingled in a very complex manner.

The Composition of Protoplasm. Protoplasm is made up mainly of the elements carbon, hydrogen, and oxygen, with smaller amounts of nitrogen, phosphorus, sodium, potassium, chlorine, calcium, iron, magnesium, and sulphur also present. The unique characteristics of protoplasm cannot be attributed to the presence of strange elements but must be due, instead, to the complexity of arrangement and combination of these more abundant elements.

Protoplasm contains both *inorganic* and *organic* compounds. Originally, the term "organic" was applied to compounds found only in living things as opposed to the inorganic compounds of the nonliving world. But chemists discovered that it was possible to manufacture some "organic" compounds in the laboratory, thus invalidating the belief that such substances could be formed only in living matter itself. The distinction now made is that compounds containing carbon are called organic and those not containing carbon are called inorganic. Because of their particular chemical characteristics, carbon atoms are capable of combining with other carbon atoms and with atoms of other elements in innumerable patterns, some of which are enormously complex. One result of this is that there are many more known organic than inorganic compounds.

The multitude of compounds and mixtures composing protoplasm may vary quite markedly in different cells of the same organism or in cells of different organisms. All protoplasm, however, includes inorganic substances such as *water* and certain *inorganic salts*, as well as various important types of organic compounds: *carbohydrates*, *fats*, *proteins*, and *nucleic acids*.

WATER. This most common of all liquids constitutes 60 to 99 per cent of all kinds of protoplasm. The adult human body is about 60 to 65 per cent water. Blood, lymph, digestive juices, urine, sweat, and tears are aqueous fluids. All embryos develop in a watery environment. The central nervous system reposes in a watery cushion. Sound and light waves are transmitted to auditory and visual receptors through an aqueous medium. These are a few of the specialized functions of water in our bodies.

The importance of water becomes increasingly evident when we consider its more fundamentally significant properties. Water is the most universal solvent known; that is, it is capable of dissolving more solids, gases, and liquids than any other known substance. This is of great importance in our bodies (and, incidentally, in industry) because substances go into solution by becoming separated into small particles, frequently of atomic or molecular dimensions. Since chemical reactions proceed more quickly and more easily when the reacting substances are in as finely divided a state as possible, the solvent power of water enables the chemical reactions so necessary for metabolism—and life itself—to take place with great facility.

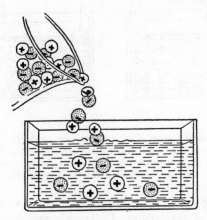

FIG. 6—A diagrammatic representation of the ionization of sodium chloride molecules in water. The sodium (+) and chlorine (−) parts of the molecule separate and become ions when they enter the water.

Certain substances upon dissolving in water give rise to particles of another type; these particles are called *ions*. Ions are electrically charged atoms or groups of atoms. The charge on the ion is negative in some cases, positive in others. Thus, sodium chloride in water *dissociates* or *ionizes* (see Fig. 6) as follows:

$$NaCl \rightarrow Na^+ + Cl^-$$

Ions are important for two reasons. Firstly, ions are more reactive chemically (combine with other chemical entities more readily) than molecules or atoms, which are electrically neutral. Since water promotes ionization, it is an extremely good medium for the consummation of chemical reactions.

In the second place, ion-containing solutions can conduct electric currents. If, from the negative and positive poles of a battery, wires are led to *electrodes* (conductors of electricity, e.g., metal rods) placed in a non-ionized fluid (such as a solution of sugar in water), no current flows between the electrodes. If in the same set-up a salt solution replaces the other fluid, current will flow. Since unlike charges attract and like charges repel one another, the positive sodium ions migrate to the negative electrode and the negative chloride ions to the positive one (see Fig. 7).

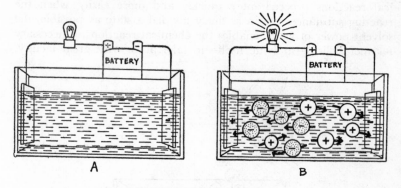

Fig. 7—Conduction of an electric current by fluids. In *A*, no ions are present, the electrical circuit is not complete, no current flows, and the bulb is not lit. In *B*, the moving ions conduct an electrical current, the circuit is completed and the bulb is lit.

Any substance which ionizes in water is called an *electrolyte*. There are three classes of electrolytes. *Acids* yield positively charged hydrogen ions (which give them their sour taste) upon ionization. Thus hydrochloric acid, HCl, ionizes as follows:

$$HCl \rightarrow H^+ + Cl^-$$

Bases or *alkalis* yield negatively charged hydroxyl ions, as in the case of sodium hydroxide, NaOH:

$$NaOH \rightarrow Na^+ + OH^-$$

Salts are neutralization products of acid and base interaction. Hydrochloric acid combining with sodium hydroxide gives rise to sodium chloride and water:

$$HCl + NaOH \rightarrow NaCl + H_2O$$

When dissolved in water, salts yield neither hydrogen nor hydroxyl ions, as shown in the ionization of sodium chloride above. Some substances give rise to both hydrogen and hydroxyl ions when they ionize; water itself ionizes slightly to fall into this category:

$$H_2O \rightarrow H^+ + OH^-$$

The importance of electrolytes in the body will be demonstrated more and more as we proceed.

INORGANIC SALTS. Sodium chloride, potassium chloride, calcium chloride, and other rather common inorganic salts are extremely important constituents of cellular protoplasm and of the body fluids. In our blood, for example, they are found in proportions much like those occurring in sea water. Since living things flourished and evolved in the seas for millions of years before venturing a terrestrial life, it is perhaps not so surprising that we retain this trace of our primitive ancestral environment.

Salts exert a deep-rooted influence upon physiological processes. In some instances salts as a group aid in determining the course of cell activities. By action upon the cell membrane they help to determine *how* substances enter or leave cells and *which* substances enter or leave. In other instances, the positive ions of certain salts have highly specific effects upon bodily activities. Calcium ion (Ca^{++}), for example, is essential for the coagulation of blood and also for the coagulation of milk which precedes its digestion.

CARBOHYDRATES. Used only to a minor degree as structural components of protoplasm, carbohydrates are primarily fuel substances. As we have mentioned, carbohydrates are organic compounds. They are composed of carbon, hydrogen, and oxygen, with two hydrogen atoms to every oxygen atom in their molecules. *Simple sugars* all have the molecular formula, $C_6H_{12}O_6$. The differences among them are due to differences in the arrangement of the atoms in their molecules. *Glucose* or *dextrose* is the most important simple sugar, since it is always present in blood and is the most widely used and readily available fuel substance of the body. *Double sugars*, $C_{12}H_{22}O_{11}$, are formed by the chemical combination of two molecules of simple sugar with the loss of one molecule of water:

$$C_6H_{12}O_6 + C_6H_{12}O_6 \rightarrow C_{12}H_{22}O_{11} + H_2O$$

Sucrose or *cane sugar* is a familiar example of this class. When a number of simple sugar molecules, each having lost a molecule of water, are linked in a chain, a *compound sugar* results. This has the formula $(C_6H_{10}O_5)_n$, where n represents a relatively large number. *Starch*, the stored carbohydrate of plants, is such a sugar, as is *glycogen* or "animal starch." The latter is stored in liver and muscle especially, ready for rapid breakdown to smaller molecules when there is a cellular demand for fuel.

FATS. Although, they, too, serve as fuel substances, fats are generally called into use only after the exhaustion of carbohydrate reserves. In a well-nourished organism we can find fat "depots" in various parts of the body. Pads of fat act as protective cushions for some organs and aid in producing a likable or unpleasing contour of the body; a layer of fat in the skin acts as insulation, thus helping to maintain body temperature.

True fats consist of carbon, hydrogen, and oxygen, but have proportionately less oxygen than carbohydrates (one typical fat, tristearin, has the formula $C_{57}H_{110}O_6$). When broken down into smaller molecules, these fats are found to be made up of only *glycerol* (an organic base) and *fatty acids* (some special organic acids). There are also *fat-like substances*, which include in their molecules other compounds as well as glycerol and fatty acids. Fat-like substances are especially important as components of the framework of cell membranes and certain other structures.

PROTEINS. Of the three large classes of organic compounds, the proteins are most characteristic of living things. Their molecules are extremely large and complex, even when compared with those of compound sugars. On chemical analysis these molecules are found to consist of carbon, hydrogen, oxygen, and other atoms. Of the latter, *nitrogen* atoms are invariably present. Protein molecules consist of long chains of *amino acids*, the simplest of which are fatty acids plus a nitrogen-containing group of atoms. Ingested proteins are eventually reduced to amino acids during digestion, and new protein molecules are formed from them in the cells.

Cells of different tissues in one individual or of the same tissue in different individuals and, especially, in different species, are generally distinct from all others. This specificity of cells is a property of the proteins which constitute the greater part of their structure. The great variety of proteins existing cannot be solely due to the different amino acids in their make-up (there are only twenty-odd amino acids known), but can be better accounted for by the numbers and arrangement of amino acids within the molecule. Although proteins differ greatly, it is true that the more closely animals are related, the more alike are their proteins. Thus, dog and wolf proteins would be much more similar than dog and human proteins.

Ordinarily, proteins are not fuel substances. In starvation, however, when carbohydrate and fat stores are depleted, proteins are burned. When this happens, it indicates that some cells are being destroyed to supply energy for maintenance of life in those which remain.

ENZYMES. Beyond what has so far been said about them, proteins are indispensable to life as *catalysts*. A catalyst is an agent that accelerates a chemical reaction. It is not used up or destroyed in the reaction; thus the same tiny amount of catalyst can function over and over again. Every cell synthesizes catalysts, which are known as *enzymes*, specific to its needs. All enzymes are protein in nature.

Probably in the great majority of cases, the chemical reactions going on in our cells would be inefficient and incomplete in the absence of catalysts. At body temperature, which is comparatively low when compared with the temperatures required for the rapid completion of many chemical processes, our essential chemical reactions would proceed at a slow pace, if at all, were they not catalyzed. Enzymes, because of their acceleration of chemical work at low temperature, are the cornerstones of metabolism.

In general, each enzyme is limited to catalyzing reactions of specific substances or specific groups of substances. A great variety are needed, then, both within and without the cell. Even though intracellular enzymes are quite difficult to isolate, a great deal has been learned about their properties and characteristics. We have already referred to some of the extracellular enzymes, since they are the active principles of the digestive juices.

NUCLEIC ACIDS. As indicated by their name, nucleic acids are found in the nuclei of cells, but we find that they are also present in cytoplasm. The nucleic acids have been very much in the news during the 1950's and 1960's; our understanding of the roles these compounds play in heredity and the maintenance of the living process has been so significantly increased that we can consider this a major breakthrough in biological knowledge.

A nucleic acid has a complex, large-sized molecule composed of many smaller molecules linked together: sugar, phosphoric acid, and four different adenine bases (the latter are nitrogenous substances). The two major kinds of nucleic acid are *desoxyribonucleic* or *deoxyribonucleic acid*, abbreviated DNA, and *ribonucleic acid*, abbreviated RNA; these two differ from each other, first, in that RNA contains *ribose* (a simple sugar with five carbon atoms) and DNA a slightly different five-carbon sugar, *deoxyribose*, and second, in that one of the four bases in DNA is different from its counterpart in RNA.

Each molecule of nucleic acid consists of a "long" strand or backbone of sugar and phosphoric acid molecules strung one after the other in bead-like fashion; attached at right angles to each sugar molecule is one adenine base. Thus, letting S = sugar, P = phosphoric acid, and A, B, C, D = the four adenine bases, structures such as the following would be possible:

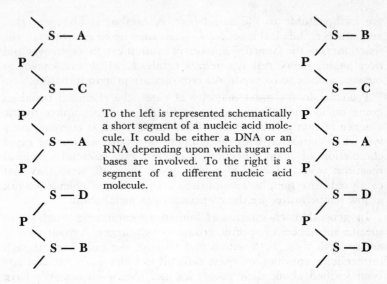

To the left is represented schematically a short segment of a nucleic acid molecule. It could be either a DNA or an RNA depending upon which sugar and bases are involved. To the right is a segment of a different nucleic acid molecule.

The schematic drawings illustrate rather simply that there can be innumerable DNA (or RNA) molecules differing from one another only in the sequence of bases. (Keep in mind that each strand would be very long in proportion to the segment illustrated.)

There is a further complication. Many DNA molecules are double-stranded, the two strands being attached as illustrated below:

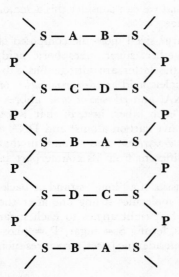

Note that A's are invariably attached to B's, and C's always to D's. Actually, we also know that the two strands are not parallel to each other as indicated here but rather wind spirally or helically about one another.

DNA in most kinds of cells would only be found in their nuclei; it is probably the most important compound in the *genes*, the hereditary units. RNA is found in far greater amount in cytoplasm than in the nucleus; its major role is that of regulator of protein synthesis. We shall examine in greater detail in Chapters XIV and XV how these substances control and contribute to life.

HOW SUBSTANCES ENTER AND LEAVE CELLS

Now that we know something about the composition of protoplasm, we can investigate its physical properties and some physical processes of great importance to the passage of substances into and out of cells. We are especially concerned with the cell membrane, that delicate film which separates the interior of a cell from its external environment, and with the membranes surrounding the nucleus and all other special "bodies" within a cell.

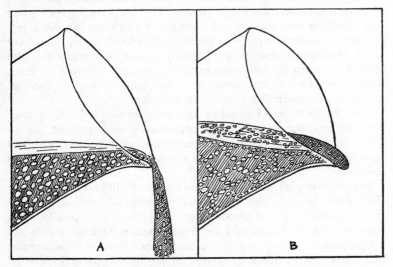

FIG. 8—A possible explanation for *sol* and *gel* states may lie in the arrangement of colloidal particles. Thus, at room temperature (*A*) the particles of gelatin (white circles) may be dispersed at random throughout the water (black); at a cooler temperature (*B*) the gelatin particles may have a definite arrangement which imprisons water. In *A* water is free to move and the fluid sol state is found; in *B* is is not free and the semi-solid gel state is seen.

The Consistency of Protoplasm. Protoplasm is a jelly-like material. It is of this consistency because to a considerable extent, it is a *colloidal solution.* This differs from a *true solution* (like sugar dissolved in water) in that the particles of dissolved substance are much larger in the former, although still not visible under the microscope. Colloidal particles are either very large molecules or groups of molecules lumped together. Because of their physical properties, the solutions which they form may exist in several different physical states. For example, gelatin in water at room temperature is in a fluid state (or is a *sol*), while at a somewhat lower temperature it is semi-solid (or is a *gel*). (See Fig. 8 for a possible explanation of this phenomenon.)

These same states are found in protoplasm, probably because of its protein content. While a considerable portion of protoplasm is in the more amorphous sol state, all of the "formed elements" that we can see microscopically are primarily in the gel condition. The latter implies far greater structural organization than the sol state; more and more evidence does point to a highly organized structure of the cell membrane and the many other intracellular membranes which electron microscopy has made visible. What is, perhaps, even more remarkable is that sol and gel portions of a cell are rapidly interconvertible under the proper conditions. Each cell must, then, have within itself mechanisms which not only control its activities but also control its structure from moment to moment. When and if we learn more about such mechanisms, we may begin to disclose the real nature of protoplasm's amazing adaptability.

The change from sol to gel or vice versa can be effected by temperature or other agents. In the proper salty environment, for instance, a cell which has had its membrane partially torn away can be acted upon by the salts in such a way that the missing section is re-formed.

Permeability of the Cell Membrane. Colloidal particles are electrically charged. This may partially explain why cell membranes are *semipermeable*, i.e., allow only certain substances to pass through them (see Fig. 9). Let us take a specific instance. Red blood cells are not permeable to positive ions, but are to negative ones. If we assume that their cell membranes consist of positively charged colloidal particles, then—since like charges repel one another—positive ions would be repelled and not enter the cell. Negative ions and uncharged particles could and would enter. However, since electrical neutrality within a given region must be maintained (that is, the number of negative charges must equal the number of positive ones), when one negative ion enters a red blood cell, another must leave it.

The above may be the explanation for the impermeability of certain cells to positively or negatively charged particles, but it will not explain all the phenomena of permeability. It is generally true that large molecules will not enter cells, while smaller ones do. So, cells are not permeable to proteins but are to their breakdown products, amino acids. This suggests that cell membranes are porous and that the size of their pores determines the size of particles which may pass through them.

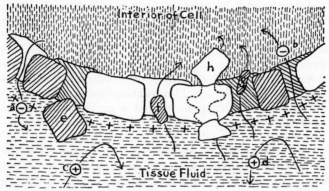

FIG. 9—Permeability of the cell membrane. On the assumption that the cell membrane is composed of protein (striped) and fat-like (white) compounds arranged in "blocks" separated by varying distances and that is has an electrically charged outer surface, it is possible to pictorialize its "acceptance" or "rejection" of substances. In this instance the positive charge on the membrane repels positively charged substances (*c* and *d*); negatively charged substances (*a* and *b*) enter and leave the cell with ease. A large protein molecule (*e*) cannot enter through the "pores" of the membrane, but smaller molecules (*f* and *g*) can. A fat-soluble molecule (*h*) can dissolve in the fat-like part of the membrane and ooze into the cell.

However, certain relatively large molecules do penetrate cells and other smaller ones do not. In some cases we find that these larger molecules are more soluble in fat than in water. When we remember that fat-like substances contribute to the structure of the membrane, we can postulate with some degree of certainty that fat-soluble molecules dissolve in the fatty part of the membrane to enter or leave a cell.

Finally, there are cases in which we do not know how it is that some substances penetrate easily, others with difficulty, and still others not at all. What is becoming somewhat clearer is that in many instances cells can take in or discharge materials by a process known as *active transport*. This can only occur while a cell is alive; it involves expenditure of energy by the cell (in the performance of work). In some cases a particular substance may, by attachment to a membrane constituent, be "pulled through" or "pumped out" of a membrane. In other cases a substance may be engulfed and "swallowed" in a manner akin to ingestion of food by an Amoeba.

Diffusion. *Diffusion* is one of the processes by which particles move into and out of cells. All molecules are in continual motion, whether they are in the gaseous, liquid, or solid state. These physical states of matter merely denote how much freedom of movement molecules have. Molecules in a lump of sugar do not have much freedom of movement, but, when the lump is placed in water, it dissolves and its freed molecules disperse themselves throughout the water (see Fig. 10). This movement of molecules is known as diffusion. It occurs whenever molecules are free to move and it involves their passage from a region of greater to a region of lesser concentration (number of particles per unit of volume). This will continue until the concentration in both regions is equal. Should a membrane separate two regions of different concentration, it will offer no hindrance to diffusion unless it is impermeable to the substance concerned.

Diffusion is an essential transport process in the body. Oxygen diffuses into blood capillaries from the air-sacs of the lungs, it being of greater concentration in the sacs. Carbon dioxide diffuses in the opposite direction since its concentration is greater in blood than in the air-sacs. All digested materials to which cells are permeable diffuse from blood to tissue fluid and then into the cells, while waste products of cellular metabolism diffuse in the reverse direction.

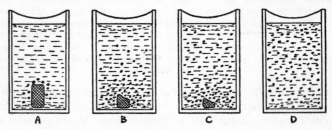

Fig. 10—A lump of sugar gradually dissolves in water. Its molecules slowly diffuse until, after some time, they are equally dispersed throughout the water.

Filtration. Whenever material is *forced* through a membrane, we call the process *filtration*. This always implies the imposition of some force greater than that of inherent molecular energy on one side of a membrane. For example, the blood pressure (set up by the pumping of the heart and other factors) forces water and certain dissolved substances to filter from the blood inside capillaries into the fluid outside the capillary walls.

Osmosis. When a semipermeable membrane is interposed between two solutions of different concentration and at least one substance in solution cannot penetrate the membrane, a special kind of diffusion occurs. Let us imagine a protein solution (e.g., a solution of egg white) on one side of a semipermeable membrane and only water on the other side (see Fig. 11). The membrane is readily permeable to water but not to protein. After some time has elapsed, we will find that the level of the solution has risen and that of the water has fallen. Evidently water has passed through the membrane into the solution. This movement of water from a region of *lesser concentration of dissolved substance* through a *semipermeable membrane* to a region of *greater concentration of dissolved substance* is called *osmosis*. In Fig. 11, water will no longer pass from A to B when the height of the column of solution exerts enough pressure (due to its weight) to cause as much water to filter out of the solution as passes into it by osmosis. The difference in height between the two columns represents the *osmotic pressure*. Osmotic pressure is determined by the number of particles that are unable to penetrate a semipermeable membrane. Therefore, the greater the concentration of protein, the greater the osmotic pressure and the osmotic flow of water.

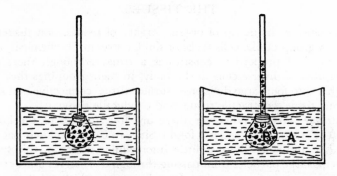

Fig. 11—Osmosis. The black dots represent protein particles which cannot penetrate the membrane. For full explanation, see text.

Note that here, as in all instances of diffusion, there is movement of molecules in that direction which will promote equalization of concentration throughout the system and which results in an equilibrium between its parts. Equilibrium in every such case is dynamic rather than static: that is, in this instance, once equilibrium is attained, water will continue to pass in, but *at the same rate* as it passes out.

If we placed Amoeba in pure water, it could not live. Many of its protoplasmic constituents cannot penetrate its membrane, but water can. Therefore, water would pass into the animal until the internal pressure on the membrane increased enough to tear it apart. Our cells would die similarly if only water were present about them.

CHAPTER III

The Organization of the Body

SINCE KNOWLEDGE of function does depend on knowledge of structure, let us investigate in a general way the parts of the body, their structural interrelationships, and their adaptation to their functions.

THE TISSUES

Systems are made up of organs, organs of tissues, and tissues of cells. A group of like cells (cells of similar structural, chemical, and physiological properties) constitutes a *tissue*. Although there are multitudes of diverse cells in the body, in their groupings they fall roughly into four large divisions—surface tissue, connective and supporting tissue, contractile tissue, and conductile tissue.

Surface Tissue. Wherever there are free surfaces in the body, "surface" tissue or *epithelium* is found. Since its cells are closely packed together and since there is little intercellular material, this tissue prevents large particles from passing through it. It serves quite often, then, as a protective covering. Its cells may be thin and flat (*squamous*), cube-shaped (*cuboidal*), or taller than wide (*columnar*); they may be found in single layers or several layers thick. Thus, the inner lining of blood vessels consists of a single layer of squamous cells, the kidney tubules are lined with a single layer of cuboidal cells, and the intestines with a single layer of columnar cells, while the outer part of the skin consists of stratified epithelium which contains layers of all three types of cells. (See Fig. 12, A-F.)

Epithelial cells of the three basic types are often modified and can perform specialized functions. Single or many-celled glands are epithelial derivatives. Columnar cells may be found with hair-like processes or extensions (*cilia*) protruding from their free ends. In the trachea, for instance, the cilia of the columnar lining are continually in motion and help to prevent foreign particles in the inspired air from getting down into the lungs.

28

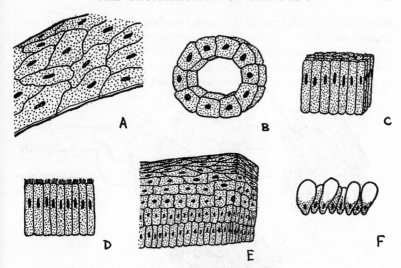

FIG. 12—Surface tissues: *A*, squamous; *B* cuboidal; *C*, columnar; *D*, ciliated columnar cells, *E*, stratified epithelium; *F*, single-celled glands (the clear spaces represent the places in the cells where the secretions are stored until they are discharged).

Connective and Supporting Tissue. There are a number of kinds of this tissue characterized by widely separated cells embedded in an abundant non-living intercellular material. This material, the *matrix*, is produced by the cells and is responsible for the connective or supporting function. The various connective and supporting tissues can be classified with reference to the type of matrix each contains.

THOSE WITH LIQUID MATRIX. These tissues are *blood* and *lymph*, which will be discussed more fully in Chapter IV.

THOSE WITH SEMILIQUID MATRIX. *Loose fibrous connective tissue* (see Fig. 13 A) is the most widely distributed type of connective and supporting tissue. It extends into and around almost all the organs of the body. If it were possible to preserve this soft tissue only, as it is distributed throughout the body, we should have a practically complete reproduction of the body, its external contours, and the position and shapes of almost all its internal organs. Note the "white" and "yellow" fibers in the matrix which impart strength and elasticity respectively to the tissue.

Adipose or *fat tissue* may be considered a modified loose connective tissue in which the cells assume greater importance. Stored globules of oil occupy the greater part of each cell, pushing the nucleus and cytoplasm to the periphery of the cell (see Fig. 13 B). Fat tissue is found in many regions of the body, but especially under the skin, around the kidneys, and in the connective tissue membranes which hold the abdominal organs in place. Most fat depots can be called upon by the body in time of need, but some are primarily protective in nature (as in the eye-socket) and do not serve as fuel stores.

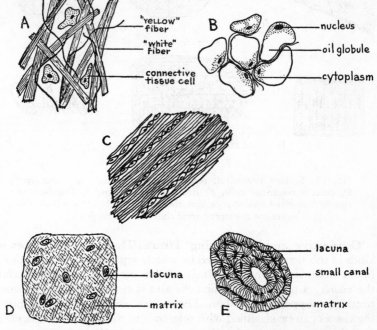

Fig. 13—Connective and support tissues: *A*, loose fibrous connective tissue; *B*, fat tissue; *C*, tendon; *D*, hyaline cartilage; *E*, bone.

Dense fibrous connective tissue has the same elements in its composition as has loose, but they are arranged differently (see Fig. 13 C). Here the fibers and cells line up parallel to one another. This structure increases the tensile strength of the tissue and orients its elasticity along a definite axis. *Tendons*, which connect muscle to bone, and *ligaments*, which connect bone to bone, are made up of this tough connective tissue.

THOSE WITH SOLID MATRIX. *Cartilage* is familiar to most of us as gristle. It is a supporting tissue whose function is to withstand pressure. Its matrix is solid but possesses the same types of fibers as the connective tissues. In some cases, however, the fibers are so fine and so tightly packed as to be invisible microscopically unless specially treated with chemicals (see Fig. 13 D). *Hyaline* cartilage (so called because of its apparently clear, homogeneous matrix) is found in the nose, larynx, trachea, and other places. *Elastic* cartilage makes up much of the ear. *Fibrous* cartilage is especially prominent in the discs between the vertebrae of the spinal column. The cartilage cells are found in *lacunae* ("lakes") within the matrix. Since cartilage contains no blood vessels, its cells are apparently nourished by the diffusion of substances from adjacent tissues through the matrix.

Bone has a structure somewhat resembling that of cartilage (from which it develops in many instances). Its cells, too, are found in lacunae which are arranged in concentric circles about canals which run lengthwise. From the canals, which contain blood vessels, tiny canals radiate to the lacunae and others pass between lacunae (see Fig. 13 E). By means of these small passageways bone cells receive nourishment and get rid of waste materials. The matrix of bone is hard and rigid because of its impregnation with the inorganic salts, calcium carbonate, and calcium phosphate. Bone makes up the skeleton of most adult vertebrates. We may also find *osseous tissue* outside the skeleton, as in the knee cap.

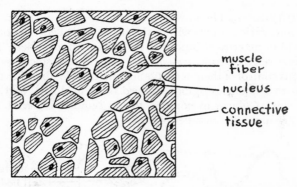

muscle fiber
nucleus
connective tissue

FIG. 14—Cross-section of part of a skeletal muscle. The connective tissue (white) separates the muscle fibers into bundles.

Contractile Tissue. Contractility is a property of all protoplasm but has developed to such an extent in *muscular tissue* that it is its distinguishing characteristic. We can recognize three kinds of muscle— *skeletal*, *smooth*, and *cardiac*.

SKELETAL MUSCLE. This type of muscle—which brings about movements of our limbs, trunk, eyes, jaws, and face—is also spoken of as *voluntary* muscle since we have conscious control of its activity. If we dissect a leg muscle (see Fig. 14) for instance, we discover that it is enclosed in a tough sheath of dense fibrous connective tissue and that connective tissue strands extend into the muscle, dividing it into bundles of muscle "fibers." (Muscle cells are called fibers because they are much longer than wide, some attaining a length of as much as two inches.) Each muscle fiber includes in its cytoplasm a number of fibrils consisting of alternate dark and light bands. These parallel each other so that the dark bands fall one beneath the other and the light ones likewise. This gives the fiber a cross-striated appearance (see Fig. 15 *B*). Each fiber contains many oval nuclei which may indicate that in the embryo many cells unite to form one adult muscle cell.

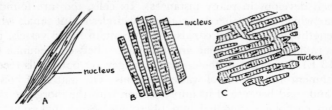

FIG. 15—Contractile tissue: *A*, smooth muscle fibers; *B*, skeletal muscle fibers; *C*, cardiac muscle.

SMOOTH MUSCLE. The muscle fibers in the digestive tract, in blood vessels and various ducts within the body are called "smooth" since they exhibit no cross-striations as in skeletal muscle fibers. They are also often referred to as *involuntary* muscle fibers, since we have no conscious control of their activity. Smooth muscle fibers have but one nucleus to a fiber, are spindle-shaped (see Fig. 15 A), and interlace into sheets of fibers, in contrast to the bundles of skeletal muscle which are more like bundles of sticks.

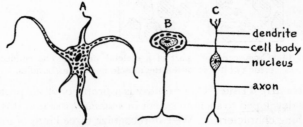

FIG. 16—Conductile tissue: *A*, multipolar neuron; *B*, unipolar neuron; *C*, bipolar neuron.

CARDIAC MUSCLE. In many of its properties heart muscle is intermediate between smooth and skeletal muscle. Its striated appearance is similar to that of skeletal muscle, but, like smooth muscle, it cannot be voluntarily controlled. It differs from both in the arrangement of its fibers. While cardiac muscle does consist of separate cells, they are structurally related to one another in such a way that they function as a network of cells (see next chapter).

Conductile Tissue. All protoplasm is irritable and responds to a stimulus by setting up a disturbance which is then conducted away from the point of stimulation. Nerve cells or *neurons*, as compared with other sorts of cells, have greatly increased properties of sensitivity and conductivity.

Neurons are of various sizes and shapes (see Fig. 16), each cell possessing a *cell body* (nucleus plus the major part of the cytoplasm) and *cell processes* (extensions of the cytoplasm). They can be classified according to the number of processes they possess—one (*unipolar*), two (*bipolar*), or more (*multipolar*). The cell processes are named *axons* and *dendrites*. Collections of these processes constitute the *nerves*, which extend to all parts of the body, and the nerve *tracts*, or pathways, whicn run up and down the central nervous system (brain and spinal cord).

THE STRUCTURE OF THE BODY

The science that deals with the fine structure of tissues is known as *microscopic anatomy* or *histology*. The science that studies larger structural aspects is called *gross anatomy*. Let us turn our attention to the gross anatomy of the body.

The More Superficial Organs. The first organ that we encounter is the elastic, semi-transparent *skin* (see Fig. 17) which covers the entire surface of the body. The skin and its modifications and accessory structures such as *nails* and *hair* act as a protective coating.

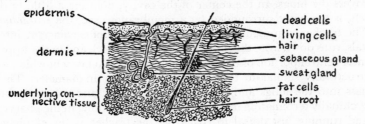

FIG 17.—A microscopic cross-section of the skin.

It is relatively resistant to injury and, unless broken, its outermost layer of stratified epithelium serves as an effective barrier against bacterial invasion. The skin is continuous with the *mucous membranes* (so called because they contain glands which secrete *mucus*) which line cavities (such as the oral, nasal, anal, etc.) communicating with the exterior. There are two zones of the skin, the outer *epidermis* and the inner *dermis*. The former is protective in function, the greater part of its thickness being occupied by dead epithelial cells. These are continually being scraped off from surface layers and then are replaced by multiplication of living cells below. The dermis is an intermingled mass of connective tissue, blood and lymph vessels, sweat and sebaceous (oil-producing) glands, and roots of hairs. In both zones many sensory nerve-endings are found, either free or leading from a particular sense organ.

Beneath the skin is a layer of connective tissue, including much fat tissue. This connective tissue serves to bind the skin closely to muscles or bone lying below, while the fat acts as insulation.

In most regions of the body the next organs that come to view are the skeletal muscles (see Fig. 77), attached to bone or overlying skin by tendons. The skeleton (see Fig. 74) lies beneath the muscles, forming the rigid framework of the body.

The Internal Organs. The interior of the body is made up of three cavities in which are found the *viscera* or internal organs.

THE CRANIAL CAVITY. The space within the skull which is filled almost completely by the brain is called the *cranial* cavity. The skull, the membranes surrounding the brain, and the watery cushion enclosed within the membranes are normally adequate protection for the brain.

THE THORACIC CAVITY (see Figs. 1, 18, 19). Within the *thorax*, or chest, is the *thoracic* cavity, containing the heart and lungs. This cavity is enclosed in the bony protective cage formed by the thoracic part of the backbone, the ribs, and the breastbone. The cavity is lined by a membrane, the *pleura*, which folds upon itself and also covers the lungs. In the center of the cavity, pointing a little to the left, is the heart surrounded by a membranous sac, the *pericardium*. The trachea, a muscular tube containing rings of cartilage at intervals, runs down from the pharynx through the neck and in the uppermost central portion of the cavity divides into two bronchi which are structurally similar to the trachea, but smaller in diameter. These pass into the lungs and break up into smaller and smaller tubes, eventually terminating in the air-sacs. Also beginning in the pharynx, and running just dorsal to (back of) the trachea is the esophagus which, on its way to the stomach, passes through the thoracic cavity behind the heart and in the mid-line of the cavity.

THE ABDOMINAL CAVITY (see Figs. 1, 18, 19). Separating the thoracic from the *abdominal* cavity is the *diaphragm*, a thin membrane of skeletal muscle.

In the *abdomen* are most of the digestive organs. Lying mainly on the right side just beneath the diaphragm is the liver, the largest gland in the body (it is red-brown in color). On the left side, opposite the liver, the esophagus connects with the somewhat pear-shaped stomach which in turn leads into the many-coiled small intestine.

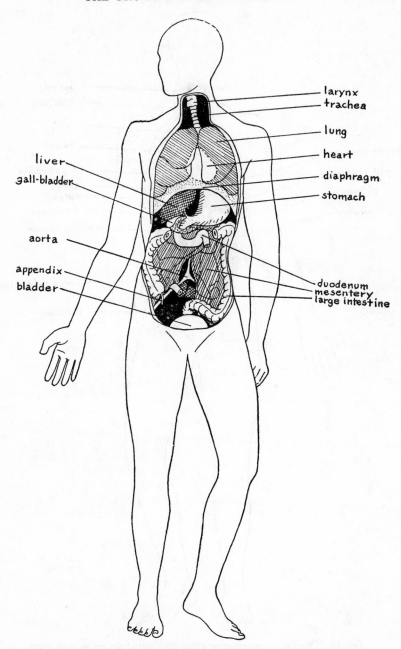

larynx
trachea
lung
heart
diaphragm
stomach

liver
gall-bladder

aorta

appendix
bladder

duodenum
mesentery
large intestine

FIG. 18—Diagram showing the abdominal organs as seen after removal of parts of the intestines. Compare with Fig. 1.

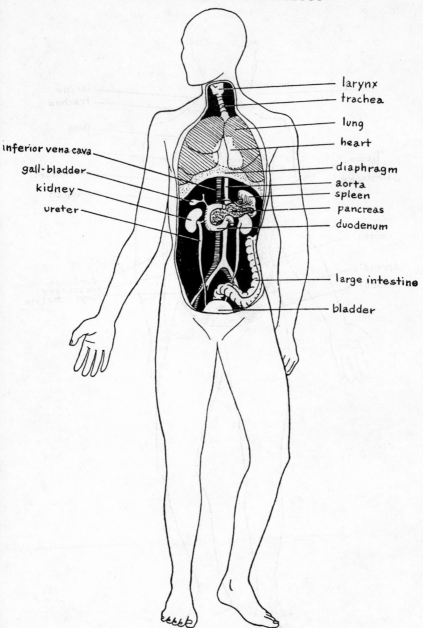

larynx

trachea

lung

heart

inferior vena cava

gall-bladder

kidney

ureter

diaphragm

aorta

spleen

pancreas

duodenum

large intestine

bladder

FIG. 19—Diagram showing some other abdominal organs as seen after removal of most of the larger ones. Compare with Figs. 1 and 18.

The latter occupies most of the central part of the cavity. At its end the large intestine begins. This organ first ascends on the right side of the cavity, turns at right angles, crosses to the left side, and descends, enclosing the small intestine on three sides. The large intestine empties into the rectum in the lower part of the cavity. At the junction of stomach and small intestine and running alongside the latter for a short distance is an elongated mass of pinkish-white tissue, the pancreas. From stomach to rectum the digestive tract is unattached except for a thin membrane, the *mesentery*, which, to some extent, anchors it to the back wall of the cavity. On either side of the cavity, high in the back, are the bean-shaped kidneys from which the two ureters descend to empty into the bladder, a muscular sac capable of great distention, located in the lowermost mid-part of the cavity. Covering all the organs in the abdominal cavity and lining its walls is a membrane similar to the pleura, the *peritoneum*.

Other Organs. No mention has been made of the many blood and lymph vessels and nerves which travel to almost all regions of the body (Figs. 20 and 84). Something will be said of these later on. The spinal cord lies within a cavity in the vertebral or spinal column, protected in the same manner as the brain.

The various glands of the endocrine system (see Fig. 131) are distributed widely. The pituitary gland hangs from the under surface of the brain. The thyroid gland rests on either side of the larynx, a thin strand crossing the mid-line to connect its two lobes. The parathyroids are embedded in the thyroid tissue and are quite small. The adrenal glands lie atop the kidneys within the large body of fat generally found about these organs. The pancreas has already been mentioned.

The principal reproductive organs (see Fig. 132) in the male, the testes, are found in the scrotal sac outside the abdominal cavity. The female reproductive organs (Fig. 134) are located within the abdominal cavity. The ovaries, one on either side, communicate with the centrally placed uterus by means of the long oviducts.

CHAPTER IV

The Circulatory System

IN ONE-CELLED ANIMALS, such as Amoeba, the problem of distributing foodstuffs and eliminating wastes is simply solved. Once food is ingested and digested, it diffuses to all parts of the cell; waste products diffuse out of the cell. In some of the simpler many-celled animal forms the problem remains essentially the same—each cell is either on the external surface of the animal or borders on a large body cavity which communicates with the exterior. Simple diffusion is still an effective means of distribution and elimination. But this sort of arrangement limits the size and complexity of the organism. In larger, more complex animals many cells are too distant from the food supply to permit effective diffusion of nutrients to them. Another system had to evolve, and this system is the more familiar arrangement of vessels ramifying throughout the body which we recognize as the circulatory system. Through these vessels flows the blood which not only transports materials to and from cells but, by the process of giving rise to the tissue fluid, also determines what the immediate environment of the tissue cells is to be.

THE BLOOD

The collecting of human blood is now a simple procedure. For this reason blood is more accessible to study than other bodily constituents. Blood is also more normal in appearance when examined outside the body than are other bodily constituents which cannot be preserved as easily as blood can.

Blood in a test tube appears to be a red, thickish fluid of the same consistency throughout. When observed under the microscope, however, it is seen as a watery fluid containing many cells. The cells are distinguished as *red blood cells* or *white blood cells*. These cells and some cell fragments, the *platelets*, are collectively spoken of as the *formed elements*. The liquid portion is the *plasma*. (See Fig. 21)

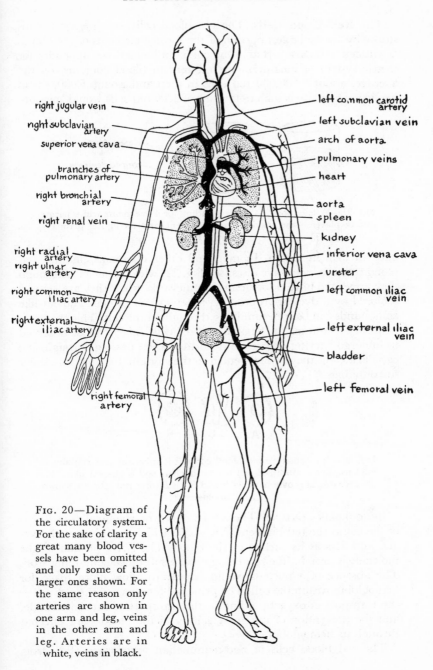

right jugular vein

right subclavian artery

superior vena cava

branches of pulmonary artery

right bronchial artery

right renal vein

right radial artery

right ulnar artery

right common iliac artery

right external iliac artery

right femoral artery

left common carotid artery

left subclavian vein

arch of aorta

pulmonary veins

heart

aorta

spleen

kidney

inferior vena cava

ureter

left common iliac vein

left external iliac vein

bladder

left femoral vein

Fig. 20—Diagram of the circulatory system. For the sake of clarity a great many blood vessels have been omitted and only some of the larger ones shown. For the same reason only arteries are shown in one arm and leg, veins in the other arm and leg. Arteries are in white, veins in black.

The Red Blood Cells. The red blood cells, or *erythrocytes*, constitute by far the largest portion of the formed elements of the blood.

NUMBER, SIZE, STRUCTURE. One cubic millimeter (see appendix for metric system of measurements) of human blood contains, on the average, about 5,500,000 red cells in men and about 5,000,000 in women. Their size is such that a row of 3200 red cells would measure

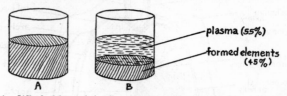

FIG. 21—Whole blood (*A*) after standing for a few hours will separate into two layers—the heavier formed elements and the lighter plasma—as seen in *B*.

only an inch in length. In man and other mammals, mature red blood cells are biconcave discs (see Fig. 22) with no nuclei. Although they appear to have no structural framework, when they are stained (colored by a dye) appropriately, a network of protein and fat-like compounds can be seen ramifying throughout the cell. This structure helps to account for the flexibility of red cells. They can be observed to undergo varying degrees of distortion when passing through fine capillaries, yet they always return to their original shape in roomier surroundings.

FIG. 22—An immature red blood cell (*C*) is spherical and contains a nucleus. The mature red cell has no nucleus and is shaped like a biconcave disc as shown in views *A* and *B*. In *B* three red cells are shown on edge.

HEMOGLOBIN CONTENT. The most important chemical constituent of the cell is the red pigment, *hemoglobin*, which combines with oxygen and acts as its carrier in the blood. The *globin* portion of the molecule is protein, the rest being *heme*, a substance containing iron. The absence of a nucleus would appear to allow more space for hemoglobin within the cell. The principal functions of the red cell— the transport of oxygen, aiding in the transport of carbon dioxide, and the prevention of too great acidity of the blood—are effected through its hemoglobin.

The red blood cells of non-mammalian vertebrates (fish, frog, snake, bird) are nucleated and of larger size than mammalian cells. Mammalian cells are favored by these differences. They contain more hemoglobin per unit of volume and have a greater proportional surface area than non-mammalian ones. Since the surface area is one factor limiting the extent to which diffusion and osmosis can occur, the greater the surface area, the more easily these processes can take place. Since the processes of diffusion and osmosis, as well as the compound hemoglobin, play important roles in the functioning of the red cells, the greater efficiency of mammalian red cells is evident.

THE LIFE-CYCLE OF THE RED CELL. It has been calculated that red cells in the blood stream live about 120 days. Since the red cell count remains comparatively *constant*, this implies that there must be processes of formation and destruction of red cells proceeding at equal rates. Red cells are produced chiefly by the *red bone marrow*. If a flat bone, such as a rib, is split open, a reddish tissue is seen. The same type of tissue is found at the ends of long bones, like the thigh bone (see Fig. 76). Upon microscopic examination of red marrow all stages in the development of the red cell are seen. Primitive connective tissue cells are the precursors of red cells. As these cells divide and multiply a series of stages results, all of which are nucleated. Late in the series hemoglobin appears and the nucleus is expelled, the resulting mature red cell passing into the blood stream. From blood passing through the liver and spleen some red cells are seized upon, devoured, and destroyed by cells which ingest and digest them much as Amoeba does its food. Such destruction is continually occurring, but the criteria for selection of red cells by these destroyers are not known.

The hemoglobin liberated from the destroyed cells is broken down in these liver and spleen cells. The destination of the globin fraction is unknown. The iron from the heme is usually carefully conserved by the body; it may be transiently stored, but it is eventually transported to bone marrow to be reincorporated into new hemoglobin molecules. The rest of the heme is converted into *bile pigments* in the liver. These pigments enter the small intestine via the bile duct and are eventually eliminated in the feces.

By estimating the amount of red cell destruction each day and the age limit of the cells, one can arrive at the astounding conclusion that 200,000,000 red cells must be produced every minute.

HEMOLYSIS (see Fig. 23). When red cells are placed in water, they swell and finally burst. Even as they swell, their hemoglobin is diffusing out. This separation of cell contents from cell framework is known as *cytolysis* in general and *hemolysis* with reference to red cells. If red cells are placed in 0.9% saline solution (0.9 grams of table salt per 100 cc. of water), they remain unchanged. In this latter case no hemolysis occurs because the concentration of salt in the solution is the same as the total concentration of salts in the plasma and in the red cell itself. There is, therefore, the same osmotic pressure on each side of the semipermeable cell membrane. In the first instance above, the osmotic pressure is much lower outside than inside the cell, water passes inward, and hemolysis results. If cells were placed in 2% salt solution, the osmotic pressure would be less inside, water would leave the cell, and the latter would shrink and shrivel.

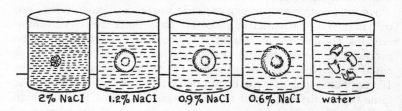

2% NaCl   1.2% NaCl   0.9% NaCl   0.6% NaCl   water

Fig. 23—The volume of a red blood cell is dependent upon the level of the osmotic pressure outside its membrane. Since the osmotic pressure of 0.9% sodium chloride (NaCl) solution equals that inside the red cell, the cell volume remains constant. When the outside osmotic pressure is lower than that in the cell (0.6% NaCl), water enters and the cell swells; if the pressure is even lower (plain water), the cell swells so much that it bursts. When the outside osmotic pressure is higher than that in the cell, water leaves the cell, and it becomes smaller (1.2% NcCl) or shrunken (2% NaCl). If the differences in osmotic pressure are not too large, it is possible to return the cell to normal volume by replacing it in 0.9% NaCl solution.

Agents other than water can hemolyze red cells. Fat solvents do so by dissolving the fatty part of the cell membrane and framework, thus releasing hemoglobin. Ether and chloroform are fat solvents as well as anesthetics. Hemolysis and cytolysis can ensue upon prolonged contract of cells with these solvents; this is one of the reasons over-anesthesia must be avoided.

Certain poisonous substances, like the toxins produced by malignant tumors or harmful bacteria, may likewise act as hemolyzing agents.

ANEMIA. When a person has too few red cells in his blood, a decreased hemoglobin content in each cell, or both, he is said to be *anemic*. Decreased hemoglobin or red cell reduction means a decreased oxygen content of the blood, subsequent poor oxygenation of tissues, and, through loss of metabolic energy, general bodily inefficiency in the performance of daily activities. Anemia can be produced by excessive loss or destruction or insufficient production of red cells or hemoglobin.

Excessive loss or destruction, as from *hemorrhage* or a *hemolyzing agent,* may produce anemia. Either cause results in a lowered oxygen content of the blood. Unless too severe, this deficiency sets into motion a compensatory mechanism which in time overcomes the loss. A reduced level of blood oxygen promotes, in some ill-understood fashion, the formation (probably in the kidneys) of a chemical substance named *erythropoietin;* the latter stimulates red bone marrow to increase production of red cells. This mechanism is involved whenever the blood oxygen level is lowered. For example, if you should stay at a relatively high altitude for several weeks, your immediate difficulties in acclimating to the lowered oxygen pressure of the air would be circumvented, eventually, by the above mechanism; within a week or so your red cell count would rise above that at sea level and the blood oxygen level return towards normal. Natives of the Andes Mountains have significantly higher red cell counts than the valley dwellers below them.

Insufficient production, resulting from any factor which decreases bone-marrow function, is a potential cause of anemia. Lead-industry workers may develop anemia by sufficient absorption of lead to destroy sizeable areas of bone marrow. Sufficient irradiation of bone marrow (from X-rays, radium, etc.) can produce similar effects. Even though the bone marrow is healthy, anemia can ensue if the nutrients necessary for red cell production are lacking in the diet. Not enough iron in the diet would curtail the production of hemoglobin and result in one type of *nutritional anemia.* In other cases, although there is no dietary deficiency, anemia can result from insufficient absorption of materials in the small intestine.

Pernicious anemia is also caused by under-production of red cells. Until 1927 it was invariably a fatal disease. At that time Dr. Whipple of the University of Rochester, who was conducting experiments on anemia induced by repeated hemorrhages in dogs, found that feeding liver to anemic dogs brought about their recovery more efficiently than other foods. Drs. Minot and Murphy subsequently tried liver feeding in controlling pernicious anemia in human patients. It was successful. After a few weeks of liver feeding the red cell count is almost normal and patients are fairly well off. Since the red cell count may drop as low as 1,000,000 per cubic millimeter and since the blood of patients shows a number of immature red cells in circulation, there is undoubtedly severe underfunctioning of the bone marrow, and liver feeding effects a striking improvement.

However, this treatment is not a cure; it is merely a check. Stopping the treatment causes almost immediate recurrence of the disease. Evidently there is some substance in liver which accelerates normal red cell production. This substance, the *antianemic factor,* results from the combination of vitamin B_{12} (the *extrinsic factor* supplied in the diet) with a protein *intrinsic factor* present in the lining of the stomach. On absorption into the blood, antianemic factor would most commonly be stored first in the liver for subsequent release and transport to the bone marrow. It can be seen, then, that inadequate production, absorption, storage, or utilization of anti-anemic factor could each be a cause of pernicious anemia and that additional treatments (other than liver-feeding) can be utilized for its amelioration depending upon which defect may be its cause in a given individual.

The White Blood Cells. Though much fewer in number than the red cells, the white cells, or *leucocytes*, appear in a greater variety of forms.

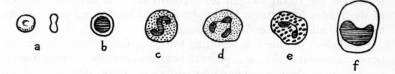

FIG. 24—White blood cells: *b*, lymphocyte; *c*, basophil; *d*, neutrophil; *e*, eosinophil; *f*, monocyte. A red blood cell (*a*) is included for a comparison of sizes.

NUMBER, KINDS, AND STRUCTURE. One cubic millimeter of blood contains from 6000 to 10,000 white cells. We may first separate them into two large groups: those *with granules* in their cytoplasm and those *without granules* (see Fig. 24). Of the granular variety, *neutrophils* are the most common of all white cells. They possess lobulated nuclei and rather fine granules which take a lavender stain. *Eosinophils* and *basophils* resemble neutrophils except that their granules are larger, those of the former staining red, the latter's blue. All three kinds are somewhat larger than red cells. The non-granular white cells include *lymphocytes* and *monocytes*. Lymphocytes are approximately the same size as red cells and have a large, somewhat bean-shaped nucleus which almost fills the cell. Monocytes are the largest of all white cells and have deeply indented nuclei. Of every 100 white cells, on the average, 70 will be neutrophils, 22 lymphocytes, 4 monocytes, 3 eosinophils, and 1 a basophil.

THE LIFE-CYCLE OF WHITE CELLS. Granular leucocytes arise in the red bone marrow, along with red cells, and develop to maturity through a series of transitional stages. Lymphocytes are formed in *lymphoid tissue* (this is widely scattered tissue in the spleen, adenoids, tonsils, thymus, and lymph nodes; the latter are enlargements found along the course of lymph vessels). Monocytes are probably formed in *reticulo-endothelial tissue* (special phagocytic tissue located in the liver, spleen, bone marrow, and lymph nodes). As yet we know little about how white cells are normally destroyed or how long they live. What indications there are lead us to believe that they have considerably shorter life-spans than red cells. However, since the white cell count remains fairly constant, rates of production and destruction must be approximately equal.

VARIATIONS IN THE WHITE COUNT. Normally, the number of white cells present in blood may fluctuate rather widely in the same individual. While not many correlations between changes in count and physiological activities can be made, exercise normally results in an increased count.

In infectious diseases, the white count may rise considerably. In appendicitis, for instance, the count may rise to about 50,000 per cubic millimeter. Such a rise is typical of infections and is often used by doctors as a diagnostic sign of infection. This type of response is a normal one, though the stimulus for greater production of white cells is not known. Abnormally, the white count may rise as high as 500,000 per cubic millimeter with the presence of many immature types in the circulating blood. This condition is called *leukemia*. The cause of the great overactivity of the bone marrow in this disease is unknown. Treatment of it has so far been ineffective, so that it generally ends in death.

Too few white cells may prove as dangerous as too many. In diseases like typhoid fever the white count may fall considerably. When this happens, individuals are very easily infected.

FUNCTIONS OF THE WHITE CELLS. Neutrophils are able to "crawl" out of the blood stream by inserting a narrow pseuodpod between cells of the thin capillary walls, the rest of their protoplasm then streaming into the pseudopod (see Fig. 141). By amoeboid movement they travel to sites of infection and combat infectious organisms by engulfing and digesting them in the same fashion that Amoeba procures and digests its food. They also remove injured or dead tissue cells in the same manner. Many of them lose their lives in the battle that follows a bacterial invasion. It would appear that bacteria liberate substances which attract neutrophils to the infected area. The bodies of dead bacteria and neutrophils and the tissue cell debris make up the *pus* which is associated with an infection. Monocytes also act as phagocytes.

The functions of other white cells are still unknown to us. It has been suggested, however, that lymphocytes are essential for the repair of injured tissue. It is believed that they flock to sites of recovery from injury or infection and are converted into connective tissue cells of less specialized character. These latter make up the bulk of the scar tissue which temporarily covers a wound. There is also a suggestion that lymphocytes manufacture substances which are essential for growth and repair of tissues in general.

The Constituents of Plasma. The liquid portion of the blood con-stitutes about 55 per cent of whole blood (plasma plus formed elements) and is mainly composed of water (about 90 per cent on the average). Of its 10 per cent of solid materials, the plasma proteins make up 7–9 per cent, inorganic salts 0.9 per cent, blood sugar (glucose) 0.1 per cent, and various other substances the remainder.

THE PLASMA PROTEINS. Of the three plasma proteins, *fibrinogen* functions mainly in the clotting of blood (which will be discussed below). *Albumin* and *globulin* are present in much larger amounts than fibrinogen and have more generalized functions. They are important in the regulation of the acidity of the blood. They also play a very important role in determining the water content of the blood. These proteins pass through the capillary walls only with difficulty while the other constituents of plasma readily penetrate the walls. Thus the only effective osmotic pressure set up in the plasma is due to its proteins. Ordinarily, this pressure tends constantly to draw water from the tissue fluid into the blood and consequently opposes the action of the blood pressure which tends continually to force water out of the capillaries. The *viscosity* of the blood depends considerably on the concentration of the plasma proteins. (We may define vis-cosity as "internal friction," the friction resulting from the rubbing together of particles as they jostle about in solution. If the tempera-ture is constant, the concentration of dissolved substances in a solu-tion determines its viscosity; thus, sugar water flows relatively easily, but molasses, a highly concentrated sugar solution, is much more viscous and flows slowly.) Blood viscosity is one factor influencing the height of blood pressure. An adequate viscosity of the plasma also seems an environmental factor essential to the life of the blood cells.

THE INORGANIC SALTS. The common salts of the plasma and the ions into which they dissociate—the positive sodium, potassium, calcium and magnesium ions; the negative chloride, carbonate, bicarbonate, sulphate and phosphate ions—are absolutely essential constituents of the environment of the blood cells and of all other cells. They help to preserve the integrity of cell membranes and regulate membrane properties to some extent. They insure the proper osmotic equilib-rium between the interior of cells and the fluid which bathes them and thus contribute to the control of the distribution of water throughout the body. They are important in determining the nature and degree of irritability in such tissues as muscle and nerve.

GLUCOSE. There are many factors operating to keep the blood sugar level at an approximately constant value. Glucose is, of course, the most widely used body fuel substance and is continually diffusing out of the blood to regions where it is needed. It is extremely important that the concentration of glucose be maintained at normal levels.

If, through some imbalance of the factors controlling this level, the concentration should be decreased to a little less than half the usual amount, convulsions, coma, and death may result.

OTHER SUBSTANCES. Many of the products of digestion are en route to cells all over the body, while waste products of cell metabolism are being transported to their sites of elimination. The hormones of the endocrine glands, various enzymes, the gases oxygen, carbon dioxide, and nitrogen, and other special compounds are present in small amounts.

The Coagulation of Blood. The clotting of blood is familiar to all of us. The value of this phenomenon in preventing excessive loss of precious blood upon injury to blood vessels is tremendously important. But straightforward as the process may seem, a number of substances is necessary for its completion.

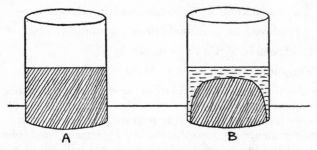

FIG. 25—Clotted blood looks like a homogeneous jelly-like mass at first (*A*). After standing a few hours, the clot shrinks and serum collects above it (*B*).

THE PHYSICAL BASIS OF COAGULATION. The essential reaction in the clotting process is the change of fibrinogen, a plasma protein, from a sol to a gel state. Let us see how this brings on coagulation. Microscopic observation of blood shows that as it is clotting, colorless threads of *fibrin*, the gel state of fibrinogen, appear. These interlace to form a tangled network in which the blood cells and plasma become enmeshed. In this way the fluid blood is converted to the jelly-like, red mass which we recognize as clotted blood. If we observe some clotted blood after it has stood a few hours, we will note that some fluid is again present (Fig. 25) and that the clot has shrunk. As it shrinks, a straw-colored liquid, *serum*, is pressed out and collects above it.

Clotting is solely a function of the plasma. If the latter is separated from the cells, it readily clots; or, if a clot is washed in water, it loses its red color—due to the washing away of the cells—but is unchanged in any other way. The cells, then, are entirely incidental in coagulation.

THE MECHANISM OF COAGULATION. The question that concerns us here is how fibrinogen is converted into fibrin at one time but remains in the sol state in blood as it circulates through the body. One widely accepted theory states the case as follows. *Fibrinogen* is converted to *fibrin* by the action of a substance, *thrombin*. Thrombin, not ordinarily present in the blood, is produced by the action of *calcium ions* on *prothrombin*, both of which are normal constituents of the plasma. However, prothrombin is ordinarily kept in an inactive state by *antiprothrombin*. When a sufficient number of blood platelets disintegrate, a substance is released which interacts with a second substance present in plasma; after several reactions an active compound, *thromboplastin*, is formed which attracts antiprothrombin to itself, freeing prothrombin for its conversion to thrombin. To summarize:

Platelet product + plasma products → thromboplastin

Thromboplastin + prothrombin-antiprothrombin →

    prothrombin + thromboplastin-antiprothrombin

Prothrombin + Ca^{++} → thrombin

Thrombin + fibrinogen → fibrin

Note also that a number of platelets tend to clump together, aiding in the stoppage of blood flow, and that injured tissue cells release *serotinin* which causes small vessels in the area to constrict.

What evidence supports this theory? *Defibrinated blood* (blood from which all the fibrinogen has been removed) will not clot, nor will blood from which only calcium ions have been removed. Fibrinogen and calcium ions must, then, be essentials of the coagulation process.

Prothrombin can be isolated from plasma. That it is prothrombin can be demonstrated by the fact that it will not cause the coagulation of a solution of fibrinogen unless it is first treated with calcium ions. The calcium ions have evidently converted it to thrombin. Now, since prothrombin and calcium ions are normal constituents of plasma, some inhibitory influence must also be present. If it were not, thrombin would be formed and clotting of the circulating blood would occur. The identity of antiprothrombin has not been established. It does not seem to be identical with *heparin*, an anticoagulant produced by liver and some other tissues.

We have accounted for everything in the above scheme but thromboplastin. This is the substance which usually initiates the clotting process. Its presence can be indicated in this manner. If blood is collected in a glass beaker, it soon clots. But, if a layer of paraffin is first deposited on the inside of the beaker, the collected blood takes a much longer time to clot. Upon microscopic observation of this phenomenon it can be noted that on a surface which water does not wet (such as a paraffin one) blood platelets disintegrate very slowly. Since this is the only observable difference between the events on a surface water wets and one which it does not, the breakdown of the platelets evidently contributes to the formation of thromboplastin.

CLOTTING WITHIN BLOOD VESSELS. Usually blood does not coagulate within the body, even though in a place like the spleen it may stagnate for some time. But if the lining of a blood vessel becomes roughened or injured at some point, platelets disintegrate and a focal point for a clot is set up. In general, such an event is a protective one, strengthening a weak point in a vessel's wall. This prevents rupture of the vessel and resultant hemorrhage. Sometimes, however, this mechanism backfires. A clot may continue to grow and may eventually completely block the vessel and prevent the flow of blood. If the vessel should supply blood to a vital region, such a clot may cause serious damage to the individual or even result in death. A clot which forms within a blood vessel is spoken of as a *thrombus* and the plugging of a vessel by it as *thrombosis*. Another danger is involved. Even though the thrombus may not plug a vessel, it may be torn loose and travel in the blood stream until it reaches a vessel too small for it to navigate. Clogging will result and again may result seriously. A travelling clot (or an air bubble, oil globule, etc.) is called an *embolus* and the condition arising from its action, *embolism*.

METHODS OF PREVENTING COAGULATION. It is often important to collect blood and prevent its clotting so that it may be studied or saved for transfusion purposes. We have already noted a number of ways this may be accomplished. One way is the removal of calcium ions by adding some compound with which calcium reacts to form a substance which will not dissociate into ions (calcium as part of a compound is not effective). Collecting the blood in a paraffined container or keeping it cool will prolong the clotting time for long periods, since in both cases the stability of the platelets is increased and no thromboplastin is formed. Adding an antiprothrombin substance will also keep the blood fluid. Defibrination is also employed. This can be done simply by whipping blood with a bundle of wooden sticks. Fibrinogen deposits as fibrin threads on the sticks and can be thus easily removed. Incidentally, this is evidence that the change from fibrinogen to fibrin is merely a change in physical state, since whipping involves no chemical manipulation of substances.

IMPAIRED COAGULATION. When the coagulatory process is normal, blood collected from an individual will clot in four to eight minutes. This period is known as the *clotting time*. In some individuals the clotting time is greatly prolonged and a slight damage to a blood vessel may end in severe hemorrhage and even death. Deficiency of any of the essential elements of the clotting process may increase the clotting time and a variety of causes may lead to such a deficiency. The most arresting condition of impaired coagulation is the hereditary disease, *hemophilia*. This disease occurs only in males and has plagued some of the former royal families of Europe. It is characterized by an excessively long clotting time. The immediate cause seems to be extraordinary stability of the platelets. Some factor present in normal plasma and aiding platelet disintegration is absent from the plasma of the hemophiliac.

The Blood Volume. By various methods it has been estimated that blood approximates 9% of the body weight. A man weighing 65 kg. (roughly, 140 pounds) would have nearly 6 liters (roughly, 6 quarts) of blood (one liter weighs approximately one kg.).

The volume of circulating blood remains surprisingly constant under a great variety of conditions. We have already seen that the number of blood cells is maintained constant by the balance between rates of formation and destruction. A number of mechanisms are also at work to maintain the constancy of plasma volume, which is largely determined by the amount of water present. Since water can reach the cells only via the blood and since water is continually being lost from the body in the expired air, sweat, feces, and urine, there must be a constant drain of water from the blood. Water is also supplied, of course, both from that which we drink and that which results from the breaking down of some chemical compounds. The kidneys are mainly responsible for maintaining water balance. If output is greater than intake, the amount of water in urine is reduced; and vice versa. The plasma proteins, as noted above, also play a role in keeping the water concentration of plasma at its normal level.

Blood volume must be maintained at its level, then, in order to supply the tissues with essential water. It is also a factor in maintaining normal blood pressure.

HEMORRHAGE. Reduced blood volume is much more common and usually more dangerous than increased blood volume. One of the more frequent causes of a lowered blood volume is hemorrhage. Since there is loss of whole blood, both the absolute number of cells and the plasma volume are lessened. After the bleeding has stopped, both of these losses must be combatted. If not more than 30 per cent of the total blood volume is lost, compensatory mechanisms within the body can bring about complete recovery in time. The reduction in red cells lowers the oxygen content of the blood and this stimulates increased production of red cells (see section on anemia). Within a few weeks the red cell count may again be normal. The plasma volume is more quickly restored by the diffusion of water into the capillaries from the tissue fluid or from cells. This may go on to such an extent that the total blood volume returns to a normal level. The ratio of cells to plasma, of course, would be less than normal under these conditions and would remain so until the number of cells attained normality. During the period of reduced blood volume the kidneys would secrete a more concentrated urine (less water in it) which would materially aid the conservation of water by the body.

TRANSFUSION. If the hemorrhage is more severe than above, the body is not capable of recuperating its losses solely through its own mechanisms and, unless external help is given promptly, death will result. The more serious deficiency in such a case is the reduced blood pressure (due to the decreased blood volume) and not the lowered oxygen concentration. The blood pressure must be maintained at a certain minimal level to keep the blood circulating. Below this level of pressure, vital regions will not be adequately supplied with blood and death results. The only way to overcome this low pressure is to increase the blood volume by injection of fluid.

The ideal transfusion fluid is whole blood itself. Many substitutes have been suggested but most are impractical or even harmful. Whole blood, however, cannot be stored for long periods; plasma can. For all those cases in which transfusion of whole blood is not a necessity, the use of plasma from "blood banks" has been invaluable. The blood from large numbers of donors is separated into plasma and cells. The plasma is pooled, frozen or dried, and stored. Dried plasma, especially, takes less storage space, is easily transported, and can be made ready for use merely by dissolving it in the correct amount of distilled water. It can be safely administered to any recipient.

BLOOD TYPES. This last advantage is of tremendous significance. It is extremely important to bear in mind that whole blood is of various types in different individuals. These types depend on no racial differences, but exist in individuals of all races. It has been determined that there are two antigens or agglutinable substances called *A* and *B* that may be found in red cells, and two antibodies or agglutinins called *a* and *b* that may be found in plasma. If *a* and *A* or *b* and *B* are present in the blood together, they cause the red cells to clump together; these clumps may prove fatal if they block small blood vessels supplying vital areas. Normally we distinguish four main blood types: *Ab*, *Ba*, *AB*, and *O* (*ab*). In transfusion of whole blood it is essential, for complete safety, to provide the same type of blood that is found in the recipient. Whenever time and facilities permit, the most reliable procedure is to mix small samples of the recipient's and donor's blood and examine the mixture microscopically. If no clumping occurs, the two are deemed compatible.

In medical practice, despite all precautions, untoward reactions sometimes followed the transfusion of seemingly compatible whole blood. Subsequent research led to the discovery of the *Rh factor*, which is the most recent antigen found in the human red cell. Blood that contains this factor is Rh-positive, while blood that does not is Rh-negative. Rh-negative blood normally contains no agglutinin comparable to *a* or *b*; if a person with Rh-negative blood receives a transfusion of Rh-positive blood, his body will react by forming an agglutinin which will cause clumping of the Rh-positive red cells. Usually not enough antibodies are formed by one introduction of Rh-positive blood to produce adverse effects. A second or third introduction may have serious consequences. Complications of a similar nature may arise in pregnancy if a woman with Rh-negative blood conceives an Rh-positive child. Antibodies may be formed in the mother's body in response to the fetal antigen and then pass into the fetal circulation and clump the fetal red cells. In a first pregnancy of this type insufficient antibodies are produced to cause harm, but in subsequent pregnancies of the same type maternal antibodies may affect the fetal blood cells.

The number of such cases is small, since there are relatively few Rh-negative individuals and since transmission between maternal and fetal blood does not invariably occur. Even when incompatibility is manifest, it is possible by intra-uterine or postnatal transfusion to save most affected infants. Therefore, Rh-negativity in a potential mother need not be a deterrent to pregnancy, provided that the situation is understood and necessary precautions are taken.

There are, then, obvious advantages to knowing the blood types of prospective parents and of individuals who require transfusions of whole blood. Fortunately, in those cases of transfusion in which only plasma is required, the *a* and *b* agglutinins in pooled plasma are apparently dilute enough to cause no difficulty in any recipient. Little wonder that dried plasma has been hailed as one of the most significant life-savers in peace and war!

THE HEART

The heart is the "pump" which drives blood through the vessels of the circulatory system. It is located in the center of the thoracic cavity and is enclosed in a tough sac of connective tissues, the *pericardium*. Day and night throughout life the heart incessantly beats at an average rate of about 70 times a minute.

The Course of the Circulation. The vessels that transport blood to the heart are the *veins;* those which carry blood away from the heart are the *arteries*. The heart in man consists of four chambers: the upper two are called *auricles* or *atria*,* the lower two, *ventricles*. Leading out from the left ventricle is the largest artery in the body,

---

*Though "auricle" is sometimes applied only to an appendage of the atrium, it is also used, as in this book, synonymously with "atrium."

the *aorta*, which distributes blood via its branches to all regions of the body except the lungs. In all tissues, the smallest arterial subdivisions break up into *capillaries*, and these in turn unite to form veins. Veins from all of the body below the heart empty into the *inferior vena cava*, those above the heart into the *superior vena cava*. These two large veins drain into the right auricle. This part of the circulation, beginning in the aorta and ending in the venae cavae, is known as the *systemic circuit*. The *pulmonary circuit* supplies the lungs only. This circuit consists of the *pulmonary artery* from the right ventricle, the capillaries in the lungs and the *pulmonary veins* which carry blood to the left auricle.

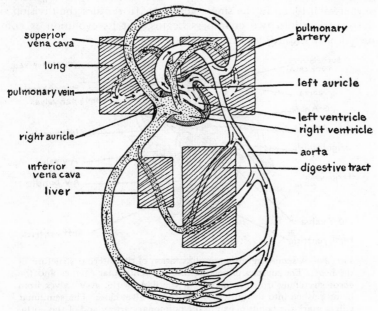

FIG. 26—A schematic representation of the course of the circulation. The stippled vessels contain oxygen-poor blood, others oxygen-rich blood. The smaller blood vessels, especially the capillaries, are omitted. Of special interest is the fact that blood leaving the digestive tract goes immediately to the liver before returning to the heart.

This four-chambered heart, two-circuit type of circulation (Fig. 26) exists in birds and mammals. It is further characterized by a complete separation of the right and left sides of the heart, the right side receiving oxygen-poor blood from the body tissues and the left, oxygen-rich blood from the lungs. If we examine the circulatory plan in the lower vertebrates, we see different schemes. In fish the heart consists of a single auricle and single ventricle. Blood leaving the heart first passes through the gills, where it is oxygenated before it goes to the body tissues. In this scheme the momentum given to the blood by the heart beat is considerably reduced by its journey through the small gill capillaries. The amphibian heart consists of two auricles and one ventricle. Blood leaves the ventricle in a single artery which quickly divides into two main branches going to the body tissues. Each of these arteries sends a branch to one lung. Blood from the lungs returns by pulmonary veins to the left auricle, while blood from the body tissues returns to the right auricle. This scheme insures pumping the blood to the tissues at relatively high pressures, but has the disadvantage of a mixture of oxygen-poor and oxygen-rich blood in the single ventricle. In reptiles the division of the ventricle into two chambers begins, but its evolution is completed only in birds and mammals.

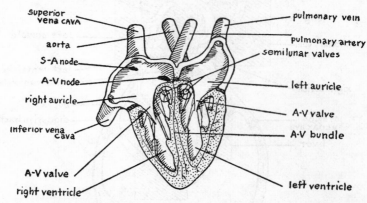

Fig. 27—A semi-diagrammatic illustration of the internal structure of the heart. The muscles projecting into the ventricular cavities and the cords stretching from them prevent the flaps of the A-V valves from being pushed into the auricles when those valves close. The semilunar valves mark the points of exit of the pulmonary artery and of the aorta. The A-V bundle should be noted as extending throughout the muscular walls of the ventricles. In this figure the auricular walls are thicker and the auricular cavities larger in proportion to the ventricular walls and cavities than they actually are.

The Structure of the Heart. The heart is a four-chambered, muscular organ about the size of your fist. The main tissue of its walls is cardiac muscle. Functionally, the muscle of the two atria acts as if it were one many-branched fiber; the ventricular muscle acts similarly. The muscle tissue is bound together by connective tissue which also connects the auricles with the ventricles. Blood vessels and nerve fibers are present in the walls, as is a special kind of conducting tissue which we shall discuss below.

The left ventricle has considerably thicker walls than the right, while the auricular walls are much thinner than even those of the right ventricle. These thicknesses can be correlated with the impetus that must be given to the blood by each of the chambers. The auricles have only to pass blood on to the neighboring ventricle. The right ventricle pumps blood to the lungs, a longer distance, while the left ventricle must pump blood throughout the entire systemic circuit.

Between each auricle and its ventricle there is a valve, an *auriculo-ventricular* or *A-V valve* (Fig. 27). These operate, unless injured, in such a way as to permit blood to pass only from auricle to ventricle and not in the reverse direction. Between each ventricle and the artery arising from it there is also a one-way valve (*semilunar valve* —so called because its flaps are shaped like half-moons) allowing blood to flow only from ventricle to artery. There are no valves at the junction of the veins and the auricles.

Properties of the Heart. Several important characteristics have been demonstrated in connection with the beating of the heart.

CONTRACTILITY. Heart muscle contracts rhythmically and auto-

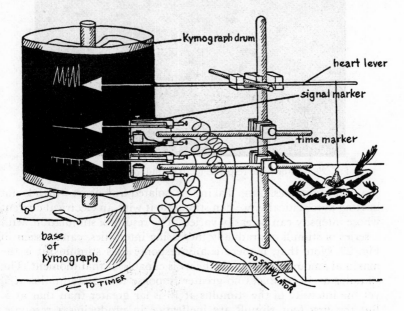

FIG. 28—Apparatus for recording the heart beat. Below the heart lever is a signal marker connected to a stimulating circuit. Below the signal marker is a time marker connected to an electrical circuit which is broken at regular intervals; each time the circuit is broken, the writing point is deflected and inscribes a line on the paper of the kymograph drum.

matically. We can assure ourselves of this fact by removing the heart of a cold-blooded animal, such as a frog, from its body and noting that it continues to beat for hours if it is in the proper salt solution.

To record the activity of the heart, an experimental set-up such as that illustrated in Fig. 28, is used. The kymograph consists essentially of a base containing a clockwork mechanism which can be made to rotate a drum resting on the base. The drum is removable. A specially prepared paper, upon which a coating of soot has been deposited, can be pasted on the drum. Any pointed instrument scratching this sooty surface will inscribe a white line on it. In Fig. 28 we see that a frog heart has been firmly fixed at one end and that a string connects its other end to a light movable lever. When the heart contracts, it pulls the unattached end of the lever upwards and this movement is inscribed on the drum by a writing point. Below the heart lever is a signal marker which is used to record the moment of application of a stimulus.

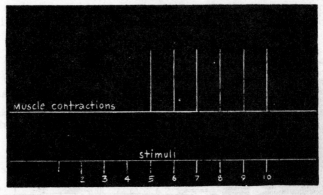

Fig. 29—All-or-none response to 10 stimuli of increasing intensity.

ALL-OR-NONE RESPONSE. Taking an isolated frog heart which is not beating automatically, we can stimulate it with an electrical current whose intensity can be easily varied. The results of stimulation, with a series of stimuli of gradually increasing intensities, can be seen in Fig. 29. Note that, if there is any response to a stimulus, it is the maximal amount of which the heart is capable at that moment. The stimulus at 10 produces no greater response than the stimulus at 5, yet the intensity of the stimulus at 10 is far greater than that at 5. But the first four stimuli are ineffective in producing a response. These results illustrate what is meant by an *all-or-none response*.

Thus, the whole ventricle, if it responds at all, responds as a unit. The advantage of this for the organism is clear. A ventricle contracting as a unit expels blood forcibly and in a short time; one which would contract in sections could not give the blood as much impetus nor expel it within the same brief period.

THE REFRACTORY PERIOD. If, while recording on a rotating kymograph drum the automatic beat of an isolated frog heart, we stimulate the heart electrically at various times during its contraction and relaxation periods, we find that sometimes we get an additional response and sometimes not (see Fig. 30). If the stimulus falls within the contraction period (upstroke), no additional beat occurs; the further into the relaxation period (downstroke) the stimulus falls, the larger the additional beat. The time during which no stimuli will elicit a response (the greater part of the contraction period) is the *refractory period*. This is the time during which the changes in the heart muscle which brought about contraction are being reversed and the muscle is being prepared for another contraction.

The refractory period of heart muscle lasts 0.1–0.2 second, a much longer time than the refractory period of skeletal muscle. It is of distinct advantage in that it prevents the heart from responding to a continuous stimulus by a continuous contraction. This ensures a rhythmic beat of the heart which is of much more value in propelling blood than a continuous contraction. It also reduces the extent to which fatigue can occur.

ELECTRICAL CHANGES. Electrical changes precede each contraction of the heart and are partly responsible for the onset of contraction. Because of the chemical and physical processes at work an active, contracting region becomes electrically negative to a resting, relaxed region. We shall investigate the electrical phenomena of activity more thoroughly in Chapter X.

Origin of the Heart Beat. It has long been disputed whether the rhythmicity of the heart beat is inherent in the cardiac muscle or originates from nervous impulses in the nerves which innervate the heart. The ultimate cause is still not known, but evidence at present indicates that this is essentially a muscular property. Embryonic heart muscle beats rhythmically when no nervous tissue is present. The adult heart continues to beat when all the nerves leading to it are cut. Some have argued that in the latter instance nerve cells within the heart muscle itself (which are present) continue to discharge impulses. This argument receives some support by analogy with the heart of the king crab. Although the latter beats in the embryo before nerve cells are present in it, in the adult animal it immediately stops and will not resume its rhythm once its nerves are cut.

It is also true that the degree of rhythmicity is not equal in all regions of the heart. If the auricles of an isolated frog heart are cut away from the ventricles, the former will continue to beat and at a faster rate than the latter. In man, too, the ventricles may beat at a different rate from the auricles in the condition known as heart block (see below).

In any case, whether the beat is of nervous or muscular origin, the exact stimulus that induces rhythmicity in the heart is a problem that still remains to be solved.

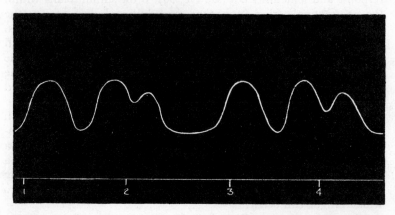

FIG. 30—The refractory period. Stimuli falling in the contraction period (1 and 3) find the heart refractory. Those given during the relaxation period (2 and 4) produce an extra beat followed by a longer rest period.

The Cardiac Cycle. Upon close examination it can be observed that the parts of the heart do not beat simultaneously. There is an orderly sequence of events, the *cardiac cycle*, which is repeated over and over again. The cycle begins with the contraction (*systole*) of the right auricle followed closely by the contraction of the left auricle. After a short pause both ventricles contract. The contraction of each chamber is followed by its relaxation (*diastole*) and then by a brief period of inactivity.

THE TRANSMISSION OF EXCITATION. The heart beat begins in the special conducting tissue we mentioned above. This tissue, *nodal tissue*, is distributed as shown in Fig. 27. There is an accumulation of it in the right auricle known as the *sino-auricular* or *S-A node*. This node is the most excitable portion of the heart and acts as a *pacemaker* for the rest of the heart. The heart beat originates here and the excitation it sets up is transmitted throughout the auricles, apparently conducted by the auricular muscle itself. This accounts for the contraction of the right before the left auricle.

The auricular and ventricular muscles are not continuous, so that excitation cannot spread directly from one to the other. The wave of excitation set up by the S-A node does activate another mass of nodal tissue in the partition between auricles and ventricles. This mass is the *auriculo-ventricular* or *A-V node*. From it an *A-V bundle* of fibers descends in the ventricular muscle, giving off branches to all regions of the ventricular walls. By means of the A-V node and bundle the excitatory state is transmitted to the ventricles which contract simultaneously.

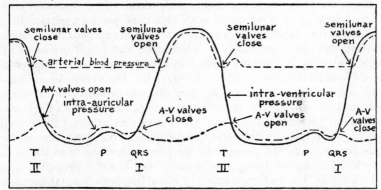

Fig. 31—Pressure changes in the auricles, ventricles, and aorta during the cardiac cycle. From the moment just before the A-V valves close until the moment the semilunar valves close the ventricles are contracting and the pressure within them is rising. During this time the auricles are filling with blood so that the pressure within them gradually rises. With the opening of the A-V valves blood passes from auricles to ventricles and the intra-auricular pressure falls. The subsequent small rise in intra-auricular and intra-ventricular pressures is due to the contraction of the auricles. *P, Q, R, S* and *T* indicate the waves in the electrocardiogram and I and II indicate the two heart sounds.

When the conducting system is functioning normally, the cardiac cycle proceeds in its usual fashion. At times, however, the conductile system between auricles and ventricles is blocked—either mechanically or because of some change in its physiological state—and the condition of *heart block* ensues. If the block is incomplete, the excitatory influence from the pacemaker will be transmitted to the ventricles some times and not at others. Thus, at intervals (which may be very regular), the ventricles will skip a beat. In the case of a complete block no impulse can reach the ventricles over the nodal tissue. This does not mean complete cessation of the ventricular beat (which would quickly bring on death). In this condition a region of the ventricle will assume the role of a secondary pacemaker and initiate ventricular contractions. The rate at which the ventricles beat now is slower than the auricular rate. In these conditions of heart block, the blood is not being pumped to the tissues as regularly or as often as normally because of the incoördination of auricular and ventricular contractions. The organism is, therefore, at a disadvantage, especially during strenuous exercise.

PRESSURE CHANGES AND THE OPERATION OF THE VALVES. As the auricles and ventricles fill with blood, contract, and relax, pressure changes occur within them which control the movements of the valves and determine the direction of blood flow through the heart. During the auricular relaxation period, venous blood flows into both auricles. As they begin to fill with blood the pressure within them begins to rise. When this intra-auricular pressure exceeds the pressure within the ventricles, the A-V valves open and blood begins to fill the ventricles. Auricular contraction then pumps the remainder of the blood in the auricles into the ventricles. The ventricles are now full and begin to contract. As they do, the pressure within them begins to mount steeply. As soon as it becomes greater than the intra-auricular pressure it closes the A-V valves and prevents the return of blood to the auricles. Rising still higher, the intra-ventricular pressure exceeds the pressure in the arteries leading from the ventricles. This opens the semilunar valves and blood is propelled into the arteries. The sudden ejection of blood increases arterial pressure and also decreases intra-ventricular pressure. When the latter drops beneath the arterial pressure, the semilunar valves snap shut. And as the intra-ventricular pressure continues to fall and the intra-auricular to rise, the latter soon exceeds the former, the A-V valves open again, and the cycle is repeated (see Fig. 31).

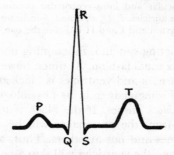

FIG. 32—The normal electrocardiogram. Compare with Fig. 31.

THE ELECTROCARDIOGRAM. We have mentioned that activity of cardiac muscle is accompanied by electrical changes. These are of sufficient intensity to be transmitted to the surface of the body where a sensitive electrical instrument can be used to show their presence. This instrument is called an *electrocardiograph*, and the record that it produces, an *electrocardiogram*. In Fig. 32 is shown a typical normal electrocardiogram. The P wave is correlated with contraction of the auricles, the QRS group with ventricular contraction, while the T wave marks the end of ventricular systole.

The electrocardiogram is useful to the physiologist and to the physician. The physician learns to recognize that certain variations or absences of waves indicate abnormalities of heart function; the physiologist finds it valuable in experimentation. For instance, the A-V bundle of a dog's heart can be injured and the injury shown on the electrocardiogram as an absence of QRS group following some P waves.

THE HEART SOUNDS. During each cardiac cycle two sounds are produced by the heart. The first is longer lasting, lower pitched, and softer than the second. The snapping shut of the semilunar valves give rise to the second sound; the first is probably due to the noises set up by the closing of the A-V valves and by the contraction of the large mass of ventricular muscle (any muscle can produce a sound when it contracts).

By placing your ear against someone's chest in the region of the heart or by listening through a *stethoscope* (the two-tubed instrument that physicians use), you can hear these sounds. An approximation of their character can be achieved by saying "lubb-dup" and accenting the second syllable. Injury to the valves of the heart can modify these sounds. If the semilunar valves do not close properly, for instance, blood leaks back into the ventricles from the arteries, producing a hushing sound. The sounds may now be simulated by "lush-sh." This condition is called a *heart murmur*.

Regulation of the Force of the Heart Beat. Even though the heart gives an all-or-none response to any particular stimulus, the force of contraction may be varied by changes in its physical or chemical state. In its changed condition it will still respond "all-or-none," but the force of its contraction will differ from that before the change.

STARLING'S LAW OF THE HEART. Muscles, somewhat like rubber bands, are elastic bodies. And the more an elastic body is stretched (within the limits of its elasticity), the greater will be the force of contraction when it is released. Thus, the more a cardiac chamber is filled with blood, the greater it will be stretched and the more forcibly it will contract. This principle was first applied to the heart by the English physiologist, Starling, and is now known as his law of the heart. Whenever the return of venous blood to the heart is increased, the heart will beat more strongly and pump out a greater amount of blood per beat.

CHEMICAL CONTROL. Carbon dioxide especially, and certain other metabolic products can alter the chemical nature of cardiac muscle. If the concentration of carbon dioxide in the blood is moderately increased, as occurs in exercise, the heart beats more forcibly than in a resting condition. This means, again, that a greater amount of blood is ejected at each heart beat.

Under resting conditions the output of each ventricle is 60–70 cc. per beat (the volume of about a fourth of a water glass). Each ventricle can, in strenuous exercise, triple its output per beat.

Regulation of the Heart Rate. The average heart rate in an adult tends to remain about 70 per minute under resting conditions (somewhat faster in children). But in severe exercise it may rise to 200 per minute or, in other circumstances, may fall to 60 or lower. The mechanisms which tend to maintain the normal heart rate or which permit changes in it can be divided into three groups: nervous, chemical, and thermal.

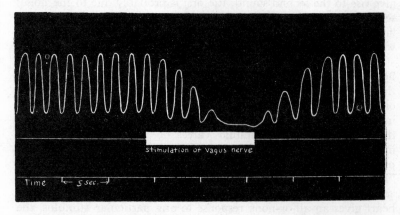

Fig. 33—Stimulation of the vagus nerve can depress, slow and finally stop the heart beat. This is a record of a frog's heart beat, but stimulation of the vagus has a similar effect on the heart beat in other animals.

NERVOUS CONTROL. Although the heart beat itself is automatic, its rate can be profoundly influenced by nervous impulses. In the absence of nervous control its ability to adapt to changing bodily conditions would largely be lost.

There are two pairs of nerves which directly control the heart rate, the two *vagus nerves* (plural, *vagi*) and the two *accelerator nerves*. The former arise in the *medulla*, a region of the hind part of the brain, and send branches to various organs, including the heart, in the thoracic and abdominal cavities. The latter originate in the thoracic part of the spinal cord and eventually terminate in the heart muscle. In man or an experimental animal, electrical stimulation of the accelerator nerves speeds the heart rate. Stimulation of the vagus nerves, however, slows the heart rate and, if the stimulus is strong enough and enough nerve impulses reach the heart muscle, may temporarily effect a complete inhibition of its beating (see Fig. 33).

We have evidence that both sets of nerves exert a continual influence on the heart. If the vagi are cut but the accelerators are intact, the heart rate speeds up and remains faster. This must indicate that impulses are continually descending from the medulla through the vagi and tending to slow the heart rate. In the absence of such inhibitory impulses, the heart is released from this "braking" action and accelerates. The reverse is true when the accelerators are cut.

Because of this nervous activity the heart can be accelerated in two ways—a decrease in the number of vagal impulses or an increase in accelerator impulses—and slowed in two ways. Through the action of these nerves, then, the heart rate is rapidly and finely adjusted to routine and emergency activities. The interplay of acceleratory and inhibitory nerve impulses always tends toward a regulation of the heart rate as economical yet as efficient as possible for the activity of the moment. Vagal and acceleratory impulses do not balance out exactly, the former exerting a more pronounced influence. We might logically expect this, since most activities of the body tend to increase rather than decrease the heart rate.

The vagi and accelerator nerve fibers which we have just mentioned are examples of *efferent* fibers, that is, fibers which lead out of the brain or spinal cord and conduct impulses to muscles or glands. In the vagus nerve to the heart there are many fibers, each of which is an extension from a nerve cell body in the medulla. The group of cell bodies which give rise to these fibers is termed a *nerve center*, or, more specifically in this instance, the *vagus* or *cardio-inhibitory center*. There are also *cardio-acceleratory centers* in the medulla and spinal cord (see Fig. 34).

The impulses which travel in the cardiac nerves originate under usual bodily conditions in the cell bodies of these centers. How are these impulses initiated? For one thing, changes in the chemical composition of the blood which reaches the centers can excite or depress them. More usually, though, stimulation of these centers is caused by nerve impulses travelling to them from many regions of the body. Many *afferent* nerve fibers (fibers bringing impulses towards the central nervous system), perhaps all, are capable of modifying the activity of the cardiac centers. Let us remember that whenever an afferent impulse activates a center to discharge efferent impulses, the resultant action is termed a *reflex* response. A great many such reflexes aid in the control of the heart rate.

As implied above, stimulation of virtually any afferent nerve can produce reflex changes in the heart rate. Apparently, afferent impulses are streaming to the cardiac centers at all times, which would mean that almost all activities of the body will have a voice in determining what the heart rate is to be at a given moment. There

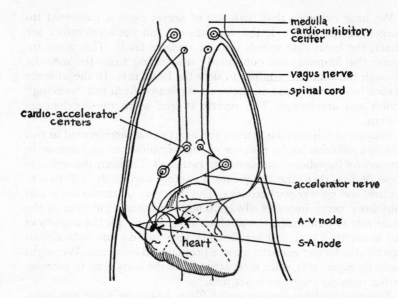

FIG. 34—A schematic diagram of the nerve centers controlling the heart rate. Impulses sent out from cardio-inhibitory and cardio-acceleratory centers reach the S-A and A-V nodes and the heart muscle itself.

are, however, some reflexes which are more specifically concerned in the modulation of the heart rate. Several specific reflexes, the *carotid sinus* and *aortic arch reflexes*, will be discussed below.

Nervous impulses from higher levels of the brain are also important in the regulation of heart rate, so that nervous impulses travelling within the central nervous system as well as afferent impulses are of importance. The clearest examples of their influence are found in the changes of heart rate produced by emotional states. Most of us are familiar with the increased heart rate that comes on through anger, excitement, or apprehension, or the slower rate produced by great fear. Undoubtedly, more rational activities of the brain can also modify the heart rate to some extent.

CHEMICAL CONTROL. Although one might expect that heart rate would be influenced by changes in concentrations of chemicals in the blood, there is little experimental evidence to support this idea. The only undisputed chemical influences on heart rate are those of hormones; for discussion of these actions, see Chapter XI.

THERMAL CONTROL. The temperature of the air about us has little or no effect on heart rate. But the temperature of the blood does influence it to a slight degree. When the body temperature rises to about 104° Fahrenheit (normal being 98.6°), the heart rate is slightly accelerated. However, this factor is significant only in relatively long-lasting feverish states and not in the short-lived periods of high temperature which occur in health (i.e., in severe exercise).

In cold-blooded animals the external temperature can markedly influence the heart rate, since it determines the temperature of such animals' blood. The heart of a frog can function (though at quite different rates) over a wide range of temperatures (see Fig. 35), whether in or out of the frog's body. Human and other "warm-blooded" hearts cannot, since they are attuned more delicately to a nearly constant temperature.

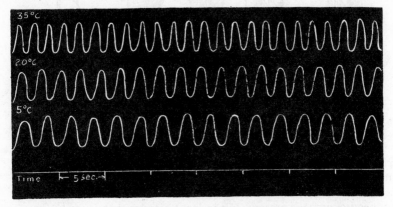

Fig. 35—A record of heart beat in the frog when the heart is bathed with salt solution of varying temperatures.

The Cardiac Output. The output of the heart per minute is called the *minute volume*. All regulation of the heart's activity is directed toward making the minute volume adequate for the situation at hand. It is the output of the heart which determines how much blood is sent to the tissues in a given time interval.

In most situations any change in the output would be in the direction of an increase. It is apparent that we can increase the output per minute either by increasing the output per beat (by increasing the strength of the beat), by increasing the rate of beating, or by a combination of the two. Thus, the regulation of the force of the heart beat and of the heart rate is pointed toward having the heart pump out sufficient blood to satisfy the needs of active tissues.

THE BLOOD VESSELS

All of the mechanisms governing the activity of the heart, the blood pressure, and blood flow are directed toward insuring an adequate supply of blood in the capillaries where the vital exchanges of gases, nutrients, and wastes occur.

Structure of the Vessels. *Arteries* and *veins* are constructed on a similar plan (see Fig. 36). Both have three layers in their walls. The innermost layer is made up of a single thickness of smooth epithelial

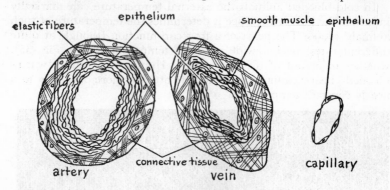

FIG. 36—Cross-sections of an artery, vein and capillary. The size of the capillary is much larger than it actually would be in proportion to the size of the artery and vein.

cells resting on connective tissue. The smoothness minimizes the friction produced by blood rubbing against the walls in its flow. The middle layer is larger than the inner and distinguishes an artery from a vein. In both kinds of vessels smooth muscle bound together by connective tissue is present, but in large arteries there are also many *elastic fibers* which impart to these vessels their characteristic resiliency. Because of their elasticity and of the thickness of this middle layer, arteries when removed from the body retain their shape to a much greater extent than veins. The outermost layer of both consists of a tough connective tissue in which some elastic fibers and nerve fibers going to the smooth muscle may be found.

The smaller divisions of arteries and veins are called *arterioles* and *venules* respectively. Arterioles differ from arteries in their size and also in the greater proportion of smooth muscle to elastic fibers in the middle layer. Venules are more nearly smaller replicas of veins.

The smallest vessels are the *capillaries* which have only one-layered walls consisting of epithelium. These minute vessels cannot be seen by the unaided eye, since their diameter may be little more than that of a red cell, and their length averages about a millimeter.

The Arterial Blood Pressure. As the blood leaves the heart, it is under considerable pressure. However, all of the energy imparted to the blood by ventricular contraction is not used in furthering the flow of blood. Some of this energy is dissipated in distending the elastic walls of the large arteries. A wave of recoil of the arterial walls then assists the heart in moving blood through the vessels. This is the *pulse wave* which is responsible for the pulse that can be felt in any artery (from those near the surface of the intact body, of course). If the arteries were rigid instead of elastic tubes, with each ventricular systole the pressure would rise sharply in them but fall steeply once the contraction was concluded. Blood flow under these conditions would be intermittent and not continuous (as it really is). The elasticity of the arterial walls, therefore, is responsible in large part for the continued maintenance of arterial pressure and of blood flow.

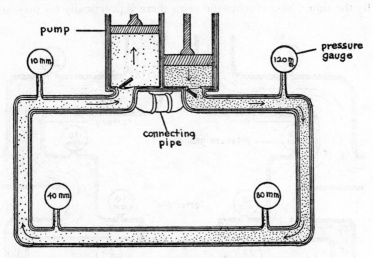

FIG. 37—A closed circuit consisting of a two-compartment pump, whose chambers are connected by a pipe, a one-way valve in each chamber and a long pipe running from chamber to chamber. The pressure of the fluid within the system (indicated by the density of the stippling and also by the figures in the pressure gauges) falls gradually with increasing distance from the pump. (Pressure is measured in millimeters of mercury.)

THE PRESSURE GRADIENT. There is a progressive fall in blood pressure from arteries to arterioles to capillaries to veins. The difference in pressure from one point to another constitutes a *pressure gradient* without which there would be no flow at all; that is, if the pressure were the same at all points, there could be no flow from point to point. If there were but a single vessel which led from the heart and eventually returned to it and that vessel had the same diameter throughout, then the pressure of the blood would fall gradually in the vessel, the drop in pressure at any one point being proportional to the distance of that point from the pumping force (see Fig. 37). The fall in pressure is due to the resistance offered to the flow of the fluid by the friction set up as the fluid rubs against the wall of the vessel. However, the arteries leading from the heart soon divide into a number of branches, each of which divides into numerous arterioles which in turn subdivide into more numerous capillaries. The net result of these many branchings is to increase the wall space offering frictional resistance and to cause a more sudden drop in pressure in the regions where many branchings occur (see Fig. 38). The pressure in the large arteries falls only gradually as the blood flows away from the heart, but there is a sudden, large drop in pressure in the arteriolar regions and a further fall in the capillaries. By the time blood reaches the veins there is practically no pressure.

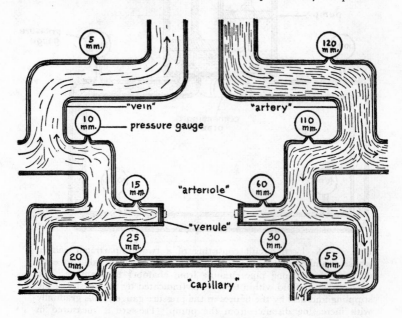

Fig. 38—A model of a closed system including a pump (not shown) based on the circulatory system. The changes in caliber of the vessels make for more sudden changes in pressure. Compare with Fig. 37. The rapid division of "arteries" into "arterioles" (much more than is indicated) causes the largest drop in pressure, the subsequent division into "capillaries" causes a good-sized but somewhat smaller drop. In the "venules" and "veins" there is a more gradual drop since there is a continued resistance to flow but decreased driving force and momentum. (Pressure is registered in millimeters of mercury.)

DEFINITION OF TERMS. With each heart beat the arterial blood pressure fluctuates. As blood is ejected from a ventricle into an artery, the pressure is suddenly increased as blood floods the artery. This pressure peak is called *systolic pressure* since it is due to the ventricular systole or contraction. During the relaxation (diastole) of the ventricle, pressure falls somewhat in the artery, but is still maintained at a fairly high level by the elastic recoil of the arterial walls. At this level it is referred to as *diastolic pressure*. The difference between systolic and diastolic pressures is called the *pulse pressure;* their average is the *mean arterial pressure.*

MEASUREMENT OF ARTERIAL BLOOD PRESSURE. In an experimental animal this can be done directly. An artery is exposed and cut. A glass or plastic tube is inserted into the end leading from the heart.

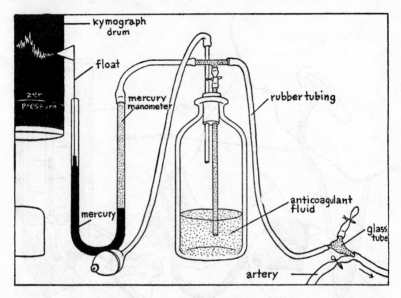

FIG. 39—A method for recording blood pressure directly in an experimental animal. A cut is made in the wall of an artery and a glass tube inserted and tied into the artery. The peripheral (away from the heart—the arrow points toward the heart) part of the artery is tied off. The other part of the artery is temporarily occluded while anticoagulant fluid is pumped through the system of tubes to raise the pressure to the approximate level of the blood pressure. This forces the column of mercury down in the right tube of the manometer and up in the left tube. When the central (towards the heart) part of the artery is released, the blood in it rushes into the glass tube. It is prevented from flooding the system of tubes by the pressure opposing it. The fluctuations of blood pressure initiate changes in the level of the mercury which are transmitted, by means of the float and writing point on it, to the smoked paper on the drum as a series of lines. The height of the blood pressure is the difference between these lines and the previously recorded line of "zero pressure."

In the tube is an anticoagulant fluid to prevent blood from clotting in it. The other end of the tube is attached to a mercury manometer (see Fig. 39). The pressure of the mercury is increased to about the height of the blood pressure and thus opposes the flow of blood; at the same time it serves as a measure of the blood pressure. The height of the latter and fluctuations in it can be recorded on the smoked paper of a kymograph drum by the writing point on the float.

In man, the foregoing procedure cannot, of course, be used. An indirect method (Fig. 40) gives fairly accurate results. A rubber bag is wrapped about the arm above the elbow and then inflated with

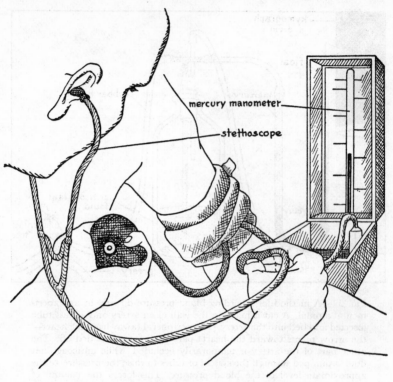

mercury manometer

stethoscope

Fig. 40—An indirect method of recording blood pressure in man. For explanation see text.

air. The bag is connected to a mercury manometer or a pressure gauge which indicates the height of pressure. The person recording the pressure places the receiver of a stethoscope over the inner side of the elbow. The brachial artery is close beneath the surface here. The pressure in the bag is raised high enough to compress the artery in the upper arm and prevent the flow of blood through it. No sound can be heard now. The pressure in the bag is then slowly decreased and, when the lumen of the artery is opened just enough to allow the passage of a jet of blood with each heart beat, a faint tapping sound is heard. The pressure recorded at this point is the systolic pressure. As the pressure in the bag is lowered more, the sound changes in quality and then disappears completely when blood is allowed to flow continuously through the artery. At the moment when the sound just disappears, the manometer or gauge records the diastolic pressure.

Measurements of pressure by this method have shown that the average systolic pressure in young male adults is about 120 mm. of mercury, diastolic about 80 mm. Blood pressure or any pressure in the body always is calculated by using atmospheric pressure (760 mm. of mercury) as the "zero" mark. That arterial blood pressure is above atmospheric pressure is evidenced by the spurting of blood from a cut artery, which could not happen if it were less than atmospheric.

The Regulation of Arterial Pressure. After we enumerate the factors that control the maintenance of arterial pressure at a roughly normal level, we will describe in more detail the dynamic process of control from moment to moment.

FACTORS MAINTAINING THE NORMAL ARTERIAL PRESSURE. A combination of five factors coöperate in the maintenance of arterial pressure at its normal level.

1) Pumping action of the heart. The heart controls the amount of blood that will be ejected into the arteries in any given period. If other factors are constant, an increase in the cardiac output (produced in any manner) will increase the arterial blood pressure; a decrease will lower it.

2) Blood Volume. To develop pressure in a closed system of tubes one must fill them to capacity. Ordinarily the arteries are thus filled. But because of their elasticity more blood can be introduced into them; the increase in the volume of circulating fluid will distend them and set up an increased pressure. Withdrawal of fluid decreases pressure. This, as we have mentioned, is the prime deficit that follows severe hemorrhage. Although it cannot endure a low blood pressure for any considerable length of time, the animal organism can withstand a large fall in pressure. In an experimental animal the arterial pressure may be reduced by two-thirds by removal of some of its blood. The pressure is restored to its normal level, however, by simply infusing back into the animal the same blood which had been withdrawn.

In instances in which a greater blood volume is needed, the *spleen* often aids in bringing this about. There are places in the spleen where arterioles empty into *blood sinuses*, relatively wide channels which can accommodate a considerable amount of blood. These sinuses are off the main line of the circulation, and the blood in them may not move at all. This splenic blood is very rich in red cells, since it is easier for the plasma to escape from the sinuses into the general circulation than it is for the cells. After hemorrhage, or in muscular exercise or emotional states, smooth muscle in the walls of the spleen contracts and the stored blood is squeezed into the circulating blood.

3) Elasticity of the arterial walls. This gives rise to and maintains the diastolic pressure; the latter is produced by the springing back of the arterial walls after they have been stretched by the sudden ejection of blood during ventricular systole. The diastolic pressure is much more constant than the systolic; that is, it is affected far less than the systolic by changes in any of the other factors maintaining blood pressure.

4) Blood viscosity. Blood is about five times as viscous as water. The more viscous a fluid is, the more resistant to flow it is and the greater is the pressure needed to force it through a narrow tube. The viscosity of the blood is largely determined by the numbers of formed elements present and to a lesser degree by the concentration of plasma proteins. If either of these factors is lowered, viscosity drops, resistance to flow is decreased, and blood pressure falls; and vice versa. It can be seen, then, that an ideal transfusion fluid must have a viscosity approximating that of blood.

5) Peripheral resistance. Arterioles are of smaller caliber than arteries and cannot, therefore, transmit as much blood in a given time interval as can arteries. There is, therefore, a resistance to the passage of blood from artery to arteriole and, for the same reason but to a lesser extent, from arteriole to capillary. This is the *peripheral resistance*. If the arteriolar diameters are decreased, resistance increases and blood pressure rises.

MOMENT-TO-MOMENT CONTROL. Rapid adjustments of blood pressure result from influences on the heart rate and force of beat and from influences on the caliber of small vessels (mainly arterioles).

The wall of every arteriole contains smooth muscle fibers which are circularly oriented. When these fibers contract, the diameter of an arteriole decreases and its resistance to blood flow through it increases; when muscle fibers relax, the effects just noted are reversed. The control of arteriolar diameter is most usually the result of local dilating influences and central constricting influences.

All arterioles receive nerve fibers whose activity causes smooth muscle to contract; such fibers are called *vasoconstrictor* ("vaso" = vessel) *nerves*. In some regions of the body, not widespread, arterioles receive a second set of nerve fibers, *vasodilator nerves*, whose activity causes smooth muscle to relax. Nervous impulses are sent along these nerves from the *vasoconstrictor* and *vasodilator centers*, respectively, located in the medulla of the brain; the former of these centers, much like the cardiac centers, is influenced by all afferent nerves.

Let us re-emphasize that all arterioles receive vasoconstrictor impulses but few receive vasodilator impulses. What is more, the vasoconstrictor center is continually sending out impulses so that, unless this influence is counteracted, arterioles will normally be constricted to some extent, a factor which undoubtedly contributes to the normal level of arterial blood pressure in an individual.

If all else remains constant, any influence that promotes increased cardiac output and increased vasoconstriction (i.e., exercise, certain emotional states) will tend to increase arterial pressure; rest and certain other emotional states will produce opposite effects.

There are, however, certain reflexes which oppose and minimize such change or, in other words, tend to keep the blood pressure as constant as possible; these are the *carotid sinus* and *aortic arch reflexes* (Fig. 41). The *common carotid arteries* arise from the aorta, and run up alongside the trachea (feel them pulsating in your neck). High in the neck, near the angle of the jaw, each divides into an *external carotid artery*, supplying superficial regions of the head, and an *internal carotid artery*, delivering blood to the brain. On each side, near the junction of the carotid branches, is a small swelling known as the *carotid sinus*. In the walls of each sinus and in the wall of the *arch of the aorta* are receptors excited by stretch of the walls.

Whenever blood pressure rises, the following sequence occurs: increased numbers of impulses are set up in afferent nerves and travel to the medulla; the cardio-inhibitory center is excited; the vaso-constrictor center is inhibited; resultant decrease in heart rate (and cardiac output) and fall in peripheral resistance tend to lower arterial pressure. When blood pressure falls, fewer impulses are sent to the medulla, the cardio-acceleratory and vasoconstrictor centers are excited, and blood pressure tends to rise.

The carotid sinus mechanism is especially influential in maintaining blood flow at adequate pressure to the brain. For example, you may have noticed at times that sudden change from a recumbent to a sitting or standing posture may cause you to feel faint. The sudden pull of gravity on blood ascending to the head may momentarily lower the pressure in the carotid arteries sufficiently to prevent adequate circulation to the brain. The carotid sinus reflex outlined above will usually soon circumvent the faintness by raising the blood pressure.

Note, then, that nervous control of blood vessels seems largely due to excitation or inhibition of the vasoconstrictor center. There is some question, in fact, whether a vasodilator center actually exists.

One might ask if vasodilation is always a passive process. The answer is no. Whenever there is increased metabolic activity of any tissues or organs (as in exercise), active vasodilation occurs in those regions. The increased chemical activity of cells augments the local levels of carbon dioxide and the latter causes vasodilation by a direct relaxing influence on the smooth muscle of the arterioles in the

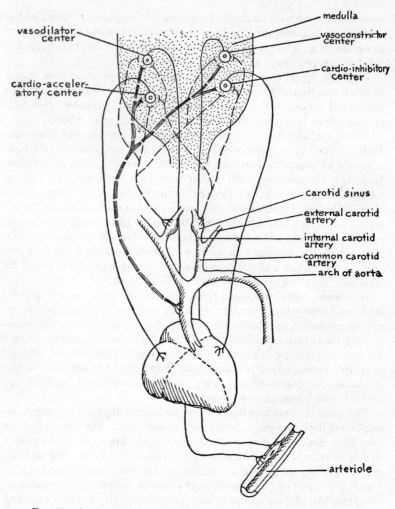

FIG. 41—A schematic diagram of the pathways for the carotid sinus and aortic arch reflexes. Afferent fibers from each carotid sinus (----) and from the aortic (≡≡≡) pass to the cardiac and vasomotor centers in the medulla. Efferent fibers from these centers (——) innervate the heart and arterioles respectively.

vicinity. A decrease in the local oxygen supply can produce the same effects, but carbon dioxide increase is the more frequent and potent factor.

On the other hand, an increase in general blood level of carbon dioxide will tend to constrict arterioles by direct excitation of the vasoconstrictor center. See Chapter XVIII for further elaboration of this role.

Variations in Arterial Blood Pressure. As we have seen, the normal adult blood pressure averages about 120 mm. of mercury for systolic and 80 mm. for diastolic. The systolic pressure is much less stable than the diastolic and fluctuates much more widely than the latter. In severe exercise, for instance, the systolic pressure may rise to as much as 200 mm. while the diastolic rises at most to 110 mm. The pulse pressure is, therefore, increased and we notice a more violently throbbing pulse.

Blood pressure tends to rise with increasing age, the systolic being about 135 mm. at the age of sixty while the diastolic is increased only to about 90 mm. At a given age, very heavy persons tend to have a higher blood pressure than lighter ones. Emotional states can cause marked variations in blood pressure, the direction of change depending upon how the heart and the caliber of blood vessels are affected.

HIGH BLOOD PRESSURE. Pathologically high blood pressure or *hypertension* is not uncommon. The blood pressure may rise to as much as 250 mm. of mercury (systolic) and 130 mm. (diastolic). This high pressure puts a strain on the heart, for the pressure in the ventricles must be built up to a greater height than arterial pressure before blood can be ejected. The increase in the work of the heart causes the left ventricle, especially, to dilate and produces thickening of its walls. The excessive pressure also causes degenerative changes in the blood vessels over a period of time. *Arteriosclerosis* (hardening of the arteries which occurs normally as we grow older and is produced by the deposition of insoluble calcium salts in the arterial walls with consequent decrease in elasticity) does not bring on the hypertension in these cases, although it may be responsible for the smaller increases in pressure that occur normally as we age. Recently, a connection has been discovered between arteriosclerosis and an excess of cholesterol in the blood stream. Cholesterol, in normal amounts, is an essential fat-like substance which is manufactured by the body as well as taken in with certain foods.

The cause of hypertension in pathological cases is an increase in peripheral resistance due to chronic constriction of arterioles. However, what causes this constriction is not clearly understood in many cases. In some instances, the hypertension is secondary to kidney disease. Such disease restricts the blood flow to the kidneys and they receive insufficient oxygen. The oxygen lack seems to bring on the production of a substance by the kidneys which causes increased contraction of smooth muscle in arteriolar walls. There is some experimental confirmation of this. If a clamp is placed about the renal artery in a dog in such a way that the blood supply is reduced and insufficient oxygen reaches the kidney cells, hypertension is produced by means of a substance elaborated by the kidneys.

In other cases, hypertension may be due to nervous factors. Possibly the vasoconstrictor center is not held in check as much as it usually is by incoming nervous impulses. Tranquilizing drugs (*reserpine* and others), which act to depress certain overactive nervous centers, have been used successfully to ameliorate the hypertensive condition in a number of cases.

The release of excessive amounts of hormones from the adrenal cortex (see Chapter XI) is also believed to be a cause of hypertension. Although no effective treatment for this condition has yet been devised, reduced intake of salt has had some beneficial results.

LOW BLOOD PRESSURE. *Hypotension* is said to exist when blood pressure is low for a given individual. Its cause is unknown, although it is not infrequently associated with some diseases and endocrine deficiencies.

The condition is less common than hypertension and does not generally produce symptoms which endanger the individual. Increased susceptibility to fatigue and dizziness accompany the condition.

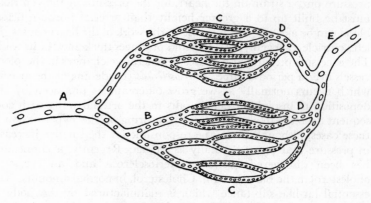

FIG. 42—Blood flow. For description see text.

Blood Flow. The blood flow, as we saw, is the result of the pressure gradient from arteries to capillaries to veins. And the pressure gradient is caused by the gradual dissipation of the energy imparted to the blood by the heart as the vessels offer resistance to the flow of blood. In addition to the pumping action of the heart (which is the primary source of pressure and flow), another factor maintaining blood flow is the elasticity of the arteries (which sustains the greater part of the pressure set up by the heart beat).

There is still another factor controlling the speed of blood flow.

This factor, the total cross-sectional area of the vessels, is responsible for the changes in the velocity of flow in the different parts of the circulatory "tree." Similar changes can be seen in the flow of liquid through any system of tubes which vary in diameter. Thus, at A in Fig. 42 the tube ("artery") is wide and the flow fast; at B and C ("arterioles" and "capillaries"), although each tube has a smaller diameter than the "artery," the total cross-sectional area of the tubes increases and the flow slackens; and at D and E ("small veins" and "large vein") the flow quickens again since the total cross-sectional area decreases. The velocity of blood flow in the body varies quite similarly. The flow in the arteries is fast, it slows in the arterioles and capillaries, and then accelerates progressively in the small and large veins.

VENOUS BLOOD FLOW. In the arteries below the heart, the blood pressure and the force of gravity work in the same direction and there is no difficulty in accounting for blood flow. In the arteries above the heart, although the gravitational effect opposes the blood flow, the carotid sinus and aortic arch reflexes maintain the pressure at regular levels and provide for a sustained blood flow.

In the veins below the heart, however, other mechanisms must be called upon to insure the return of blood to the heart. The venous pressure is very low and cannot force the blood up against the pull of gravity. The important accessory mechanism in the lower regions of the body is the "pumping" action of the skeletal muscles. When these muscles contract, they compress the relatively thin-walled veins and squeeze blood upward. The blood is prevented from moving back toward the capillaries by the action of *valves*, spaced at frequent intervals along the veins, which open only toward the heart (Fig. 43). When the skeletal muscles relax, the veins expand and are filled with blood from below. This mechanism is of particular importance to the venous return during strenuous exercise. In the thoracic cavity another mechanism aids in the venous return, the significance of which will become clearer in Chapter V.

Since the flow of blood in veins above the heart is aided by the pull of gravity, no accessory mechanisms are needed to insure this flow.

THE CIRCULATION TIME. If a substance is injected into the blood stream at one point, the time it takes to reach some other point in the circulatory system can be recorded. By the use of dyes or other materials it has been found that the *pulmonary circulation time* (the shortest time required for blood to pass through the heart and lungs) is about eleven seconds in man. The *total circulation time* from one arm to the other is about 24 seconds. The total circulation time varies according to the region of the body selected; the total circulation time from heart to foot will be greater than from heart to arm.

The circulation time varies in health and in disease. In muscular exercise, it will be decreased; in heart failure, it will be increased.

THE CONTROL OF BLOOD FLOW TO AN ORGAN. The amount and the rate of blood flow to a particular organ is regulated by nervous and chemical factors. Of these, the chemical effects seem predominant. When an organ is active, its rate of metabolism increases and more carbon dioxide is produced than at rest. The excess carbon dioxide diffuses into the blood stream and causes dilation of the arterioles of the organ by direct action on the smooth muscle in their walls. With increased caliber of the arterioles more blood is delivered to the organ and at a faster rate.

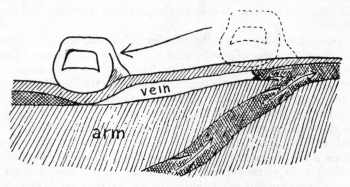

Fig. 43—Action of the valves in veins. If you select a prominent vein on your arm and run your finger along it toward your hand, you will note that a section of the vein collapses and seems to disappear. This happens because you are preventing blood from flowing toward the heart by your pressure on the vein and because the valves in the vein prevent blood from flowing back into the emptied section of it.

The vasomotor nerves also control blood flow. Stimulation of vaso-constrictor nerves reduces the amount and rate of flow through arterioles; stimulation of vasodilator nerves, when present, produces the opposite effects. There can be reflex control as well as chemical control of blood flow in an active organ.

Since there is a relatively constant blood volume, if the blood flow to one region is increased, it must be decreased in some other place. Note how smoothly the reactions are synchronized during muscular exercise. A greater blood flow is needed by the active skeletal muscles. Their activity increases the carbon dioxide concentration locally and their arterioles are caused to dilate. The excess carbon dioxide in the circulating blood increases the force of the heart beat, excites the vasoconstrictor center, causing generalized vasoconstriction and rise of blood pressure. But the local excess of carbon dioxide maintains the dilation of arterioles in the muscles, despite the vasoconstrictor impulses. Thus, more blood is supplied at greater pressure to the active muscles, while the inactive regions receive less blood.

Shock. In such seemingly diverse situations as severe hemorrhage, burning or crushing of tissues, severe emotional disturbances, and the postoperative condition (especially after abdominal surgery), individuals may suddenly go into a state of shock. Such an individual pales, evidences extreme weakness, and usually lapses into unconsciousness. What seems to happen internally is that the capillaries suddenly become much more permeable than is normal and a large volume of fluid escapes from them into the tissue spaces; this marked reduction in blood volume lowers the blood pressure precipitately. The reason for the change in state of the capillaries is not understood.

The obvious treatment is to increase the blood pressure, and this is best accomplished by prompt infusion of plasma in amounts sufficient to maintain the blood pressure within normal limits. If this treatment is too long delayed or, unfortunately sometimes, even when it is not delayed, the state of shock may be irreversible. A vicious circle of events occurs: the liver, inadequately supplied with blood, releases a potent vasodepressor substance; the latter markedly dilates the blood capillaries, and blood stagnates in them. Once this condition is present, transfusion is not effective.

THE LYMPHATIC SYSTEM

The purpose of all the circulatory adjustments is to provide a sufficient flow of blood in the capillaries. In these minute vessels occur the vital exchanges between tissue fluid and blood.

The Formation of Tissue Fluid. Tissue fluid, execpt for its protein concentration, has the same composition as blood plasma. How is this fluid derived from the blood? The thin capillary walls are permeable to all of the constituents of blood except the formed elements and, to a large extent, the plasma proteins. Some of the smaller protein molecules do penetrate the walls, but only enough to keep the protein concentration of tissue fluid at about 3 per cent. At the arterial end of the capillaries the blood pressure amounts to about 30 mm. of mercury. This pressure tends to drive water and the dissolved substances in it out of the capillaries. The tissue fluid, however, exerts some pressure, too, which opposes the driving force of the blood pressure. The tissue fluid pressure is much less than blood pressure. Assuming that it is about 5 mm. of mercury, the *effective filtration pressure* (see Chapter II) would be 25 mm. of mercury. On the other hand the proteins which do not filter out of the blood exert osmotic pressure (about 25 mm. of mercury) which tends to draw fluid into the capillaries. The proteins in the tissue fluid also exert osmotic pressure, although considerably less than that of blood because of the lower protein concentration. If the tissue fluid osmotic pressure amounts to 10 mm. of mercury, the *effective osmotic pressure* will be 15 mm. Since the effective filtration pressure is greater than the effective osmotic pressure, there will be a force of 10 mm. of mercury (25–15) tending to drive fluid out of the capillaries at the arterial end (see Fig. 44).

At the venous end of the capillaries the osmotic pressure may be a little higher than at the arterial end because of the loss of water and consequent rise of protein concentration. The blood pressure, however, falls somewhat. If the osmotic pressure becomes greater than the blood pressure, fluid will be drawn into the capillaries.

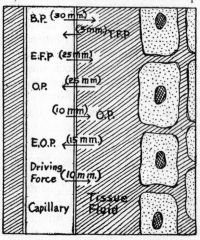

Fig. 44—The formation of tissue fluid. B.P. = blood pressure; T.F.P. = tissue fluid pressure; E.F.P. = effective filtration pressure; O.P. = osmotic pressure; E.O.P. = effective osmotic pressure. For explanation see text. Pressures are in millimeters of mercury.

Any decrease in blood osmotic pressure, any increase in blood pressure or in tissue fluid osmotic pressure (other factors remaining constant) will cause an increased formation of tissue fluid. An increased capillary permeability would have the same effect. If any of these changes persist for some time, tissue fluid will accumulate in the tissue spaces in greater amounts than normal and a condition of *edema* or *dropsy* will result. For example, edema can result if the protein content of plasma falls because of insufficient protein in the diet or because of kidney disease and consequent loss of protein in the urine.

Structure of the Lymphatic System. There are a vast number of small, very thin-walled vessels, the *lymph capillaries*, which drain fluid from the tissue spaces. These vessels merge with one another to form larger and larger lymph vessels. From regions below the heart all lymph vessels finally empty into two large vessels, the *right lymphatic duct* and the *left lymphatic* or *thoracic duct*. These ducts then empty into veins which are returning blood from the right and left arms respectively. The smaller lymph vessels above the heart eventually terminate in the right and left *cervical lymphatics*, which empty into the same veins as do the lymphatic ducts.

In the course of the larger lymph vessels there are enlargements called *lymph nodes* or *glands*. The lymph vessels entering these nodes break up into finer branches which ramify throughout the nodes and then once more unite to form larger vessels which leave the node.

The Flow of Lymph. The excess tissue fluid is carried back to the blood by the lymph vessels. Once inside the lymph vessels this fluid is called *lymph*. The lymph capillaries are closed vessels which end blindly in the tissue spaces; the permeability of lymph capillary walls is greater than that of blood capillary walls. However, just how fluid enters the lymph capillaries is obscure.

The flow of lymph is very slow. There is little driving power behind its flow (there is no effective pump like the heart). If tissue fluid formation is increased, the flow of lymph accelerates because of the push of freshly formed fluid against that in the lymph vessels. Lymph flow in vessels below the heart, like the venous flow, is impeded by the pull of gravity. The "pumping" action of the skeletal muscles is, therefore, of even greater importance for lymph flow than for venous return. Numerous valves which allow lymph to flow only toward its outflow into the blood stream are also important in maintaining whatever flow there is.

If the lymphatic system is blocked at any point, edema will result.

Functions of the Lymphatic System. We have already noted that this system provides for the return of tissue fluid to the blood. This is especially important for the proteins which "leak" out of the blood stream. They do not return to the blood through the capillary walls, but only via the lymphatic system. Water, on the other hand, can return directly to the blood stream if necessary.

The lymph nodes are the site of formation of the lymphocytes. Lymph contains a greater concentration of lymphocytes than blood for this reason.

The lymph nodes and other accumulation of lymphoid tissue (such as the tonsils and adenoids) act as strainers of foreign particles or bacteria and thus help to prevent the spread of injurious materials throughout the body. Lymphoid tissues, especially that of the thymus, may be of considerable importance in the formation of antibodies (see Chapter XXI).

CHAPTER V

The Respiratory System

THE INTAKE of oxygen and the release of carbon dioxide are processes essential to life. Respiration involves these two processes at two different levels. The more obvious kind of respiration is breathing or *external respiration*, which involves the procurement of oxygen and the excretion of carbon dioxide by the body. *Internal respiration*, the

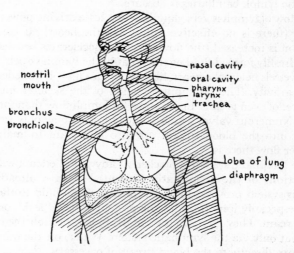

nostril
mouth

nasal cavity
oral cavity
pharynx
larynx
trachea

bronchus
bronchiole

lobe of lung
diaphragm

FIG. 45—The respiratory system. The ribs and intercostal muscles (see Figs. 48, 74 and 77) are not included here, although they are important parts of this system.

use of oxygen and production of carbon dioxide by the cells of the body, involves the multitude of chemical reactions which make up the metabolism of the cell. These reactions constitute the subject matter of *biochemistry* which is beyond the scope of this book. Unless otherwise indicated, we shall mean external respiration when we use the word "respiration."

In one-celled animal forms, respiration consists of a simple exchange of oxygen and carbon dioxide across the *cell membrane*. More complex animals evolved different mechanisms. In some types of worms the respiratory gases diffuse through the *skin* into or out of blood vessels in the skin, and the blood carries them to or from the body cells. Even in as comparatively advanced an animal as the frog, a considerable portion of the respiratory exchange is effected through its moist skin.

Insects possess a series of air tubes which branch and rebranch throughout their bodies and open to the outside through pores in their abdominal walls. Circulation of air is produced by contractions and expansions of the abdomen, air being brought directly to the cells.

In most higher animals another mechanism is introduced—the collection of air in a respiratory organ across whose thin, moist walls gases diffuse into and out of the blood, which transports the gases to and from the cells. The respiratory organs of fishes are called the gills; those of amphibia, reptiles, birds, and mammals are the *lungs*. Water or air is pumped through these organs and the gaseous exchange occurs between them and their blood capillaries.

THE ANATOMY OF THE RESPIRATORY ORGANS

Air is sucked in through either the *nostrils* or the *mouth* and passes into the *pharynx*. Opening from the pharynx is the respiratory tube proper which begins as the *larynx* or voice box (the receptacle of the vocal cords). The continuation of the respiratory tube is the *trachea*, which extends into the thoracic cavity. (See Fig. 45.)

In the walls of the larynx there are plates of cartilage which act as supporting structures for the vocal cords. Cartilage is also present in the trachea (Fig. 46) in the form of incomplete rings. These rings make the trachea a more rigid tube than it would otherwise be, and prevent it from being easily collapsed. They are only three-fourths complete, however, so that the trachea can be somewhat constricted. The trachea contains smooth muscle in its walls. Constrictor and dilator nerves control the muscle and thereby regulate the caliber of the trachea. Another important structural part of the walls is elastic tissue (also present in the lung tissue), with which we shall be concerned in the mechanisms of breathing.

The trachea finally divides into two *bronchi*, one going into each *lung*. There each bronchus subdivides further and further until a great number of very small branches, *bronchioles*, end in air-sacs (see Fig. 47). The bronchial walls are very similar to those of the trachea until the finest bronchioles are reached, when the walls become thinner and cartilage is no longer present.

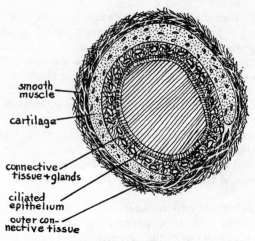

FIG. 46—A cross-section of the trachea showing the incomplete ring of cartilage in its wall.

Lining the inner surfaces of the bronchial tubes, trachea, pharynx, larynx, and parts of the nasal passageways is a layer of columnar epithelium. Its cells are modified in many places to form glands which secrete mucus or a watery fluid. These secretions lubricate the respiratory passageways and preserve a moist environment for the surface cells. The columnar cells are further modified by the presence of fine, hair-like processes, *cilia*, on their free surfaces. Movement of

FIG. 47—Lung tissue. Each bronchiole opens into a number of air-sacs. Each air-sac has a number of tiny bulges in its wall which form the alveoli between which and the capillaries the respiratory gases are exchanged.

the cilia is continually going on in the direction away from the lungs. By their movements they sweep small foreign particles, such as dust, outwards and prevent their passage into the lungs.

The smallest branches of the bronchial "tree" divide into a number of *air-sacs*, each of which has a number of bulges in its walls. These bulges form little chambers or *alveoli* (see Fig. 47), which are lined by a single layer of flat epithelial cells. The lungs are richly supplied with blood vessels, and capillaries lie immediately adjacent to the alveolar walls. Thus, the respiratory gases have only to diffuse through two delicate walls (in some places the alveolar wall is lacking so that only one wall separates the blood and air) to pass from alveoli to blood or vice versa.

THE MECHANISMS OF BREATHING

Unlike the frog, which swallows air and thus forces it into its lungs under pressure, man sucks air into his lungs by decreasing the pressure in them. When we inhale, a series of events occurs: the chest increases in volume, the pressure in the chest cavity, and that inside the lungs falls, and air is sucked into the lungs; when we exhale, the opposites of these events take place: the chest decreases in volume, the pressures just noted rise, and air is forced out of the lungs. These events are possible only because the thoracic cavity is completely closed, yet can exhibit changes in volume.

The Mechanisms of Inspiration. Inhalation or *inspiration* is an active process, exhalation or *expiration* a passive one ordinarily. In inspiration the capacity of the chest is increased from front to back, from side to side, and in the vertical plane. The latter is accomplished by the contraction of the *diaphragm*, the muscular partition between the thoracic and abdominal cavities. At rest, the diaphragm is dome-shaped (see Fig. 45), but tends to flatten out during its contraction (Fig. 48). This movement will increase the volume of the chest from top to bottom. At the same time, contraction of the *intercostal* (between the ribs) *muscles* moves the ribs upward and forward. The rib movements increase the chest volume from front to back (upper ribs) and from side to side (lower ribs).

Because of the increase in chest volume the lungs expand and air is drawn in. Let us trace the mechanism behind this. At the moment of birth there is no air in the lungs and they are in a deflated condition. But at that moment the chest expands and the pressure falls in the space between the lungs and the chest wall (if nothing else changes in a system, an increase in volume is accompanied by a decrease in pressure). The decrease in pressure on the *outside* of the lungs causes them to inflate. Since now the volume inside the lungs increases, the pressure *inside* the lungs falls. With the pressure inside the lungs less than the atmospheric pressure outside the body, air rushes through the respiratory passageways into the lungs.

From the moment that air first enters the lungs, they are never completely deflated and almost completely fill their portion of the thoracic cavity. The space between the lungs and the chest walls, the *intrathoracic cavity*, is, then, only a potential cavity; in reality it contains nothing but a thin film of fluid between lung and chest walls. That thin fluid film, however, is important. The force of its surface tension actually keeps the lungs adherent to the chest wall; thus, when the chest wall moves outward (or inward), the lungs correspondingly expand (or deflate).

The elastic tissue in the lungs tends to make them resist expansion; this resistance to expansion, plus the actual expansion of the thoracic cavity, lowers the pressure in that cavity.

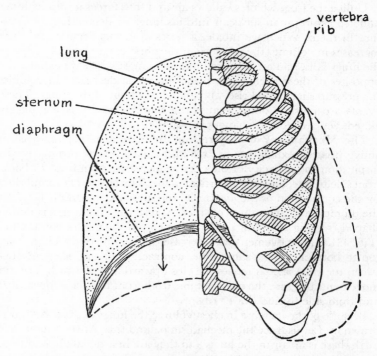

Fig. 48—The ribs, lungs and diaphragm in their resting or expiratory positions. The dotted lines indicate the extent of movement of the ribs and diaphragm during inspiration and, consequently, the increase in capacity of the thoracic cavity.

Expiration. Ordinary expiration comes about by the reversal of the changes occurring during inspiration. The muscles that produce the inspiratory movements relax, so that, as the diaphragm ascends and the ribs return to their resting positions, the volume of the chest decreases. The lungs, adhering to the chest wall, decrease in volume, aided by the recoil of their elastic tissue. As lung volume decreases, pressure in the lungs increases above atmospheric pressure (air in the lungs becomes somewhat squeezed) and air is forced out of the lungs and respiratory passageways. As the intrathoracic volume decreases, intrathoracic pressure increases.

When we expire forcibly, there are contractions of muscles that aid in the process. The muscles in the wall of the abdomen contract and compress the abdominal organs which in turn push upward against the diaphragm, hastening its rise. Other intercostal muscles contract and move the ribs downward and toward the back. These latter muscular movements assist the normal pull of gravity, thus hastening the change and increasing its extent. The net result of these more active events is a greater decrease in the volume of the thoracic cavity than occurs normally. The lungs react to this by a more vigorous elastic recoil, consequently expelling air more rapidly and more forcibly.

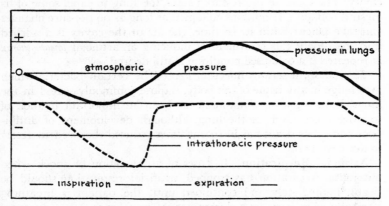

Fig. 49—Pressure changes during respiration. See text.

Pressure Changes (see Fig. 49). From what has been said above, we can see that in inspiration the pressure within the lung first decreases as the lung expands. Toward the end of inspiration, however, it begins to rise as air is drawn in, and by the end of inspiration, it equals the atmospheric pressure. At this point no more air enters. During the first part of expiration the pressure rises as the lung recoils, and then it falls again as air is forced out. At the end of expiration the pressure again equals atmospheric, and no more air is exhaled.

The intrathoracic pressure, on the other hand, declines steadily during inspiration, reaching its greatest depth at the end of inspiration. It rises sharply during the early part of expiration and then levels off at a maximal height. Note that intrathoracic pressure is always below atmospheric pressure; this is so because, even at rest, the lungs are partially inflated and their *tendency* to pull away from the chest wall sets up a strain in the intrathoracic space which keeps its pressure lowered.

As we mentioned above, the intrathoracic cavity contains only a thin film of fluid. If, by any means, more fluid or a quantity of air should get into this space, then respiration would be impaired or stopped. This occurs because the intrathoracic pressure rises and the lung deflates to an extent dependent upon how great the rise in pressure is. This condition may be brought about accidentally (by a knife or bullet wound) or by disease (inflammation of the pleura and accumulation of fluid, hemorrhage into the cavity, etc.).

Doctors, however, may make good use of the phenomenon. If one lung becomes infected, it has a better chance of healing if it can be rendered motionless. Since each lung is in a compartment separated from the other lung by membranes and by the space containing the heart, it is possible to inject air into one side of the intrathoracic cavity. The increase in pressure causes the lung to expel some of its air and collapse. It remains collapsed as long as no pressure changes can take place within it. In time, the air in the cavity is absorbed into the blood; this treatment of inducing an artificial *pneumothorax* is repeated if a collapsed condition is still desired.

Tuberculosis, a serious infection caused by certain bacteria which may lodge in any tissue of the body, is quite commonly seated in the lungs. Inducing a pneumothorax has been an important method of treating tuberculosis of the lung, although development of antibiotics and other drugs has in recent times reduced the need to resort to this treatment.

Artificial Respiration. In cases of asphyxiation or shock when automatic respiration has stopped, artificial respiration should be begun immediately and continued until the patient is breathing normally once more or a doctor has taken charge.

The mouth-to-mouth method is easiest to apply, even for the person untrained in first-aid measures. You force air from your mouth into the subject's mouth, bringing about inflation of his lungs, and then allow him to exhale the air by natural elastic recoil. Continue the procedure at normal breathing rate. This method has the added advantage of forcing some carbon dioxide into the subject; as we shall soon see, this can act as an additional stimulus for resumption of breathing.

When prolonged artificial respiration is desirable, as in some severe cases of *poliomyelitis*, machines can be employed. The "iron lung" works by alternately increasing and decreasing the pressure outside the body, thereby producing alternate compression and expansion of the chest wall.

Composition of Inspired and Expired Air. The air about us is a mixture of gases. Nitrogen makes up almost four-fifths of the total (79 per cent). Oxygen constitutes about 20 per cent, carbon dioxide 0.04 per cent, and the remainder consists of water vapor and traces of rarer gases. The expired air contains about the same percentage of nitrogen and rare gases, but the other contents are significantly different. Oxygen now makes up only about 16 per cent of the total, the carbon dioxide volume has increased to 4 per cent, and the air is just about saturated with water vapor.

The important respiratory change is the decrease of 4 per cent in oxygen content and the similar increase in carbon dioxide volume. It is evident that not all the oxygen of the inspired air is taken up by the blood and, therefore, that expired air could be rebreathed for a short time before discomfort would be felt.

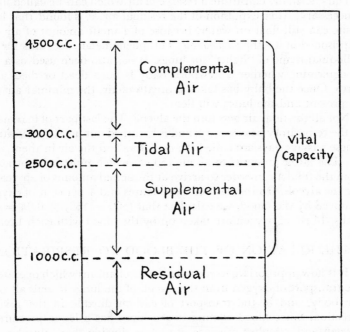

Fig. 50—The capacity of the lungs. See text.

The Capacity of the Lungs. With each normal inspiration of an adult man at rest about 500 cc. of air are inhaled. A like amount is exhaled. This ebb and flow of air is called *tidal* respiration and the volume of air concerned, *tidal air*. We are familiar with the fact that we can inhale more than this amount. In addition to the tidal air, we can inhale another 1500 cc. of air, the *complemental air*. After a normal expiration, we can also exhale 1500 cc., the *supplemental air*. The sum of tidal, complemental, and supplemental airs is called the *vital capacity* (see Fig. 50). The average man can, then, breathe in about 2000 cc. (that is two liters, which is approximately the same as two quarts) of air and he can expel about 3500 cc. The figures for women may be some 20 per cent less than these and for trained athletes 20 or more per cent greater. The vital capacity can be increased by training. Chest expansion, however, is not a good index, since some persons with powerful chest muscles can expand their chests to a greater extent than their lungs can fill.

Even after the greatest amount of air possible has been expired, a considerable volume of air remains in the lungs. When the lungs are removed from the body, it is found that an additional liter of air can be collected from them—the *residual air*. The supplemental and residual airs normally constitute a reserve of air which can be called upon if necessary. After expulsion of the residual air, it is found that lung tissue can still float on water, because of a small amount of air still imprisoned in it—the *minimal air*. This phenomenon accounts for the colloquial name of "lights" for lungs. It has also been used as a test to determine whether a newborn baby is born dead or died after birth. Once the baby has taken a breath of air, the minimal air will be present and the lungs will float.

Not all the tidal air gets into the alveoli. The last part of it remains in the respiratory passageways and is breathed out first in expiration. These passageways are called the *dead space* and the air in them, *dead air*. The latter amounts to about 150 cc. which must be subtracted from the tidal air in order to arrive at the actual amount of air reaching the alveoli. On the basis of these figures and 4 per cent of oxygen removed by the blood, we calculate that $(500 - 150) \times 0.04 = 14$. Thus, 14 cc. of oxygen are taken up by the blood with each breath.

THE RELATION OF THE BLOOD TO RESPIRATION

It is now appropriate to consider the mechanisms which operate in the transport of oxygen from the alveoli of the lungs to cells all over the body, and in the transport of carbon dioxide in the reverse direction. Since blood coming to the lungs has a lesser pressure of oxygen and a higher pressure of carbon dioxide than alveolar air, and since the two layers (at most) of thin cells which separate these regions are extremely permeable to both gases, the simple process of diffusion seems adequate to explain the passage of oxygen into the blood and of carbon dioxide into the alveoli. Similar reasoning explains the passage of oxygen out of the blood and carbon dioxide into it in the body tissues in general.

But the process is not as simple as it seems. It is more complex because of the nature of the blood. For example, if we expose 100 cc. of *plasma* to the air and allow equilibrium to be attained (as many molecules of gas leaving the fluid as entering it), we will find on analysis that only about 0.2 cc. of oxygen was in solution. On the other hand, 100 cc. of *whole blood* under the same conditions will contain about 20 cc. of oxygen. Since the same pressure of oxygen in the air is available to both blood and plasma, and different amounts of oxygen enter each, other factors must be influencing the diffusion of the gas.

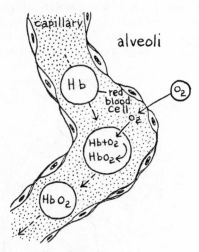

Fig. 51—Passage of oxygen from alveoli into blood. The same red blood cell is shown in three different positions during its journey through the capillary.

The Transport of Oxygen. The examples just quoted make it plain that though there is oxygen in solution in the plasma, it is only a small part of the total amount in whole blood. Evidently it is something in the blood cells that is mainly responsible for its uptake by the blood. That something is the hemoglobin of the red cells; 100 cc. of a solution of hemoglobin (containing as much hemoglobin as would be present in 100 cc. of whole blood) will also take up about 20 cc. of oxygen. Hemoglobin (which we will symbolize by "Hb") combines with oxygen to form *oxyhemoglobin:*

$$Hb + O_2 \rightarrow HbO_2$$

Thus combined, oxygen is carried in the red cells to the capillaries of the tissues. The oxygen content of the tissues and tissue fluid is less than that of blood. In the presence of lowered oxygen pressure, oxyhemoglobin breaks up into hemoglobin and oxygen, and the freed oxygen diffuses out of the blood:

$$HbO_2 \rightarrow Hb + O_2$$

Diffusion of oxygen is regulated by pressure differences and by the nature of the medium that takes up the oxygen. The pressure of oxygen in the air is about 152 mm. of mercury. Its pressure in the alveoli is only 105 mm., since oxygen is diffusing out of the alveoli into the blood at all times. The oxygen pressure in blood coming to the lungs is 40 mm. Because of this pressure difference, oxygen diffuses into the blood. There it first dissolves in the plasma (Fig. 51). We have seen that very little can be dissolved in this way. However, from the plasma it diffuses into the red cells where it is taken up by hemoglobin. This process goes on quickly enough to raise the oxygen

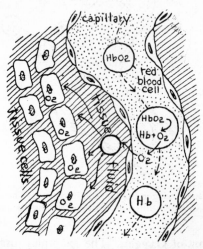

FIG. 52—Passage of oxygen from blood into the tissues. The same red blood cell is shown in three different positions during its journey through the capillary. Compare with Fig. 51.

pressure to 100 mm. in the blood leaving the lungs and to saturate hemoglobin almost completely (95 per cent). Thus, in the lungs there is an equilibrium between the oxygen in the alveoli and that in the plasma, and another between that in the plasma and in oxyhemoglobin. In this setup the plasma acts as a middle-man, passing oxygen either in or out of the blood, depending upon the pressure of oxygen outside the blood. In the tissues and tissue fluid the pressure of oxygen is low (0 − 40 mm.). Here, then, oxygen diffuses out of the plasma into the tissue fluid (Fig. 52). This disturbs the equilibrium between dissolved oxygen and oxyhemoglobin; some of the latter breaks down and releases oxygen which diffuses into the plasma. This process continues until the oxygen pressure of the blood has fallen to 40 mm.

The Transport of Carbon Dioxide. The pressure of carbon dioxide in the tissues and tissue fluid (45 or more mm.) is higher than that in the arterial blood (40 mm.) coming to the tissues. It therefore diffuses into the plasma and dissolves (Fig. 53). But, as in the case of oxygen, comparatively little can be carried in this fashion. It diffuses into the red cells where, under the influence of an enzyme, it combines with water to form *carbonic acid:*

$$CO_2 + H_2O \rightarrow H_2CO_3$$

Carbonic acid then reacts with salts of the blood proteins (hemoglobin and plasma proteins) to form *sodium* and *potassium bicarbonates* ($NaHCO_3$ and $KHCO_3$). These ionize in the water of the blood, i.e.,

$$NaHCO_3 \rightarrow Na^+ + HCO_3^-$$

The greater portion of the carbon dioxide is carried as the *bicarbonate ion*, HCO_3^-. Another small fraction combines directly with hemoglobin to form *carboxy-hemoglobin.*

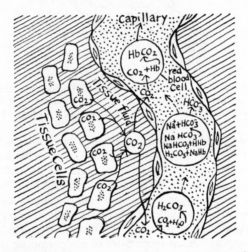

FIG. 53—Passage of carbon dioxide from the tissues into the blood. The same red blood cell is shown in three different positions during its journey through the capillary. NaHb = the sodium salt of hemoglobin, HHb = an acid form of hemoglobin, $HbCO_2$ = carboxy-hemoglobin. Some hemoglobin reacts with carbonic acid, some combines with carbon dioxide.

In the venous blood the pressure of carbon dioxide has now been raised to 45 or more mm. The pressure of the gas in the alveoli is about 40 mm. Therefore, in the lungs carbon dioxide diffuses out of the plasma (Fig. 54). This upsets the equilibrium between dissolved gas and that in the bicarbonate form. Thereupon the bicarbonates react with the blood proteins in the reverse direction to that above, carbonic acid is re-formed and, under the influence of the red cell enzyme, breaks down to water and carbon dioxide. The latter dissolves in the plasma and diffuses out of the blood until its pressure falls to 40 mm.

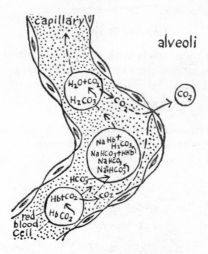

Fig. 54—Passage of carbon dioxide from the blood into the alveoli. The same red blood cell is shown in three different positions during its journey through the capillary. Compare with Fig. 53.

An interesting interrelationship between carbon dioxide and oxygen exists. The blood becomes slightly more acid when carbon dioxide enters (due to formation of carbonic acid) and the greater acidity favors the breakdown of oxyhemoglobin. Thus, carbon dioxide entry speeds oxygen release. These phenomena are reversed in the lungs—carbon dioxide exit favoring oxygen entry.

Carbon Monoxide Poisoning. Colorless and odorless, carbon monoxide is responsible for more cases of gas poisoning in peacetime than is any other gas. Since it is a component of the exhaust gas of automobiles, special precautions have to be taken in places like long automobile tunnels to prevent its accumulation. Its poisonous effects are due to its great affinity for hemoglobin, with which it combines to form *carbon monoxide hemoglobin*. Since the affinity of this gas for hemoglobin is some 300 times greater than that of oxygen, it is small wonder that a relatively low concentration of it in the air can cause the formation of a considerable amount of carbon monoxide hemoglobin in place of oxyhemoglobin. The resultant lowered oxygen content of the blood may be, and often is, severe enough to cause death. However, in the presence of an excess of oxygen, carbon monoxide hemoglobin is reconverted to oxyhemoglobin, so that effective treatment involves removal of the patient from the poisonous atmosphere to one rich in oxygen and immediate institution of artificial respiration if breathing has stopped. Recovery of the patient will be complete if the concentration of the gas was not too high or the exposure to the gas not too long.

THE CONTROL OF RESPIRATION

Unlike the heartbeat, breathing can be voluntarily controlled to a certain extent. But most often it goes on quite rhythmically and automatically. The rate of respiration at rest averages, in most of us, some sixteen to eighteen breaths per minute. Both rate and depth of respiration can vary widely under different conditions. How are these changes brought about and what is responsible for the automaticity?

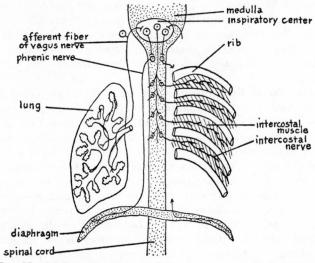

FIG. 55—A schematic diagram of the nervous control of respiration. Only the right lung and some of the left ribs and intercostal muscles are shown. The efferent paths from the inspiratory center to the diaphragm and intercostal muscles are indicated. On the afferent side only the vagal fibers from the lung to the respiratory center are seen.

The Respiratory Centers. In the medulla of the brain there are two clusters of nerve cell bodies named the *inspiratory* and *expiratory centers*. In the pons of the brain lies a third center influential in respiration. (For the sake of simplicity, only the inspiratory center is shown in Fig. 55.) The inspiratory center discharges automatically and rhythmically and is responsible for initiating each inhalation. What causes its automaticity is still as unclear as what causes that of the heartbeat. However, the rhythm of breathing, as you know from your own experience, can often be far more irregular than that of the heart. Whether regular or irregular, the rhythm of the inspiratory center is modified by a variety of influences—often nervous, sometimes nervous and chemical combined—which will be discussed in the following section.

When the neurons of the inspiratory center discharge, impulses are conducted down their nerve fibers to other neurons in the spinal cord which, in turn, discharge impulses to the muscles whose contraction leads to inspiration. On either side of the cervical (neck) region of the spinal cord lie nerve cells from which arise the *phrenic nerves* (Fig. 55); the latter travel through the thoracic cavity, each nerve innervating half of the diaphragm. The *intercostal nerves* arise from neurons on either side of the thoracic portion of the spinal cord (Fig. 55); these nerves control the intercostal muscles. Inspiration can normally occur only when impulses follow the paths just indicated to the appropriate muscles. Expiration is most usually the result of cessation of discharge of impulses and consequent relaxation of the inspiratory muscles. Injury or destruction anywhere along the nervous pathway could, obviously, seriously interfere with, or even prevent, breathing.

Rhythmicity of Respiration. If no other influences acted upon the inspiratory center, it would tend to keep discharging at regular intervals but with a rhythm considerably slower than that usually observed. A combination of nervous and chemical factors usually cooperate in driving this center at a somewhat faster rhythm.

Let us first note some intrinsic nervous influences. Each inspiration sets into motion two mechanisms, each of which tends to inhibit the activity of the inspiratory center. As the lungs inflate, the alveolar walls distend and receptors in them initiate impulses in sensory fibers of the *vagus nerve*. These impulses ascend to the expiratory center and excite it; its neurons send impulses to the inspiratory center which, on reaching the latter, tend to inhibit (prevent the discharge of) inspiratory neurons. Also, the inspiratory center as it discharges sends impulses not only to the spinal cord but to the center in the pons as well. The pontine neurons fire impulses to the expiratory center which then functions as mentioned above. The expiratory center is, we see, stimulated both reflexly and via the pontine center to send impulses which inhibit inspiratory activity. The net effect is to shorten the inspiratory discharge which, when repeated time after time, accelerates the breathing rate. In experiments, cutting the vagus nerves (Fig. 56) slows the respiratory rate (the inspiratory center can now discharge for a longer time). If, subsequently, connections between the pontine center and the centers in the medulla are severed, breathing is further slowed in rate.

The excitability of the inspiratory center is, in addition, affected by certain chemical influences. Whenever the level of carbon dioxide in the blood that courses by the inspiratory center rises sufficiently high, inspiratory activity is increased. Since the inspiratory neurons are very sensitive to small changes in carbon dioxide level and since that level is almost continually fluctuating (because of expiratory activity as opposed to the metabolic activity of the tissues), we can see that the moment-to-moment level of carbon dioxide must have important consequences for breathing.

Thus, there are nervous and chemical agencies which *regularly* control the rhythm of breathing. To these must be added a variety of irregular factors that may temporarily supersede the above or, at least, importantly modify them.

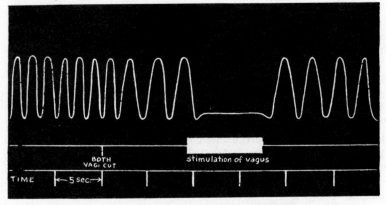

Fig. 56—A graphic record of respiration in the dog. Note that after both vagus nerves are cut, respiration slows. When the end of a vagus nerve— the end leading to the brain—is stimulated, respiration is completely inhibited.

Special Means of Control. The breathing process can, of course, be voluntarily modified (by impulses from highest brain centers reaching those in the medulla and pons) in quite precise fashion; depth and rate can be varied in a multitude of patterns. Voluntary control cannot, however, completely override inherent or reflex influences: try to breathe while swallowing or try to hold your breath indefinitely.

One cannot breathe while swallowing because the swallowing process sets up sensory impulses in the pharynx which reflexly inhibit breathing—and inhibit very potently. Inhibition of breathing while swallowing prevents solids or liquids from entering the respiratory passageways and is an example of a *protective reflex* associated with breathing. When the larynx is stimulated mechanically (by foreign particles) or chemically (by harmful or irritating gases), breathing is again reflexly inhibited and this may be followed by reflex coughing. Similar stimulation of the nasal lining can result in reflex sneezing.

Holding the breath indefinitely is impossible because the voluntary inhibition of breathing is overcome by the increasing level of carbon dioxide which is the result of metabolic activity. Carbon dioxide excitation of inspiratory neurons overpowers their inhibition from higher centers. We see an opposite effect when the carbon dioxide level is reduced as the result of forced (rapid and deep) breathing. After such breathing one can hold the breath longer than after normal breathing; swimmers take advantage of this phenomenon to remain longer under water. Forced breathing causes more carbon dioxide to be lost through expired air than can enter the blood from the tissues; the fall in blood level of the gas depresses the inspiratory center for a short time until the carbon dioxide level builds again.

It may seem odd to you that carbon dioxide levels, rather than oxygen levels, are more important in respiratory regulation, but such is incontrovertibly the case. Actually, the inspiratory center is depressed when directly exposed to a lowered blood oxygen level. Peripherally, however, there are receptors in the carotid arteries and the aorta which are excited by a lowered blood oxygen (or increased carbon dioxide) level. Impulses from these receptors reflexly activate the inspiratory center. This mechanism is, perhaps, more important in emergency situations than in moment-to-moment control.

It should also be mentioned that breathing rate and depth can be altered by any environmental change. Just as do other vital centers in the medulla, the inspiratory center receives and reacts to sensory impulses from a wide variety of sources.

OTHER FUNCTIONS AND ACTIVITIES OF THE RESPIRATORY SYSTEM

Sneezing and Coughing. These acts are reflexes induced by irritation of the lining of the nasal cavities or of lower regions of the respiratory tube. Their function is, of course, to expel the irritant. Both begin with a short inspiration followed by the drawing together of the vocal cords (thus closing off the lungs from the outside) and a powerful expiration. As expiration starts with the respiratory passageway closed, a high pressure is developed within the lungs. Then the vocal cords separate and a strong gust of air sweeps the irritant out of nose or mouth.

Yawning, Sighing, Hiccoughing. These acts are respiratory reflexes whose significance and initiating stimuli are obscure. Yawning may be an indirect circulatory reflex response which serves to stimulate the circulation. The fact that it is frequently accompanied by stretching lends some support to this conclusion.

Talking and Singing. Voiced sounds are produced by the vibrations of the vocal cords which are set into motion by the expired air. The quality of the sound depends upon the degree of tension of the vocal cords, a condition which we can modify at will. It is also evident that we must voluntarily control the respiratory movements to permit the wide range of inflections and the continuity of utterances of which the human voice is capable.

The Head Sinuses. In the frontal and maxillary (cheek) bones (see Fig. 74) there are some air-filled cavities, the *frontal* and *maxillary sinuses*. The functions of these cavities are obscure. Many of us are never aware that we possess such sinuses, but some of us become acutely conscious of their presence during sieges of "sinus trouble" or *sinusitis*.

The head sinuses are lined by a thin membrane and are connected with the upper part of the nasal cavities by narrow passageways. Sometimes "germs" enter the sinuses via these passageways and set up an inflammation or infection.

Aiding Blood and Lymph Flow. In Chapter IV we noted that respiratory movements aided the flow of venous blood and lymph. This assistance is made possible by the changes of pressure in the intrathoracic and abdominal cavities. During inspiration the pressure in the former falls but rises in the latter (because of the descent of the diaphragm which squeezes abdominal organs to some extent). The relatively thin-walled veins and lymph vessels are expanded in the thorax and compressed in the abdomen as a result of these pressure changes. During expiration the effects are reversed as the pressures swing in the opposite directions. When the vessels are enlarged, more blood or lymph enters them from below and when they are compressed blood is forced upward. This accessory "pumping" action with every respiration considerably aids the return of blood to the heart and lymph to the blood.

CHAPTER VI

The Digestive System

DIFFUSION OF nutrients from a food vacuole to the other parts of the cell is a satisfactory process for the nourishment of Amoeba. In the simpler multicellular animals there is a central cavity into which food is taken and digested. Branches of this cavity extend to within short distances of all the cells, so that diffusion is still an adequate process

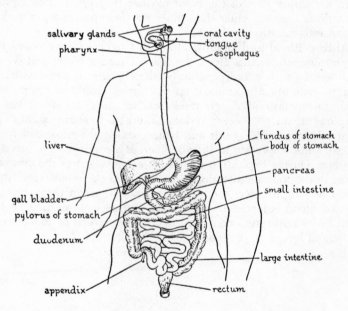

FIG. 57—Diagram of the digestive system.

for supplying them with nourishment. As more complex animals evolved, however, a more complex body plan came into being in which the site of digestion of foods was quite distant from many body cells. The coincident development of the circulatory system, which could transport digested materials to all parts of the body, made it possible for a group of organs to be limited to the specific function of breaking down ingested food into materials useful to the organism.

ANATOMY OF THE DIGESTIVE ORGANS

Food enters the mouth, is swallowed, and passes successively through the pharynx, esophagus, stomach, and small intestine. In the latter two the digestible material is broken down. The products of digestion are absorbed in the small intestine. The residue proceeds through the large intestine and rectum and is eliminated through the anus.

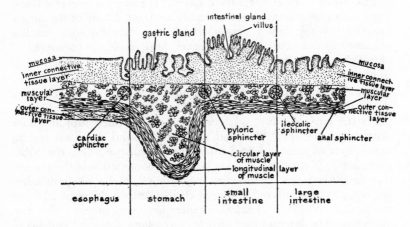

Fig. 58—A schematic sketch of the layers of the alimentary canal in its four main regions. For full description, see text.

The mouth is lined by a *mucous membrane* or *mucosa* which is lubricated by the mucus secreted from many tiny glands in it. The teeth and the muscular tongue are important in chewing, and the latter starts the food on its journey through the digestive tract. Most of the saliva that pours into the mouth is secreted by three pairs of salivary glands. The gland cells secrete saliva into small ducts which unite to form larger ones and finally one or two large ducts which carry the fluid into the oral cavity.

The alimentary canal proper has the same basic construction plan in all its parts. Each part is essentially a tube consisting of four-layered walls. From the *lumen* (cavity) outwards these layers are the *mucosa*, the *inner connective tissue layer*, the *muscular layer* and the *outer connective tissue layer* (see Fig. 58). Modifications of these layers can be correlated with the functions of the different parts.

The Mucosa. In the esophagus the mucosa consists mainly of stratified epithelium, which is the kind generally present where considerable friction may be developed. Throughout the stomach and intestines the cells of the mucosa are columnar. The lining of the stomach has many visible folds which increase its surface area and numerous tiny glands which dip down below the surface. The small intestine's lining looks and feels velvety smooth. On microscopic examination, however, it is seen that, in addition to many glands, the mucosa extends countless finger-like processes into the lumen. In the large intestine the mucosa is less modified than in other regions but it does contain many mucus-secreting cells. Thus, in each part of the tract, the mucosa is distinctively varied.

The Inner Connective Tissue Layer. The inner connective tissue layer varies little throughout the digestive tract. Many of the larger branches of the blood vessels travel here, sending out smaller branches to the other layers of tissue. Also, a plexus (network) of nerve fibers and nerve cell bodies is found throughout the length of this layer.

The Muscular Layer. In all regions but the upper two-thirds of the esophagus (which contains skeletal muscle) smooth muscle comprises the muscular layer. It generally is subdivided into an inner layer of muscle whose fibers run circularly around the canal and an outer layer of muscle whose fibers run lengthwise along the tube. Contraction of the circular layer will cause constriction of the lumen. The muscular layer of the stomach is much thicker than in other regions and its subdivisions are not clearly defined. Here in addition to circular and longitudinal fibers there are many others which run obliquely. The longitudinal muscle of the large intestine consists of three separate bands of muscle, and thus does not form a continuous layer. These bands are not so long as the large intestine and when they are contracted give this part of the tract a puckered appearance.

In certain regions—the junctions of esophagus and stomach, of stomach and small intestine, of small and large intestines, and at the anus—the circular muscle is greatly thickened to form a ring of muscle capable of closing off the lumen entirely. These rings or *sphincters* regulate the passage of material from one part of the tract to another. Between the circular and longitudinal layers of each sphincter there is another nervous plexus which contains more cell bodies than those in the inner connective tissue layer.

The Outer Connective Tissue Layer. Around the esophagus, the outer connective tissue layer is a tough, protective coating; but in the rest of the tract it secretes an aqueous fluid which lubricates the outer surfaces of these organs as they rub against one another.

THE CHEMICAL BREAKDOWN OF FOOD

Although two days may elapse before all traces of a meal are completely eliminated from the digestive tract, the digestible portions will have been absorbed into the blood stream and be available for use by the cells within four to ten hours. Before we consider how food travels through the tract, let us trace its digestion.

Prior to the mid-eighteenth century, scientists believed that digestion was a mechanical process, nutritive juices being squeezed out of food as it was ground up in the stomach. As a result of the work of Réaumur, Stevens, and Spallanzani, it was found that gastric juice could digest meat outside of the body without mechanical aid and that therefore digestion must be a chemical process. An interesting experiment performed at this time was that of having a man swallow a small perforated metal ball containing food. The holes in the ball allowed the gastric juice to attack the food but the ball would resist any mechanical force. Some time later the ball was retrieved and the experimenters then noted that the food had been digested.

Salivary Digestion. An enzyme in saliva begins the process of digestion. However, the digestive action of saliva is less important than its other activities.

If salivary secretion is insufficient, the membranes of the mouth and pharynx become dry and the sensation of *thirst* may be aroused. But, mere drying of these membranes is an insufficient stimulus for that sensation. It is only when the dryness is due to a real depletion of the water in the body (when there is insufficient water for normal salivary secretion) that thirst is aroused.

The saliva rinses and cleans the mouth and teeth and thus helps to prevent accumulation of materials which could bring about decay of the teeth. It moistens and lubricates the structures in the mouth. In addition to preserving a moist, healthy environment, this action facilitates movements of the tongue and lips in talking. And, since only dissolved solids can be tasted, the dissolving action of saliva allows for the sensation of taste.

When food enters the mouth, it is thoroughly mixed with saliva. This makes the food much more plastic and aids tremendously in swallowing. For instance, swallowing dry crackers in the absence of saliva is extremely difficult. The mixing of starchy food and saliva also enables the enzyme, *salivary amylase (pytalin)*, to begin its action on starch. Starch, you will remember, is a compound sugar; in the presence of salivary amylase it is broken down to the double sugar *maltose*.

Several factors may influence the activity of any one enzyme. Each works best within a certain limited temperature range. Since body temperature varies only slightly, this factor is not of great functional import. Outside the body, the influence of temperature can easily be demonstrated, low temperatures slowing and higher ones accelerating their action. A temperature of about 110° F., however, can destroy most enzymes. Each enzyme also works best at a certain acidity. If this is varied too greatly in one direction or the other, an enzyme becomes inactive. Saliva is slightly acid as a rule, but may be slightly alkaline. Salivary amylase works best in solutions which are nearly neutral (as much acid as alkali present).

Because of their great specificity, each adapted to a special purpose, enzymes attack only certain substances. They also may not be able to attack the products so produced. Thus, amylase acts only on starch and cannot cause the breakdown of maltose.

Since foods remains in the mouth only a short time, salivary digestion is not completed before food reaches the stomach. Ordinarily, it may proceed for a half hour or so in the stomach. The starchier portion of a meal generally comes toward the end of the meal. The food swallowed earlier tends to line the walls of the stomach and form a protective coating about that entering later, preventing a rapid mixture of the latter with the gastric juice. Under such conditions amylase continues to break starch down until the very acid gastric juice inactivates it.

Gastric Digestion. Many of the gastric glands secrete a watery juice which contains a considerable amount of hydrochloric acid. "Acid stomach" is, therefore, a normal and, as we shall see, useful condition which should not be tampered with except on the advice of a physician. The enzymes of the gastric juice work properly only in a strongly acid medium.

The three parts of the stomach are called the fundus, body, and pylorus (see Fig. 57). The glands of the fundus and body contain two important types of cells. One type secrets acid, the other secretes the gastric enzymes.

Pepsin is the most important of the three enzymes produced. It attacks the proteins of ingested food, splitting them into smaller substances. Ordinarily, this digestion does not proceed to the amino acid stage but only to the formation of some intermediate products, the *polypeptides*.

Rennin is an enzyme which brings about the coagulation of milk. This process resembles the coagulation of blood. The milk protein, *caseinogen*, is changed from its sol to its gel state. In the latter form it is called *casein*. Since casein is insoluble, it cannot leave the stomach quickly in solution and remains to be acted upon by pepsin. As in the clotting of blood, calcium ions are necessary for the completion of the process. The clot in this case is the *curd* and the liquid portion that separates from it is the *whey* (comparable to blood serum).

Gastric lipase is a fat-splitting enzyme (the ending "-ase" signifies an enzyme). Its action is weak, however, and it is questionable whether it is at all effective in adults. There is more evidence that both rennin and it are of value to infants.

Digestion in the Small Intestine. The major portion of digestion occurs in the small intestine. Secretions from the liver, pancreas, and intestinal mucosa insure the splitting of foods into substances which can be absorbed into the blood.

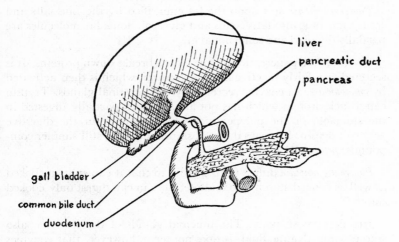

Fig. 59—A sketch of the liver and pancreas, their ducts and the entrance of the latter into the duodenum.

THE BILE. Liver cells are continually secreting *bile*, a brown or greenish-brown fluid. From the liver a duct carries bile toward the small intestine (Fig. 59). If the intestine is not ready to receive the bile, it passes via another duct into the *gall bladder* where it is stored until called into use. At such a time it flows from the duct of the gall bladder into the *common bile duct* (formed by the union of ducts of the liver and gall bladder) and through it to the *duodenum* (the first part of the small intestine).

In addition to water, the important constituents of bile are the *bile salts*, *bile pigments*, and two fat-like compounds, *cholesterol* and *lecithin*. (Cholesterol has already been mentioned in connection with arteriosclerosis in Chapter IV.) From the standpoint of digestion the bile salts are of greatest interest. They have the property of emulsifying fats in the duodenum. (An *emulsion* is a colloidal suspension of one liquid in another, e.g. fat in water.) The globules of fat are reduced in size and have much less tendency to join with one another. Thus, the total surface of fat exposed to the action of the pancreatic fat-splitting enzyme is greatly increased. Bile salts also increase the activity of this enzyme.

THE PANCREATIC JUICE. The pancreas is a diffuse, whitish gland which lies in the *mesentery* (the membrane anchoring the small intestine to the abdominal wall) alongside the duodenum. Its cells secrete an alkaline solution rich in enzymes and pass them via the pancreatic duct into the duodenum (Fig. 59).

Pancreatic lipase acts upon the fat emulsified by the bile salts and splits some of it into fatty acids and glycerol. Some fat molecules are partially digested and some not at all.

Trypsin is the pancreatic enzyme which breaks down proteins. It is secreted as a fairly inactive form, *trypsinogen*, which is then activated by *enterokinase*, an enzyme secreted by the intestinal glands. Trypsin can attack protein which has not already been partially digested in the stomach, or the polypeptides which result from the digestive action of pepsin. It breaks these substances down to still simpler compounds, *peptides*.

Pancreatic amylase differs from ptyalin in that it can split uncooked as well as cooked starch into maltose; ptyalin can digest only cooked starch.

THE INTESTINAL JUICE. The mucosal glands of the intestine also secrete some alkaline fluid. It does not seem, however, that enzymes are present in this fluid. Rather, enzymes are located in the membranes of or in the interior of the mucosal cells.

These intestinal enzymes complete the digestion of ingested foodstuffs. The *peptidases* are a series of enzymes which split peptides of varying complexity into amino acids. There may also be an *intestinal lipase* weaker in action than pancreatic lipase. Finally, there are a few enzmes which attack carbohydrates: *maltase* converts maltose into glucose; *lactase* splits lactose (milk sugar) into glucose and galactose; *sucrase* splits sucrose (cane or table sugar) into glucose and fructose.

Summary of the Digestion of Food. Ingested food is acted upon by a number of enzymes from its entrance into the mouth until its digestion is completed in the small intestine. The following diagram illustrates the action of the various enzymes.

Carbohydrates:

$$\text{Starch} \xrightarrow[\text{pancreatic amylase}]{\substack{\text{salivary} \\ \text{or}}} \text{maltose} \xrightarrow{\text{maltase}} \text{glucose}$$

$$\text{Sucrose} \xrightarrow{\text{sucrase}} \text{glucose} + \text{fructose}$$

$$\text{Lactose} \xrightarrow{\text{lactase}} \text{glucose} + \text{galactose}$$

Fats:

$$\text{Fat} \xrightarrow{\substack{\text{gastric, pancreatic,} \\ \text{and/or} \\ \text{intestinal lipase}}} \text{fatty acids} + \text{glycerol}$$

Proteins:

$$\text{Protein} \xrightarrow{\substack{\text{pepsin} \\ \text{or} \\ \text{trypsin}}} \text{polypeptides}$$

$$\text{Polypeptides} \xrightarrow{\text{trypsin}} \text{smaller peptides} \xrightarrow{\text{peptidases}} \text{amino acids}$$

The simple products of digestion—amino acids, fatty acids, glycerol, and the simple sugars—are absorbed into the blood while the undigested residue passes on into the large intestine.

In mammals such as the cow, rabbit, etc. which feed solely on vegetable matter, there is some further digestion in the *cecum*, a part of the large intestine. Certain bacteria present in this region secrete enzymes which are able to split the cellulose of the plant cells into usable products. Digestion of cellulose does not occur in man whose cecum is very much reduced in size and lacks these special bacteria.

REGULATION OF THE DIGESTIVE SECRETIONS

The secretion of the digestive juices is going on continually, but at the times that they are especially needed, processes are set into motion that insure a more copious flow. The factors controlling the activity of the digestive glands may be nervous, chemical, or mechanical in nature.

The Control of the Salivary Glands. We all know that when anything is introduced into the mouth an increased flow of saliva results. Moreover, the mere sight, smell, or even thought of food can produce the same result. (Think of your favorite food and note the accumulation of saliva in your mouth.) Increased salivary flow under such conditions has been experimentally found to be under reflex nervous control.

Substances in solution chemically stimulate the taste buds of the tongue, afferent nervous impulses are sent to *salivary centers* in the hind part of the brain, and efferent impulses are relayed to the salivary glands (see Fig. 60). The latter impulses cause greater activity of the glands. Afferent impulses are also sent to the salivary centers by mechanical stimulation of the membrane lining the mouth or as the result of smell, sight, or thought of food. The reflexes set up when the mouth is empty are examples of *conditioned* or *learned reflexes* (see Chapter X), acquired by an individual through his experiences and not inherited. The salivary responses to stimulation of structures in the mouth are inherited, not acquired, reflexes.

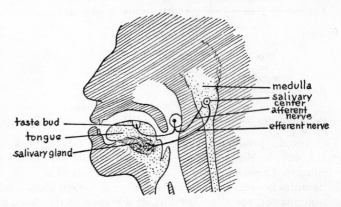

Fig. 60—A diagram of the pathway involved in the production of reflex salivary secretion.

The salivary responses to stimuli are remarkably purposive. For example, if acid is taken into the mouth, a profuse salivary flow results. This dilutes the acid and tends to prevent injury. Food, on the other hand, evokes a relatively scanty amount of saliva which is rich in mucus and enzymes. The food is mixed with salivary amylase, lubricated, and more easily swallowed. These two types of salivary secretion come from different cell types in the salivary glands: one produces the watery saliva, the other gives rise to the mucous, enzyme-rich secretion. Since different nerves innervate the two kinds of cells, their secretions can be called forth independently or coöperatively.

The Control of Gastric Secretion. In man the gastric glands are continually active, even in sleep. Nervous, mechanical, and chemical factors can, however, modify their activity.

As in the case of salivary secretion, the presence of food in the mouth or the sight, smell, or thought of food can reflexly bring on the secretion of gastric juice. This ordinarily precedes the entrance of food into the stomach and is known as the *psychic phase* of gastric secretion. The efferent nerves for this reflex response are the vagus nerves which send branches to the stomach. If they are cut, psychic gastric secretion is abolished.

Food, after entering the stomach, distends the stomach walls; this mechanical effect stimulates the mucosal glands to secrete more gastric juice. This occurs in the *gastric phase* of gastric secretion. During this period there is also chemical stimulation of gastric secretion. The pepsin liberated earlier by the psychic secretion of gastric juice begins to digest the proteins of the food. The products of partial protein digestion—polypeptides—stimulate the pyloric mucosa to produce a substance called *gastrin*. Gastrin is absorbed into the blood and is carried by it to the glands of the fundus and body of the stomach. Under the influence of gastrin the glands secrete more gastric juice.

Because of the psychic secretion gastric juice is already present in the lumen of the stomach before the food arrives and can start to digest it immediately. The food itself and its partially digested products then further the secretion of more juice to complete the gastric part of digestion.

The Control of Pancreatic and Biliary Secretions. The vagus nerves also send fibers to the pancreatic and liver cells. Stimulation of a vagus nerve can increase the secretion of pancreatic juice and of bile. A psychic flow of both of these digestive juices can be reflexly induced, but this flow is not so important as in the cases of salivary and gastric secretion. Cutting the vagus nerve does not prevent the formation of bile and pancreatic juice.

The chemical control of these secretions is more important than the nervous. When the acid contents of the stomach enter the duodenum and come into contact with its mucosa, a chemical substance named *secretin* is liberated. Secretin is present in the mucosa in an inactive form, *prosecretin*, which is activated by the acid from the gastric juice. Once released, secretin is absorbed into the blood, carried to the pancreas and liver and promotes the secretory activity of these glands (Fig. 61). That it is the acid and not any other constituent of the gastric contents which is responsible for the liberation of secretin can be demonstrated by the increased secretion of pancreatic juice and bile following the introduction of acid into the duodenum. Bile salts present in the duodenum aid the absorption of secretin but are not essential for it.

Although the flow of pancreatic juice in response to stimulation of the vagus is relatively scanty, the juice is rich in enzymes. Secretin induces a profuse, watery secretion relatively poor in enzymes. It may be that the secretin-induced flow washes out the enzymes secreted under vagal influence and furnishes a good medium of transport into the duodenum for them.

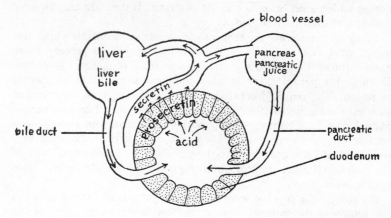

Fig. 61—A scheme for the influence of secretin on the secretion of bile and pancreatic juice.

While secretin does increase the secretion of bile, it does not cause the gall bladder to expel its stored bile. *Cholecystokinin*, a substance liberated by the action of fat on the duodenal mucosa, passes into the blood, is transported to the gall bladder and causes the latter to contract. The gastric contents thus provoke increased secretion of bile and, if fat is present, the emptying of that stored in the gall bladder. Adequate emulsification of fat is insured in this manner.

The Control of the Intestinal Glands. There appear to be both nervous and chemical means of control of the intestinal glands, but the evidence still is inconclusive with respect to the exact mechanisms involved. Intestinal juice is secreted continuously but its amount is augmented when food is in the small intestine.

THE PASSAGE OF FOOD THROUGH THE DIGESTIVE TRACT

Let us now trace how ingested food is mixed with the digestive juices and its consistency changed as it is moved through the digestive tract.

Mastication. The movements of the lower jaw—up and down, in and out, and from side to side—serve to break up the food into small pieces and mix it thoroughly with saliva. Tongue and cheek movements are important in pushing food between the teeth and then forming a rounded mass (*bolus*) of the finely divided material.

Swallowing. The bolus of mashed food is placed upon the tongue and then rolled backward by contractions of the tongue muscles until it rests upon the back of the tongue. A muscle underneath the tongue next contracts, moving the tongue upward against the roof of the mouth and backward and propelling the bolus into the pharynx. This first stage of the swallowing act is under voluntary control; once food reaches the pharynx, however, involuntary reflex control is established.

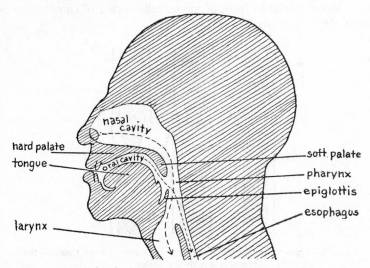

FIG. 62—The reflex elevation of the soft palate until it rests against the back of the pharynx prevents food from passing into the nasal cavity during the swallowing process. The maintenance of the position of the tongue against the hard palate and its backward movement does not allow food to reenter the oral cavity. The upward movement of the larynx under the base of the tongue and the epiglottis, plus other factors (see text), prevents food from passing into the respiratory passageways. In this diagram all of the organs mentioned are shown in their resting positions.

The muscles of the pharynx contract and the bolus is forced into the esophagus. Accessory reflex acts are necessary at this point to prevent the bolus from passing into the nasal cavity, into the larynx or back into the mouth instead of into the esophagus (see Fig. 62). Food cannot pass back into the mouth because the tongue remains in the position attained in the first stage; it cannot move upward into the nasal cavity because the soft palate is reflexly elevated and blocks the pharynx at this point; and it cannot enter the larynx because reflex muscular contraction moves this organ upward under the base of the tongue and under the epiglottis. At the same time the vocal cords are drawn together and respiration is inhibited. Swallowing and respiration are thus prevented from proceeding simultaneously and swallowed material has only one place to go—into the esophagus.

Peristalsis in the Esophagus. Once in the esophagus, the bolus is moved downward by *peristalsis*. Peristalsis is a type of movement common to most regions of the digestive tract. It consists of a wave of constriction preceded by a wave of relaxation, the constriction being produced by contraction of the circular muscle in the walls of the tract. Any material in front of the travelling ring of constriction is forced along by it (see Fig. 63).

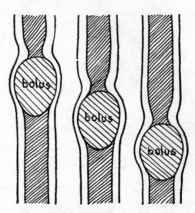

Fig. 63—Three stages in the transport of a bolus of food through the esophagus by peristalsis.

Ordinarily each swallow reflexly initiates a wave of peristalsis which sweeps the length of the esophagus. Mechanical stimulation of the base of the tongue or of the posterior wall of the pharynx readily elicits such a wave. Afferent nervous impulses are sent to a swallowing center in the medulla of the brain which in turn relays impulses over efferent nerves to the circular muscle of the esophageal wall. A peristaltic wave can also be set up reflexly by the distention of the esophageal wall. A large bolus which cannot be carried the length of the esophagus by a single peristaltic wave can give rise to secondary waves in this manner. It is carried nearer and nearer to the stomach by each successive wave.

Peristalsis in the upper two-thirds of the esophagus depends upon the integrity of the vagus nerves which innervate the muscle in its walls. The lower third contains smooth muscle whose activity is controlled by the nervous plexuses lying within the wall.

Solid or semi-solid food passes from the mouth to the stomach in 6 to 7 seconds. The peristaltic wave reaches the *cardiac sphincter* (the ring of muscle at the junction of esophagus and stomach) before the bolus; the sphincter, which had been contracted, now relaxes and food passes into the stomach. Liquids reach the cardiac sphincter in less than a second because they are squirted into the pharynx under pressure and travel down the esophagus under the influence of the force of gravity rather than peristaltic action. The liquid collects above the cardiac sphincter until the peristaltic wave, which travels more slowly, reaches the sphincter and causes it to relax.

Animals that swallow liquids in the above manner can drink when the head is down, since they can squirt liquid down the esophagus even against the force of gravity. In certain birds liquids cannot be squirted into the esophagus. Consequently, such birds must raise their heads to allow liquids to trickle into the esophagus; peristaltic waves then transport liquids down the esophagus.

Movements of the Stomach. In experimental animals it is possible to observe the movements of the digestive tract by direct inspection. In man this is not feasible. The best method devised to observe movement of the tract in man is to take X-ray photographs of the stomach and intestines during digestion of a meal. The meal fed to the subject contains substances opaque to X-rays (such as barium salts). These substances outline the contours of the organs in which they are present.

By this method it has been determined that the stomach is quiescent before food enters and its cavity, except for that of the fundus which is dilated by gas, is non-existent because of the drawing together of its walls. The entering food separates the walls by its own weight and moves downward. Soon afterwards, peristaltic waves begin about halfway down the stomach and travel downward to the pyloric region (Fig. 64). These waves are more intense in the region of the pylorus than in the body and the waves as a whole become stronger as digestion proceeds. In the pyloric region wave after wave churns the food, breaks it into smaller and smaller particles, mixes it thoroughly with gastric juice, and reduces it to a semi-fluid consistency.

The stomach is completely emptied of an ordinary meal within 3–5 hours. Emptying, of course, does not occur all at once, but is a gradual process. Every so often a little material is squirted from the pylorus into the duodenum. The *pyloric sphincter*, separating stomach and small intestine, is apparently open most of the time and functions somewhat as a strainer. When the gastric contents are of the proper consistency, they pass through. Thus, liquids pass through the stomach very quickly (a matter of minutes). Of the solid constituents of food, carbohydrates pass through most rapidly, then proteins, and finally fats. Fats specifically inhibit or reduce gastric motility, so that a fatty meal is slow to digest.

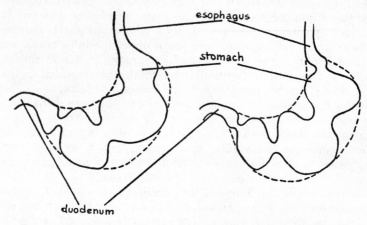

Fig. 64—Two stages in the peristaltic activity of the stomach. Note that more than one peristaltic wave can be present simultaneously. The dotted lines indicate the boundaries of the relaxed stomach.

Other factors influence the emptying time, too. If the duodenum is full, emptying of the stomach will be slower than if the former were empty. The stronger the peristaltic waves are, the faster the stomach will empty. The presence of bulk in the stomach distends its walls and accentuates peristalsis. Two sets of nerves also exert some influence. Cutting them does not abolish movements of the stomach, so that the nerve plexuses within the walls appear to be more essential than these extrinsic nerves. However, when present and stimulated, one set (the vagus nerves) usually augments or initiates peristalsis while the other decreases or inhibits it. Emotional states and exercise generally depress gastric motility.

Movements of the Small Intestine. When the gastric contents enter the intestine, they are moved along by peristaltic waves. For the most part, these waves travel slowly and only a short distance. At times, faster waves, travelling somewhat further, occur. The latter are known as *peristaltic rushes*. The intestinal contents are moved very gradually through the great length (20-odd feet) of the small intestine.

Another type of movement is prominent here—*rhythmical segmentation*. This consists of sharp contractions of segments of the circular muscle of the intestinal wall at regularly spaced intervals. Neighboring segments alternately relax and contract as shown in Fig. 65, resulting in thorough mixture of food and digestive juices. Rhythmical segmentation is also important in making intimate contact between the intestinal contents and mucosa, which allows for the absorption of digested substances. In the ordinary sequence of events, rhythmical segmentation proceeds for a time in an intestinal loop and a peristaltic wave then moves the contents onward. This sequence is repeated over and over again.

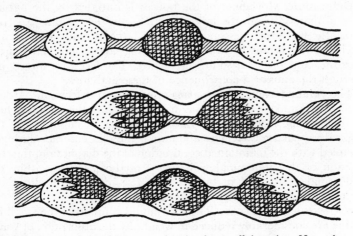

FIG. 65—Rhythmical segmentation in the small intestine. Note the mixing of intestinal contents that this type of activity promotes.

Two sets of extrinsic nerves modify intestinal motility in the same way as similar nerves do in the stomach. These nerves are not necessary for the maintenance of peristalsis, which is apparently controlled by the nerve plexuses within the intestinal walls. Even when these plexuses are paralyzed by drugs, rhythmical segmentation occurs. This movement must, then, be an inherent property of the intestinal smooth muscle. The normal stimulus for intestinal movements is the distention of the walls by the intestinal contents.

Movements of the Large Intestine. The intestinal contents are still semi-fluid when they enter the large intestine. Some churning movements which aid in the absorption of water occur there. Most of the time there is little movement in this part of the alimentary canal. Two or three times a day a strong peristaltic wave sweeps over a considerable distance of the large intestine. It is similar to, but stronger than, the peristaltic rush seen in the small intestine. This movement is known as *mass peristalsis* and carries material into the lower portions of the large intestine. The entrance of food into the stomach serves as a stimulus for mass peristalsis. The desire to move one's bowels after breakfast, a rather common experience, is probably the result of this reflex.

The intestinal contents take about twelve hours to pass through the intestines. They usually remain in the terminal portion of the large intestine for another twenty-four hours or longer before evacuation. The character of the food eaten, however, can influence the rate of movement of materials through the intestines. Exercise and emotional states generally increase intestinal activity.

Defecation. Movement of the bowels is initiated by the passage of fecal material from the large intestine into the rectum. A strong peristaltic wave then descends along the large intestine and rectum, the longitudinal muscle contracts and brings about shortening of the intestine, and the anal sphincter relaxes. The feces are forced out through the anus as a consequence of these activities.

The voluntary action of *straining* often aids in defecation. A deep inspiration is taken, the diaphragm descends, and the breath is held by the drawing together of the vocal cords and the closing off of the respiratory passageway. The abdominal muscles contract strongly. Coupled with the maintained contraction of the diaphragm, the contraction of the abdominal wall increases the pressure within the abdominal cavity and its organs. The rise in pressure within the rectum materially aids the expulsion of the feces.

FORMATION OF THE FECES. The semi-liquid contents of the small intestine are considerably reduced in weight by the absorption of water after having passed into the large intestine. The feces consist of undigested or indigestible food residues (such as cellulose), digestive secretions, bacteria, and shed epithelial cells. Of these, food residues make up very little of the fecal mass. Feces continue to be formed during starvation and their composition is little different from those formed on a normal diet. While the mass of the feces may be reduced in starvation, the reduction is primarily due to the lack of stimulation of secretory activity ordinarily brought about by the ingested food.

Bacteria are normally present in large numbers in the large intestine. Their action on the bile pigments produces compounds which give feces their characteristic color. Bacterial action on other compounds produces ill-smelling and poisonous substances; the latter are rarely absorbed into the blood in amounts which are capable of doing harm, but are eliminated in the feces.

DIARRHEA, CONSTIPATION, CATHARTICS. If for some reason the contents of the large intestine move through it too quickly, not as much water is absorbed. Loose, frequent bowel movements—*diarrhea*—result. The opposite of this—*constipation*—occurs when movement of the intestinal contents is slow. More water than usual is absorbed and the dry, hard feces that are produced are passed with greater difficulty. Constipation is much more rarely caused by some organic defect than by the *habit* of voluntarily restraining defecation. Under the latter conditions, the rectum adapts itself to the increased bulk of feces and the desire to move the bowels subsides. Regular habits of defecation will do more to relieve the condition than subscribing to the use of cathartics or laxatives. Repeated use of cathartics tends to aggravate rather than cure constipation; it is as if the bowels come to "expect" the assistance of some outside force to aid their movements. If constipation is chronic, it is far better to get medical advice than to depend on widely advertised "panaceas."

Antiperistalsis. Peristalsis, as we have seen, is a wave-like movement carrying materials in the alimentary canal away from the mouth. Normally and abnormally similar movements travelling in the opposite direction are common to various parts of the digestive tract and are known as *antiperistaltic* movements.

"*Heartburn*" is attributed to the stimulation of the esophageal lining by acid fluid moved upward by antiperistalsis in the stomach. *Belching* is believed due to antiperistaltic expulsion of gas from the stomach. Antiperistalsis occurs normally in the small intestine and may cause material to be returned to the stomach. It apparently functions, in most cases, to prevent too rapid movement of food through the intestine. Abnormally, antiperistalsis can result from *obstruction of the intestines*, the intestinal contents passing back into the stomach and then being vomited.

Vomiting. *Vomiting* is a reflex act aroused by afferent impulses from the stomach or some other part of the body or by impulses originating in parts of the brain. These impulses pass to the *vomiting center* in the medulla which relays impulses to the various muscles involved in the process. The act of vomiting begins with some strong peristaltic waves followed by a powerful constriction of the lower part of the stomach and relaxation of the stomach and cardiac sphincter above the constricted ring. Strong contractions of the diaphragm and abdominal muscles then force the gastric contents through the relaxed stomach and equally relaxed esophagus. Respiration is inhibited during the process.

Hunger Contractions. A few hours after a meal, when the stomach is nearly empty, we sometimes begin to feel hungry. The feeling that results is difficult to localize and its origin is obscure. As time goes on, *hunger pangs* develop. These we are able to localize to the upper part of the abdomen, that is, to the "pit of the stomach." These pangs are unpleasant sensations which follow one another for some time. They then disappear but will return periodically so long as the stomach remains empty.

Dr. Cannon of Harvard University and Dr. Carlson of the University of Chicago were mainly responsible for demonstrating that hunger pangs were caused by the contractions of the empty stomach (Fig. 66). About three hours after a meal, strong peristaltic movements occur in the stomach. These follow one another for about thirty minutes, hunger pangs being felt at the time of the contractions. Contractions generally disappear for one-half to two hours following a "hunger period." A new hunger period then begins. This periodic alternation of activity and quiescence continues throughout fasting. After a few days, however, the pangs may lessen in intensity and disappear. Hunger contractions and pangs may be lessened by compression of the abdomen ("tightening the belt"), smoking, exercise, and taking a cold bath or shower.

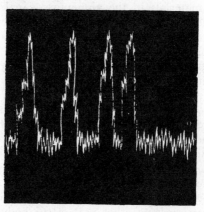

Fig. 66—Hunger contractions. A balloon connected by rubber tubing to a recording system is passed into the empty stomach of a man and there inflated. The pressure of the peristaltic contractions of the stomach is transmitted through the balloon to the recording system and inscribed on smoked kymograph paper. A record like the above is recorded during a hunger period. A hunger pang is usually associated with the large contractions.

What causes these contractions is not at all clear; nor is it known how the peristaltic contractions of the empty stomach give rise to conscious sensations while the same type of contractions pass entirely unnoticed during digestion of a meal.

Hunger is a crude, painful sensation, inherited by the individual and not modified by his experience. *Appetite*, on the other hand, is the desire for food which may accompany hunger but is not the same thing. Appetite is a sensation capable of modification by experience and is not inherited. We may still have an "appetite" for dessert, for instance, after our hunger has been satiated.

THE ABSORPTION OF FOOD

The end products of digestion—simple sugars, amino acids, fatty acids, and glycerol—plus other elements of food (such as vitamins, salts, and water) are of no use until absorbed into the blood and carried to cells all over the body.

Most absorption occurs in the small intestine. The exceptions to this are the absorption of alcohol by the stomach, the absorption of water, some inorganic salts, and, at times, glucose by the large intestine. The absorption of alcohol by the stomach accounts for the rapidity with which alcoholic drinks may take effect. The ability of the large intestine to absorb glucose is made use of in rectal feeding; solutions of glucose are given by enema and absorbed into the blood.

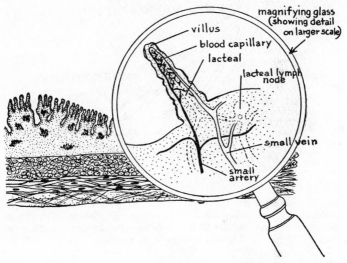

Fig. 67—A section of the wall of the small intestine. One villus with its blood and lymph supply is shown greatly magnified.

The finger-like extensions of the mucosa of the small intestine, the *villi*, project into its lumen and expose a huge surface through which absorption may take place. Movements of the villi from side to side and up and down are brought about by smooth muscle in the intestinal mucosa. In helping to stir up the intestinal contents these movements aid in the digestion and absorption of substances. Within each villus (see Fig. 67) there is a blood capillary loop and a small lymph vessel. Sugars and amino acids, after passing through the epithelium of a villus, diffuse into the capillary and are taken off by the blood. Fatty acids and glycerol, however, seem to be re-formed into fat in their passage through the epithelium. Most of the fat then passes into the lymph vessel. The latter is called a *lacteal*, because, after a meal, it is filled with milky-white fat. Water and salts are also absorbed into the blood here, though much water absorption takes place in the large intestine.

The processes of osmosis and diffusion play important parts in the transfer of substances from the intestinal lumen into the vessels within a villus. But these processes cannot account for all the phenomena of absorption. For instance, a salt solution of lesser concentration than that in the blood can be absorbed; or, if some of the

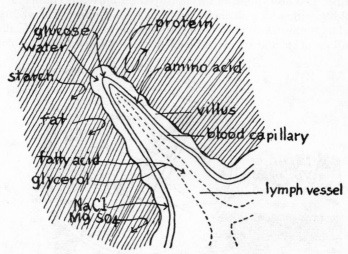

Fig. 68—Absorption in the small intestine. Very large molecules cannot penetrate the wall of the villus. Most others enter the blood stream in the villus, fat entering the lacteal, however. NaCl = sodium chloride; MgSO4 = magnesium sulphate.

animal's own blood is introduced into the intestine, it can also be absorbed. These facts cannot be explained on the basis of physical processes alone. Evidently the cells of the mucosa are doing actual work in absorbing some substances. The cells also show a preference as to which substances they will "accept." Thus, sodium chloride is easily absorbed but magnesium sulphate (epsom salts) is not. This is not a matter of the size of the molecules because, although the magnesium sulphate molecule is larger than that of sodium chloride, glucose, which has a larger molecule than magnesium sulphate, is readily absorbed (see Fig. 68). Although much of the mechanism of absorption requires further clarification, it is evident that many substances are absorbed by one or another form of active transport.

SOME DISEASES OF THE DIGESTIVE SYSTEM

Gallstones. Substances insoluble in the bile may act as the nuclei for *gallstone* formation. Cholesterol, found in the bile, is a frequent component of gallstones. Calcium carbonate, bile pigments, and perhaps masses of bacteria are also found in some gallstones. The stones usually begin to form in the gall bladder and grow larger there. If they remain in the bladder, nothing of great consequence results. If, however, when the gall bladder contracts, they are forced into the bile duct, they can obstruct the passage of bile. In such a situation a great deal of pain may result and surgical removal of the stones is necessary. The stones will not dissolve of their own accord nor can they be made to dissolve in the body.

Jaundice. Bile pigment is ordinarily present in blood to a very slight extent. If too many red blood cells are destroyed and more bile pigment formed than the liver can excrete, or if the liver is damaged or the bile ducts blocked, bile pigment is diverted into the blood in greater than normal amounts. In time some of this excess pigment diffuses into the tissues and imparts to them the characteristic yellow color of *jaundice*.

Appendicitis. The appendix (see Fig. 57), a vestigial structure (evolutionary remnant) of the human digestive tract, has no known function. Infection of this organ, *appendicitis*, is dangerous because rupture of the appendix can liberate many infectious organisms from the appendix and intestines into the abdominal cavity. If this should happen, *peritonitis* (inflammation of the peritoneum) and death may result. As you know, an infected appendix can be easily removed by surgical means.

Ulcers. A rounded, eroded area (*ulcer*) of the wall of the stomach or duodenum is a not uncommon occurrence. There is some evidence that the action of pepsin and hydrochloric acid on the gastric mucosa may produce an ulcer. At any rate, when an ulcer is not due to a specific disease or to some nervous disorder, it is found only in those regions of the digestive tract that are exposed to acid. And even if such ulcers are not produced by acid or peptic action, the presence of acid aggravates the condition. Treatment is generally dietary in nature. The diet of patients with ulcers is calculated to avoid mechanical irritation of the ulcers and to reduce gastric secretion. The elimination of bulky foods from the diet reduces mechanical irritation; meat, alcohol, and highly spiced foods (which stimulate the gastric glands) are excluded but large amounts of milk and cream (whose fat content tends to inhibit gastric secretion) are included. Alkali, such as sodium bicarbonate, may also be included for the purpose of neutralizing the acid in the stomach.

Severe ulceration can often be surgically alleviated. Before the condition becomes too severe, the use of tranquilizing drugs has also been found helpful. A possible implication of the latter treatment is that mental or emotional state may contribute to ulceration (nervous impulses may cause increased secretion of acid gastric juice).

CHAPTER VII

The Excretory System

THE contractile vacuole acts as the "excretory system" of Amoeba. In some of the early multicellular animals, cell wastes diffuse into the general body cavity on which many cells border, and thence out

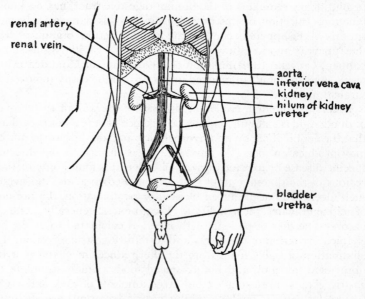

renal artery
renal vein

aorta
inferior vena cava
kidney
hilum of kidney
ureter

bladder
urethra

FIG. 69—Diagram of the excretory system.

the same opening through which foods enter. In some more advanced kinds of invertebrates in which a segmental body pattern is found, each segment (except those of the "head" region) contains two tubes or series of tubes, one on each side of the body; waste materials from the cells of the segment eventually enter these tubes and pass out of the body through pores on the external surface.

In vertebrates the *kidneys* take over most, though not all, of the excretory function; other excretory organs are the *lungs, skin,* and *large intestine.* As we have noted, the lungs excrete carbon dioxide and some water. The sweat glands of the skin excrete water and salts, though, as we shall see in Chapter XVI, the elimination of water here is more important in the regulation of body temperature than it is in excretion. The lining of the large intestine excretes calcium and iron into the lumen and these metals are then eliminated with the feces. Most other constituents of the feces are not considered as excretory products since they are not metabolic wastes. The bile pigments may, however, be classed as excreted substances since they result from the breakdown of hemoglobin in the liver. It may also be mentioned that the salivary glands help to excrete heavy metals, such as mercury and lead, when they are introduced into the body. In lead poisoning the blue line on the gums is produced by deposition of lead sulphide, the latter being formed by the reaction of lead excreted in the saliva with sulphur present in the tartar on teeth.

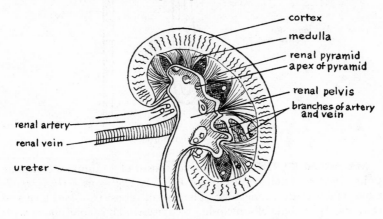

cortex
medulla
renal pyramid
apex of pyramid
renal pelvis
branches of artery and vein
renal artery
renal vein
ureter

FIG. 70—A vertical section through the kidney and ureter.

We shall mean by excretion the extraction by certain cells of metabolic wastes from the blood. The body then rids itself of the wastes by accessory mechanisms. For example, the kidney cells are responsible for the removal of many wastes found in the blood. These wastes dissolved in water constitute the urine, which is removed from the body via ureter, urinary bladder, and urethra.

THE ANATOMY OF THE URINARY SYSTEM

The *kidneys* are two bean-shaped organs lying in the back of the abdominal cavity, not far below the diaphragm and just outside the peritoneum. When a kidney is sliced in half vertically, two main layers of its substance can be seen (as shown diagrammatically in Fig. 70). Just beneath the tough, connective tissue sheath which encases the kidney is the outer layer, the *cortex*. This layer merges with an inner layer, the *medulla*, consisting of a number of cone-shaped divisions, the *renal pyramids*. The apex of each pyramid extends into a central sac, the *renal pelvis*.

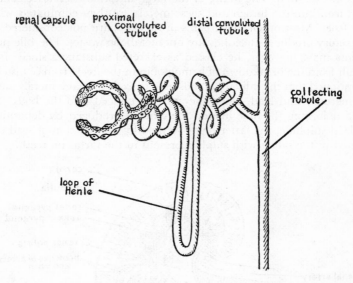

FIG. 71—The nephron.

Microscopically the kidneys are composed of a number of tubular units, *nephrons*. Each nephron (see Fig. 71) begins as a *renal capsule* from which leads a long tube. The capsule consists of two layers of thin, flat epithelial cells enclosing a cavity which is continuous with the lumen of the tube. The tube can be subdivided into a number of distinct parts. Leading directly from the capsule is a much twisted portion called the *proximal* (near) *convoluted tubule*. This is followed by *Henle's loop* and then a second twisted portion, the *distal* (far) *convoluted tubule*. These tubules have walls composed of cuboidal epithelial cells except for a small part of Henle's loop. The distal convoluted tubule leads into a collecting tubule (not considered part of the nephron) which joins with other similar tubules to form larger ones. The latter empty into the renal pelvis. The capsule and the proximal and distal convoluted tubules are in the cortex; Henle's loop and the major portion of the collecting tubules are in the medulla. Each kidney contains about one million nephrons, each of which is about two inches long when straightened. The combined length of the nephrons in the kidneys is about forty-five miles.

Several features of the kidney's blood supply are of special importance to an understanding of its function in urine formation. The *renal artery* enters the kidney at the *hilum* (see Figs. 69 and 70) and breaks up into many branches which run through the medulla and eventually into the cortex. Arterioles stem from the arteries in the cortex and run to the renal capsules. Each arteriole then breaks up into a number of capillary loops which push into the cup formed by the capsule (see Fig. 72). This tuft of capillaries is called a *glomerulus*.

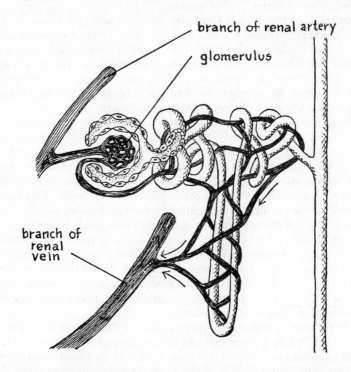

branch of renal artery

glomerulus

branch of renal vein

Fig. 72—The blood supply of the nephron. Compare with Fig. 71. Arrows indicate the direction of the flow of blood. See text for complete description.

Each capillary loop is separate from and has no connection with any other. The capillary loops reunite to form an arteriole which leaves the capsule only to break up into a number of capillaries once more. The latter supply blood to the tubules. The capillaries then unite to form small veins and these eventually merge into the large *renal vein* which leaves the kidney at the hilum.

The *ureter* is the tube which conducts urine from kidney to bladder. It has three layers of smooth muscle in its walls as has the *bladder*. The latter is a very distensible, hollow organ. Urine is voided from the bladder via another tube, the *urethra*, which runs through the penis in the male and into the vestibule in the female.

THE FORMATION OF URINE

Former controversies as to whether the kidneys act merely as filters in urine formation or whether they actively secrete urine have been resolved. Current ideas on renal function combine certain elements of both older theories, but in modified form.

Function of the Renal Capsule. The anatomical features of the renal blood supply and the fact that the inner layer of capsular cells fits over the glomerular capillaries like a "glove over fingers" strongly suggest that materials filter out of the glomerulus into the renal capsule. The cells of the capillary and capsular walls which separate their respective cavities are thin and flat. They would, then, be well adapted for filtration of materials through them.

There are two lines of evidence that support such a functioning of the glomerulus and capsule. First of all, to enable filtration to occur there must be an adequate pressure difference between the fluid in the glomerular capillaries and that in the capsule. Measurements have shown that the glomerular capillaries have very high blood pressure compared to those in other regions of the body. This exists because of the peculiar arrangement of the renal blood supply. The renal artery is a direct branch of the aorta and quickly branches into smaller divisions. Thus, the pressure in it is not so quicky diminished as it is when the arterial course is longer. Also, the arteriole leading out of the glomerulus has a diameter only half that of the one leading into it (see Fig. 72). This condition causes considerable resistance to outflow of blood from the glomerulus and consequently increases the pressure in the glomerular capillaries.

The pressure of blood in the glomerular capillaries has been found to be considerably greater than the sum of the osmotic pressure of the blood proteins (which tends to draw fluid into the blood) and of the fluid pressure in the cavity of the renal capsule (which opposes the blood pressure in the capillaries). From the standpoint of pressure differences, then, a filtration mechanism is possible and plausible. Experimental evidence bears this out. If the pressure in the glomerular capillaries is raised, urine formation is increased. If the blood osmotic pressure is reduced, there is also an increase. But, if the ureter is clamped off (thus increasing the pressure within the capsule), urine flow diminishes.

More striking evidence was provided by Dr. Richards and his co-workers. Fluid was sucked out of the renal capsule of the frog kidney by means of a very fine tube. This is a very delicate procedure, precise manipulations being directed by microscopic observation. Having drawn out a sample of the fluid in the capsule, these physiologists them chemically analyzed it. They found that it had the same composition as the blood plasma, except that none of the plasma proteins was present. Since the protein molecules and the blood cells are too large to diffuse through these capillary walls, this is the composition of solution we should expect to be present when blood filters into the renal capsule.

Function of the Renal Tubules. When the capsular fluid is compared with urine in the bladder, marked differences in composition are detected. Since the ureter and the bladder do nothing but transport and store urine, changes in composition must occur in its passage through the renal tubules. It has been estimated that about 200 liters of fluid are filtered into the kidneys each day, yet only about 1½–2 liters of urine are voided during an average day. Obviously a great deal of water must have returned to the blood from the tubules.

Other changes also take place. Plasma and capsular fluid contain sugar (glucose); urine normally does not. Urea (a waste product of protein metabolism), on the other hand, is relatively much more concentrated in urine than in blood. Changes of concentration of solid wastes in the urine as compared with blood and capsular fluid must occur in the tubules. The latter must reabsorb solid materials as well as water. However, as the examples just mentioned illustrate, not all solids are reabsorbed to the same degree. While all sugar is ordinarily reabsorbed, a much smaller proportion of urea is normally returned to the blood.

Because of properties as yet unknown, the tubules carry on *selective* reabsorption of solids. Some solids are called *high threshold substances* because the tubules can reabsorb relatively large concentrations of them; only when their concentration in the blood exceeds that which the tubules can absorb will they appear in the urine. Glucose, for instance, is generally completely reabsorbed. But, if we raise the blood glucose concentration above normal (by injecting glucose into the blood or by eating a bar of candy), the amount in excess of the threshold concentration will "spill over" into the urine (see Fig. 73). Other solids are *low threshold substances;* that is, they need have only a relatively low concentration in the blood before beginning to appear in the urine. Urea is such a substance. Those substances which the body cannot utilize have lower thresholds than substances valuable to the body. The wastes are largely excreted, then, while essential blood constituents are largely conserved. Excesses of the latter, though, are wastes and are also excreted.

As the capsular fluid makes its way through the rest of the nephron, the following activities occur. The cells of the proximal convoluted tubule actively reabsorb glucose, amino acids, sodium ions, chloride ions, bicarbonate ions, and probably a number of other substances. As noted above, not all of these are reabsorbed to the same degree, but all of them are reabsorbed to a considerable extent. Nitrogenous waste products of metabolism tend, however, to be reabsorbed to a lesser extent; *urea* is relatively slightly reabsorbed and *creatinine* is not reabsorbed at all.

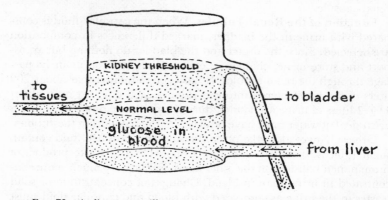

Fig. 73—A diagram to illustrate excretion of glucose by the kidney. Normally glucose is being supplied to the blood from the liver and drained from the blood by the tissues. At its normal blood level no glucose "spills over into the urine." Upon reaching a certain concentration in the blood, however, the tubules are unable to reabsorb the excess amount of glucose which then appears in the urine.

When we say these substances are reabsorbed, we mean that they are actively transferred from the lumen of the nephron into the blood of nearby capillaries. Blood concentrations of dissolved substances in the capillaries are thereby markedly increased; and, as a consequence, osmotic pressure of the blood rises above that of the fluid in the nephron. A secondary consequence of the active reabsorption of solute materials is the passive reabsorption of water by osmosis into the blood capillaries. At least 80% of total water reabsorption occurs in this fashion, as the fluid passes through the proximal convoluted tubule and Henle's loop.

As fluid reaches the distal convoluted tubule, its character is quite different from the original capsular fluid, but not as different as the eventual urine will be. In this portion of the nephron there is further reabsorption of sodium ions (the principal positive ions of body fluids). In part, this reabsorption is accomplished in exchange for potassium ions; the exchange is an active process facilitated by a hormone secreted by the adrenal cortex (see Chapter XI). Other sodium ions are exchanged for hydrogen ions or for *ammonia;* both of these latter are secreted by the distal tubular cells into the lumen. The over-all effect of this complex phenomenon is to conserve sodium and also to reduce the acidity of the blood (see below).

Lastly, as fluid moves through the distal convoluted tubule and the collecting tubule, their walls are made more permeable to water by the action of a hormone from the posterior pituitary gland (see Chapter XI). Although the reabsorption of water occurring here is by no means as great in volume as that in previous sections of the tubule, it is nonetheless a large amount. If the hormonal action is lacking, daily urine output may rise to twenty liters; obviously this can be an extremely dangerous development for the individual.

Summary of Urine Formation. A protein-free filtrate of plasma passes into the renal capsules from the glomerular capillaries. In its passage through the renal tubules, this filtrate loses water and some of its dissolved substances by selective reabsorption and may gain some substances by secretory activity of the tubules. The urine is then conveyed by collecting tubules to the ureter and then to the bladder. Urine is composed especially of water and waste materials. The kidneys are essential for the maintenance of normal blood composition.

The Control of Urine Volume. Anything which will increase the blood pressure in the glomerular capillaries will increase the filtration of fluid into the renal capsules. If a large amount of water is drunk, blood volume tends to increase; the consequent rise in general blood pressure and in glomerular blood pressure increases the rate of filtration; consequently the volume of urine formed is augmented. When fluid intake is cut down or when states of fever and dehydration exist, the converse holds true, and a scantier urine flow results. To a large extent the work of the kidney thus controls the volume of circulating blood.

Another factor in the control of urine volume is the concentration of solids in the capsular and tubular fluids. The greater the concentration of substances, the greater the osmotic pressure of the fluid. When the osmotic pressure is higher and tends to draw fluid into the tubules, less can be reabsorbed into the blood and a greater urine flow results.

The excretion of greater amounts of urine than normal is called *diuresis* and a substance producing it a *diuretic*. Many substances act as diuretics in the way just described in the preceding paragraph. *Glucose* (in large amounts) and *urea* act as such diuretics. *Alcohol* acts as a powerful diuretic, probably by slowing up tubular reabsorption. *Caffeine*, the drug present in coffee, produces diuresis by increasing the blood flow through the kidneys.

Urination. Urine is continually being formed and transported to the bladder by peristaltic movements of the ureters. When the amount of urine in the bladder is about 300 cc., the distention of the bladder's walls give rise to the desire to urinate. The act of urination is essentially an unconscious reflex which, however, is subject to voluntary control.

The necessary reflex movements involved in urination are contraction of the muscular walls of the bladder and relaxation of a sphincter which surrounds part of the urethra. Considerable pressure (which may be increased by straining movements) is set up in the bladder and the urine is forced out through the urethra. Voluntary restraint of urination is effected by maintaining the contraction of the sphincter.

REGULATION OF ACIDITY OF THE BLOOD

Blood is normally slightly *alkaline;* that is, it contains a slight excess of hydroxyl over hydrogen ions (see Chapter II). The proportion of these ions must be maintained for the proper functioning of most of the tissue cells which are bathed by the blood and other body fluids derived from it. Under normal physiological conditions bodily mechanisms adequately preserve the balance between these ions, never allowing more than slight variations to occur.

Much of the regulation of acidity is accomplished within the blood itself by its proteins (both hemoglobin and the plasma proteins). These proteins are called *buffers* because they can react with either acid or basic substances and immobilize their hydrogen or hydroxyl ions. And, since the resulting "protein-acids" or "protein-bases" ionize to a slighter degree than the acids or bases with which they react, fewer hydrogen or hydroxyl ions will be in solution.

For example, carbon dioxide when it diffuses into blood reacts with water to form carbonic acid:

$$CO_2 + H_2O \rightarrow H_2CO_3$$

Carbonic acid then reacts with the potassium (K) salt of hemoglobin as follows:

$$H_2CO_3 + KHb \rightarrow KHCO_3 + HHb$$

The acid form of hemoglobin (HHb) ionizes to a lesser degree than carbonic acid so that the number of hydrogen ions in the blood is reduced. By such reactions the entrance of acid into the blood is prevented from making blood more acid than is healthful. Excess alkali in the blood is treated similarly.

There are, however, more acid than alkaline products of metabolism, so that neutralization of acid is generally a more urgent problem than neutralization of alkali. The distal convoluted tubules of the kidney also aid in regulation of acidity. For one thing, their cells produce ammonia (NH_3) from urea and from amino acids. Ammonia reacts with water to form a base, ammonium hydroxide:

$$NH_3 + H_2O \rightarrow NH_4OH$$

This base in turn can react with acids to neutralize them. The neutral salt that results is excreted by the kidneys. In addition to neutralizing the acid, the ammonium hydroxide serves in place of a sodium or potassium alkali; that is, the latter would have to be used to neutralize the acid if ammonia were not present. Since ammonia is a waste product and sodium and potassium salts are very useful to the body, this series of reactions conserves valuable materials.

The kidneys also excrete some acids of the blood directly and convert some alkaline substances into more acid ones. The urine, therefore, is generally acid although the blood is slightly alkaline. The kidneys, then, by excreting an acid urine help to maintain the blood at a constant acidity.

ABNORMAL FUNCTIONING OF THE KIDNEYS

During infectious diseases, bacteria or the toxic substances they secrete may get into the blood and thence into the kidneys. Severe and prolonged kidney disease can prove fatal, since waste products will not be adequately eliminated from the blood.

Poisoning by lead, arsenic, mercury, or other chemical poisons can also lead to disturbances of kidney function.

Arteriosclerosis of the renal blood vessels may prevent some parts of the kidneys from receiving a proper blood supply. Such parts will die and the kidneys may have insufficient nephrons functioning to maintain the health of the individual. There is a considerable margin of safety, however, for even when one kidney is removed, the organism will survive with no ill effects.

CHAPTER VIII

The Skeleton

MANY OF THE lowest forms of animal life have no rigid structural framework at all. In the *invertebrates* (animals without backbones) the skeleton, when it is present, is a rigid case deposited on the outside of the body. The shells of oysters and clams and the hard outer coverings of insects are examples of such *external* skeletons. External skeletons are adequate for these animals but limit them both as to body size and flexibility of movement.

The *vertebrates* (animals with backbones) have *internal* skeletons which are basically very similar for organisms ranging from fish to man. There are, of course, various modifications that occur in animals whose modes of living and locomotion are very different. Since the internal skeleton is capable of growth, vertebrates can grow very large (elephant, whale, dinosaur). The different ways in which the various bones are attached to one another permit varying types of locomotion and, in some vertebrates, quite complex kinds of movement (movements of the hand, thumb, and fingers in monkeys, apes, and man).

THE BONES OF THE SKELETON

Some fish (sharks, dogfish, etc.) have skeletons composed of cartilage; man, like most vertebrates, has a bony skeleton. The human skeleton consists of the *skull*, the *vertebral column* (backbone), and its *attachments*. The latter include the *ribs*, the *pectoral* (shoulder) *girdle*, and the *pelvic* (hip) *girdle*. The *limbs* in turn are attached to the girdles, and the *sternum* (breastbone) is attached to the ribs.

The skull is made up of a number of fused bones, the only movable one being the *mandible* (lower jaw). The backbone consists of a chain of thirty-three *vertebrae*. These relatively small bones, which fit on top of one another, are composed of a solid base, on the dorsal side of which is an arch (Fig. 75). In the cavity formed by the holes in the

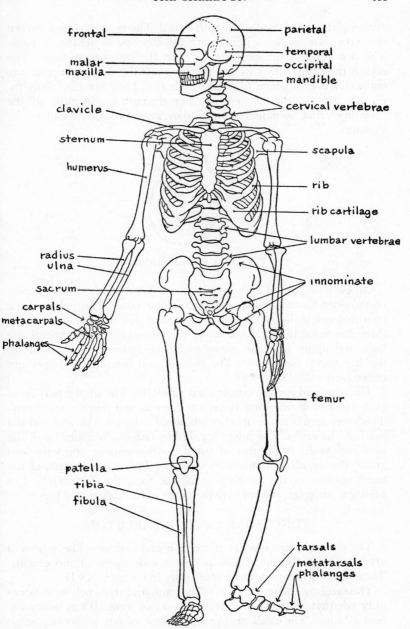

Fig. 74—Diagram of the skeleton.

arches of the vertebrae lies the spinal cord. The twelve pairs of curved ribs articulate (make a joint) with the thoracic vertebrae in back. The first seven articulate directly with the sternum in front. The eighth through tenth ribs are shorter than the first seven and are connected by cartilage to the seventh rib. They are thus only indirectly attached to the sternum. The eleventh and twelfth are the "floating" ribs, so called because they have no attachment to the sternum.

Fig. 75—A typical vertebra.

On each side of the body, the pectoral girdle consists of the *scapula* or shoulder blade and the *clavicle* or collar bone. The pelvic girdle consisted originally of three bones on each side. In man each set of three has fused into a single bone, the *innominate*. Each innominate bone articulates with the *sacrum* (the bone formed by the fusion of the five sacral vertebrae). The sacrum and innominate bones are collectively called the *pelvis*.

The arm and leg are constructed similarly. The upper portion of each consists of one long bone, the *humerus* and *femur* respectively. The lower arm is made up of two bones, the larger, the *ulna* and the smaller, the *radius*. The lower leg, in like fashion, is made up of the *tibia* and *fibula*. A number of small bones comprise the wrist and ankle, the *carpals* and *tarsals* respectively. The major portion of the hand consists of the *metacarpals*, of the foot, the *metatarsals*. The *phalanges* (singular, *phalanx*) are the bones of the fingers and toes.

FUNCTIONS OF THE SKELETON

The skeletal functions are protection and support. The modes of articulation of the bones also permit a wide range of movements. These latter will be discussed more fully in Chapter XVII.

The skull completely encloses the brain, and its closely-knit bones offer adequate protection to this vital organ from all but heavy external blows. The skull also protects some of our important sense organs. The eyes are sunk fairly deep into bony sockets and further protected by the overhanging bony brows. The internal ears (in which the sense organs for sound are located) are embedded within the *temporal* bones of the skull. The sense organs for smell and taste are in the nose and mouth cavities, protected by the bones which surround these cavities. The bones of the face also give it its characteristic contours.

The vertebral column encloses and protects the spinal cord. It also furnishes a somewhat rigid support for the body. At its head end it allows for movements of the skull, in the thorax it serves as one attachment for the ribs, and at its lower end it fits into the pelvic girdle to form a solid support for the weight of the body above this region. The last four vertebrae make up the *coccyx* which has no function but is the vestige of the tail we lost during evolutionary development.

The "cage" formed by the thoracic vertebrae, ribs, and sternum offers some protection to the heart and lungs. These bones are, of course, of great importance in allowing for the essential respiratory movements.

The pectoral girdle serves mainly as a place of attachment for the arm. The latter functions as a grasping, balancing, and defensive organ. The *opposable* thumb of monkeys, apes, and man is a great evolutionary advance, enabling such animals to grasp and wield objects in ways that were never possible before its advent.

The pelvic girdle, besides serving as a place of attachment for the legs, distributes the weight of the body to them. The legs are more sturdily constructed than the arms, a fact correlated with the weight they have to support. The body weight is distributed by the femurs and tibias to the arches of the feet. The arch then distributes the weight to the ball and heel of the foot, making for a stronger base of support and for better balance. Women's high-heeled shoes, although an aesthetic adornment, distort this distribution and also tend to cramp the feet. Such shoes can in time seriously impair the normal function of the feet.

THE STRUCTURE OF BONE

Bone is composed mainly of mineral matter. Even so hard a tissue as fresh bone, however, contains 25 per cent water. Another 30 per cent consists of organic material, mainly protein. The remaining 45 per cent is made up of inorganic compounds, especially calcium phosphate. Calcium carbonate, one form of which we know as marble, is also present.

Such is the composition of bone exclusive of its fatty marrow. On splitting a long bone longitudinally, we may see the yellow marrow filling up the cavity of the shaft. The osseous tissue itself constitutes the thick outer shell (Fig. 76). In the ends of such a bone, red blood

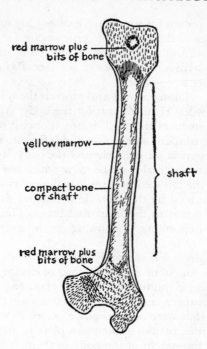

red marrow plus bits of bone

yellow marrow

shaft

compact bone of shaft

red marrow plus bits of bone

FIG. 76—A longitudinal section through a long bone.

cell-forming marrow is interspersed with thin, needle-like bits of bone.

As pointed out in Chapter III, layers of osseous tissue are laid down in concentric circles around small canals which run lengthwise in the shaft. These canals contain blood vessels. Nutrient materials are carried from the blood to bone cells by a network of even smaller canals. Waste materials pass in the reverse direction.

Flat bones (ribs, skull bones, etc.) contain only red marrow in their cavities but are otherwise much like long bones.

CHAPTER IX

The Muscular System

By MEANS of its *neuromuscular* apparatus an organism can respond to changes in its environment. The structures comprising this apparatus were not present in the lowest forms of animal life, but appeared only gradually during the course of evolution.

In Amoeba there is no specialized part of the cell to respond to an external stimulus. When a change in the environment occurs, the cell as a whole responds. In a slightly more advanced animal, the sponge, muscle cells make their first appearance. These cells contract in direct response to stimuli. In animal forms succeeding the sponge, muscle cells usually do not respond directly to stimuli, but contract in response to nervous impulses which control their activity. However, even in man there is the suspicion that some muscle (for example, some intestinal smooth muscle) may not be nervously activated.

THE PROPERTIES OF SKELETAL AND SMOOTH MUSCLE

We have already discussed the activity of cardiac muscle in Chapter IV and have seen various manifestations of *smooth muscle* in involuntary activity. The latter type of muscle is concerned with movements of internal organs other than the heart. Skeletal or voluntary muscle, on the other hand, makes possible the movements of the skeleton and, in some instances, the skin.

Since *skeletal muscle* is primarily concerned with movements adjusting the body to its external environment, and smooth muscle with movements in response to internal environmental changes, we might expect to find differences in their anatomical and physiological properties. In Chapter III we have noted differences in their gross and microscopic structures. There are also differences in their nervous connections. Skeletal muscle cells have only one nerve fiber innervating them while smooth muscle cells usually have two differ-

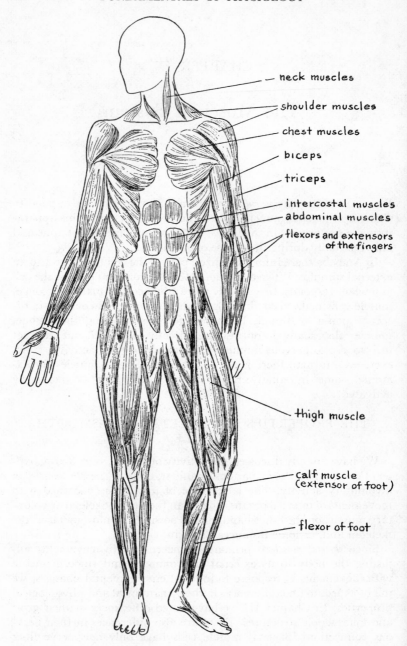

neck muscles

shoulder muscles

chest muscles

biceps

triceps

intercostal muscles
abdominal muscles

flexors and extensors
of the fingers

thigh muscle

calf muscle
(extensor of foot)

flexor of foot

Fig. 77—Diagram of the muscular system.

ent kinds of nerve fibers innervating them. Skeletal muscle contracts when nerve impulses reach it, relaxes when impulses are no longer sent to it; smooth muscle contracts when impulses along one kind of nerve fiber reach it, relaxes when impulses along the other kind are relayed to it. Skeletal muscle is not able to function normally in the absence of the nerves that control it, but some, at least, of the smooth muscles can—those responsible for rhythmical segmentation in the small intestine.

Both smooth and skeletal muscle are characterized, when compared with other kinds of tissue, by their especial contractility. Both, too, are more irritable than most tissues. Skeletal muscle, however, is much more sensitive to electrical stimulation than smooth, (a weaker current being needed to activate the former) while the reverse holds true for their sensitivity to chemical stimuli (smooth muscle being more easily affected by drugs, for instance).

Skeletal muscle contracts and relaxes more quickly than smooth, while smooth muscle is able to maintain a contracted state over longer periods of time than can skeletal. Changes in the external environment can occur more quickly as a rule than in the internal environment, and adjustments to such changes often have to proceed just as quickly. The rapidity with which skeletal muscles react may mean the difference between life and death.

THE PHYSIOLOGY OF SKELETAL MUSCLE

We know comparatively little about the mechanisms at work in the contraction of smooth muscle, so that we shall concern ourselves with the activity of skeletal muscle.

Excitation of Muscle. In the body, skeletal muscle is normally excited only when nerve impulses reach it. There is not, however, a one-to-one relationship between nerve fibers and muscle cells. Rather, one nerve fiber branches considerably and innervates a number of muscle cells (ratios vary between 1:3 and 1:165). The motor nerve cell plus the muscle cells it controls is called a *motor unit* (Fig. 78). Since one muscle may contain thousands of muscle cells, many nerve fibers may be required for its control. The smaller the motor unit ratios for a muscle (the greater the number of nerve fibers innervating it), the more delicate its action is likely to be. Thus, muscles controlling finger movements are innervated by proportionately greater numbers of nerve fibers than are arm or leg muscles.

At the very tip of each nerve fiber ending in muscle, electron microscopy reveals a slight gap between the nerve and muscle fibers. It also discloses that the muscle fiber membrane in this region is quite specialized in contrast to the membrane in other parts of the fiber. This modified portion is known as the *motor endplate* or *myoneural junction*.

It is experimentally demonstrable that a nerve impulse, arriving at the nerve fiber tip, causes the release of a small amount of the substance *acetylcholine*. The latter diffuses the small distance to the motor endplate and, by altering its permeability, sets up an electrical change in the endplate. The electrical change spreads from the junctional region (in the middle of the muscle fiber) along the muscle fiber membrane to both ends of the fiber. In some manner this "muscle impulse" triggers the release of energy which is used for fiber contraction.

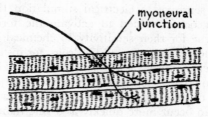

Fig. 78—Part of a motor unit—a nerve fiber sending branches to three skeletal muscle fibers.

Even though muscle is normally only excited by a nerve impulse, it can be shown to be independently irritable. Direct stimulation of the muscle causes it to contract. But, to prove this point, we must make sure that the contraction of the muscle was not due to excitation of the ends of the nerve fibers embedded in the muscle. Removal of the nervous influence can be accomplished in two ways: by cutting the nerve and allowing time for its degeneration, or by injecting into the blood of an experimental animal the drug "curare." This drug prevents the action of acetylcholine at motor endplates so that nerve impulses, in its presence, become ineffective stimuli for muscle activity. After either of these procedures, stimulation of muscle can cause it to contract. It must then be irritable in its own right.

We find also that a muscle is sensitive to, and will respond to, all kinds of stimuli (changes in the environment)—electrical, mechanical (pinching), thermal (touching it with a hot rod), or chemical (placing some salt on it).

Not every stimulus will activate a tissue. To be adequate, a stimulus must fulfill certain conditions. First of all, it must be of minimal intensity. For instance, an electric current that is too weak is not effective. Then the stimulus must last for a minimal length of time. An electric shock that is too brief will not excite. And lastly, there must be a minimal rate of change of intensity; that is, the intensity must build up to adequate strength quickly enough in order to be effective.

Muscle Contraction. To study the mechanisms at work in muscle contraction it is necessary to record the contractions graphically. An apparatus like that in Fig. 79 is very often used. This is practically the same as the apparatus for recording heart beat (Fig. 28, p. 55). When the muscle contracts, the muscle lever moves upward.

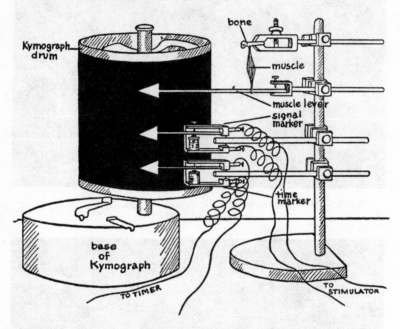

Fig. 79—Apparatus used for recording muscular contractions. The contracting muscle pulls toward the clamped bone to which it is connected and moves the muscle lever upward. The contraction is inscribed upon the kymograph paper by the writing point.

ALL-OR-NONE RESPONSE. Taking the isolated calf muscle of a frog and stimulating it with a series of electrical stimuli of increasing intensity, we can get a record like that in Fig. 80. Note that with very weak stimuli (1, 2) the muscle does not respond. This means that muscle has a certain *threshold* of irritability, that stimuli must be of a certain minimal intensity to excite it. With gradually increasing intensity, stimuli 3 through 8 evoke gradually increasing muscular contractions. But although stimuli 9 and 10 are of greater magnitude than 8, the responses to them are of the same height as the response to 8. Stimulus 3 is called a *minimal stimulus* because it evokes the first observable response. Stimulus 8 is called a *maximal stimulus* because it produces the greatest observable response.

The explanation for these results runs as follows. The muscle is made up of a number of muscle fibers, each of which may have a different threshold. A minimal stimulus will call into play those fibers with the lowest threshold. Stronger stimuli will cause more and more

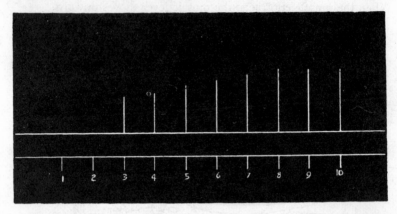

FIG. 80—Muscular contractions in response to stimuli of gradually increasing intensity. See text.

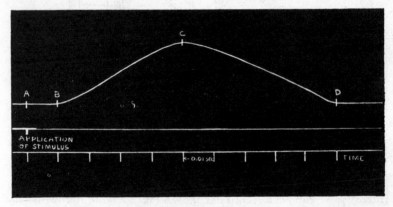

FIG. 81—The simple muscle twitch. The time between *A* and *B* is the latent period, between *B* and *C* the contraction period, and between *C* and *D* the relaxation period. See text.

muscle fibers to respond, and the height of contraction will increase. A maximal stimulus will excite all the muscle fibers. The assumption is that once a muscle fiber is adequately stimulated it will give the greatest response of which it is capable at the moment; when the stimulus is not adequate, no response will occur. Each muscle fiber, then, is said to give an *all-or-none* response to stimuli. Thus, since stimulus 8 produces the maximal response of all the muscle fibers, stimulus 9 can produce no greater response, even though it is a stronger stimulus.

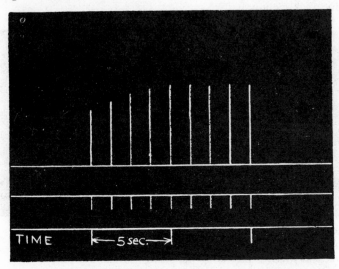

FIG. 82—The staircase phenomenon. See text.

A whole muscle, as Fig. 80 shows, does not give an all-or-none response, but a muscle fiber does. Actually it has been questioned whether the muscle fiber can or cannot give graded responses to varying strengths of stimuli under certain experimental conditions. However, in the body the simplest explanation is that muscle fibers follow the all-or-none "law."

THE SIMPLE TWITCH. A single adequate stimulus results in a brief twitch of the muscle. If we record such a muscular contraction on a moving kymograph drum, we see that the twitch may be divided into three periods (Fig. 81). The time (0.01 sec.) between the application of the stimulus and the start of the response is the *latent period*. The time for the height of the response to be attained (0.04 sec.) is the *contraction period*. The time for the return of the muscle to its resting state (0.05 sec.) is the *relaxation period*. During the contraction period the muscle can do work. As we shall see below, during the 0.1 sec. that a twitch lasts and for some time afterward many processes are occurring in the muscle.

THE STAIRCASE PHENOMENON. If a number of stimuli of adequate and equal intensity are sent into a muscle in rapid succession, a record like that in Fig. 82 is obtained. Note that the first few contractions successively increase in height (staircase effect) and the remainder tend to level off. As a result of the first contraction chemical changes occur in the muscle which make it more irritable and enable it to contract to a greater extent when a second stimulus is sent in quickly enough.

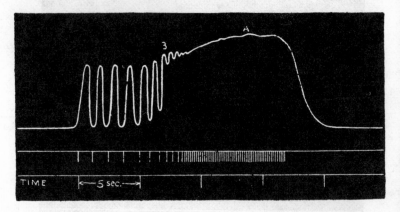

Fig. 83—Tetanus. At *A*, the fused contraction called tetanus is seen. At *B* is shown a good example of the phenomenon of summation of contractions which is part of the mechanism behind the production of tetanus.

TETANUS. Fig. 83 shows the record obtained when stimuli are sent into a muscle at a faster and faster rate. A new phenomenon can be observed here. A second stimulus coming into the muscle while it is still contracting in response to a preceding one evokes a greater height of contraction than either stimulus alone can call forth. In other words, *summation of contractions* occurs: the second contraction adds with the first. This occurs even if all of the muscle fibers are activated by each stimulus, so that it is not due to the contraction of more muscle fibers. The change in chemical state of the muscle as the result of its activity, plus the summing of contractions, accounts for the increased height of contraction.

When a series of stimuli come into a muscle rapidly enough, the contractions fuse into a maintained one which is called *tetanus*. (This is a normal muscular response and is not the same as the muscular rigidity, "lockjaw," caused by the tetanus bacillus.) For the reasons just outlined above, a tetanic response is greater than a corresponding simple twitch.

REFRACTORY PERIOD. If a second stimulus is sent in too quickly after a first, it will not be effective. For a short time after it has responded to one stimulus a muscle will not respond to any other. This time is the *refractory period*, lasting only 0.005 sec. in skeletal muscle (a much shorter period than for cardiac muscle).

THE CHANGES OCCURRING IN ACTIVE MUSCLE

Preceding, during, and after the actual contraction of skeletal muscle, a series of interrelated changes take place. For convenience, these can be talked about in the following categories.

Electrical Changes. As noted previously, when the motor endplate of a muscle fiber is adequately stimulated by a nerve impulse, an electrical change is set up. This change, in turn, initiates a sweep of negativity along the muscle fiber membrane to both its ends. The latter electrical event is known as the *action current* (if measured as current flow in milliamperes) or as the *action potential* (if measured in millivolts). This same phenomenon occurs in nerve and will be more fully explained in that connection in the next chapter.

The electrical changes just described occur during the first part of the latent period. (The refractory period also occurs concomitantly with the action potential or current.) As the current moves along the fiber, still within the latent period, it triggers the first of a long series of chemical reactions liberating the energy used for contraction.

Physical Changes. Refer to Chapter III for the structure of muscle fibers. Within each fiber are long fibrils, each of which is alternately dark- and light-banded. A dark section plus an adjacent light section is believed to constitute a unit for contraction. As the wave of excitation proceeds from the endplate toward both ends of the fiber, it causes energy release near or in successive units of the fibrils, and unit after unit shortens. Thus a wave of excitation is soon followed by a wave of contraction; since the latter occurs very rapidly, it is not perceived as a wave by our sense of sight.

Within the above units are still smaller units, composed especially of protein molecules, but undoubtedly including other kinds of compounds as well. We do know that in the fibrils there is a special, complex protein, *actomyosin*, which is capable of contracting. This substance has actually been extracted from muscle in quite pure form and it can be made to shorten in a test tube, given the proper conditions. Perhaps the most probable explanation (not a complete one by any means) of its contraction is that certain portions of the actomyosin molecule slide by one another; and on relaxation they slide back to resting position. The net result when all myofibrils contract simultaneously is the production of a shorter, wider fiber (there is no change in volume) which pulls against its attachments at either end (see Chapter XVII).

Chemical Changes. Although we cannot as yet give a complete explanation of the tissue chemistry underlying cellular activities, here, too, we have learned a great deal from experimentation.

Much as other tissues, muscle needs oxygen for continued activity. Active muscle needs more oxygen than resting muscle; in the absence of oxygen, muscle dies comparatively quickly. These relatively simple observations were made long ago and have since been repeatedly verified. Modern testing, however, has led to the discarding of the old idea that the energy released from oxidations is directly used for contraction. What follows will be a shortened and simplified version of the exceedingly complex sequence of chemical reactions that are now known to occur in muscle.

First, some further basic knowledge of chemistry is required. Let us take a fairly simple compound as an illustration. *Acetic acid*, the acid present in vinegar, consists of two carbon atoms, four hydrogen atoms, and two oxygen atoms, all linked together to form a molecule. A shorthand version of this is $C_2H_4O_2$. Even better, because it shows us graphically the relations between the various atoms, is:

$$
\begin{array}{ccc}
 & H & \\
 & | & \\
H - C & - \ C & = O \\
 & | & | \\
 & H & O \\
 & & | \\
 & & H
\end{array}
$$

Each letter stands for an appropriate atom and each line or dash for a chemical bond, the energy required to hold any particular atoms together. The amount of energy in a bond between C and H is different from that in a bond between C and O, etc. Putting a molecule together requires energy which is used to bind the atoms to one another; taking a molecule apart will therefore liberate energy. Thus, any time a more complex compound is broken down to a simpler compound, some energy will be freed.

Suppose that acetic acid is completely oxidized:

$$C_2H_4O_2 + 2\ O_2 \rightarrow 2\ CO_2 + 2\ H_2O + \text{energy}$$

We see that carbon dioxide and water result, but that energy is also released. Since this kind of reaction was known to occur both outside and inside the body, and to yield considerable energy, it was not illogical to conclude that oxidation of organic compounds was the source of energy for muscular contraction.

Subsequent observation, however, that a muscle could continue contracting for a short time in the absence of oxygen, necessitated revision of ideas on the subject. It was not until much later and only after much more experimentation that a better answer was found. What is even more significant is that the answer was soon shown to apply to and have relevance for all kinds of cells throughout the animal and plant kingdoms.

It had been known that muscle contains several *organic phosphates*, and that these become reduced in concentration after muscle is made to contract, while *inorganic phosphates*, also present, increase in concentration, and energy is released. Re-examination of these compounds with more refined and powerful techniques led to a most important revelation. An organic phosphate called *adenosine triphosphate*, or ATP for short, was shown to release more energy than was expected for a relatively simple breakdown. More work demonstrated that the bonds linking two of the phosphate groups to the molecule are special—they involve more energy than most chemical bonds. Without going into great chemical detail, letting A = adenosine, and P = a phosphate group, we can indicate ATP structure as follows: A − P ∼ P ∼ P. Between A and P the bond is the more usual one; but the two connecting the P's are *energy-rich* bonds.

The splitting of an energy-rich ATP bond is now known to be involved in many, many, energy-requiring activities of all kinds of cells. We still do not comprehend all the intricacies, but it is clear that ATP is formed in cells and serves as a "storehouse" of readily releasable and peculiarly available energy for cellular purposes.

In muscle, the action current triggers the breakdown of ATP, thus releasing energy utilized for contraction. All of the remaining chemical reactions (and there are a great many of them) are concerned with *recovery* processes. These can be summarized as follows:

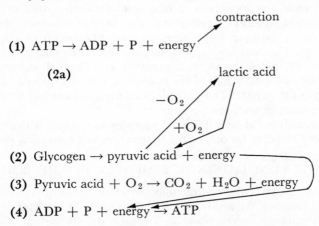

contraction

(1) ATP → ADP + P + energy

(2a)

lactic acid

$-O_2$

$+O_2$

(2) Glycogen → pyruvic acid + energy

(3) Pyruvic acid + O_2 → CO_2 + H_2O + energy

(4) ADP + P + energy → ATP

In (1) of the above sequence, when ATP breaks down, an energy-rich bond is broken (releasing energy which is used for contraction); a phosphate group is thereby freed (becoming inorganic phosphate, here represented by P) and two phosphates are left still attached to adenosine (forming *adenosine diphosphate*, ADP).

All the rest of the chemical machinery now set moving has one primary goal, the replenishment of ATP. Although it must be kept in mind that a muscle fiber does not use up all of its ATP in a single contraction or even during a bout of contraction, ATP is not present in large concentration and it is also used by a muscle cell for other energy-requiring activities as well as contraction (see Chapter XIV).

Reactions (2) and (3) are over-all summaries, actually representing some twenty-odd, enzyme-controlled reactions. Reactions (1) and (2) need no oxygen and are the basis for muscle's ability to contract for a while when oxygen supplies are not adequate. Reaction (2), however, does not provide enough energy for much resynthesis of ATP, so that strenuous activity cannot proceed very long when supplies of oxygen are not sufficient.

Whenever oxygen supplies are adequate, the oxidation of pyruvic acid provides for more energy than does reaction (2), and this can account for much ATP resynthesis. If oxygen is in short supply, however, little pyruvic acid can be oxidized, and most of it is, instead, converted to lactic acid (reaction 2a). Only when oxygen is re-supplied in sufficient amounts will reaction (2a) reverse and allow further oxidation of pyruvic acid. This will be further discussed in Chapters XVIII and XIX for its significance in exercise and fatigue.

Reactions (2), (3), and (4) occur during the contraction and relaxation periods and beyond them in what is called the *recovery period*. Even after a few seconds of contracting, a muscle continues to be chemically active (above its resting levels) for a minute or more.

Thermal Changes. During and after activity a muscle liberates heat. As we have just seen above, energy is liberated from chemical reactions. The heat liberated is that portion of the energy which is neither expended in work nor stored in chemical compounds. Actually, more than half of the energy cannot be captured by cells and goes off as heat. The latter is not simply wasted but is used in maintenance of body temperature.

Measurement of heat liberated provides additional evidence that recovery activities far outlast the contraction and relaxation periods.

THE FUNCTIONING OF MUSCLE IN THE BODY

Normally, muscular contractions are tetanic in nature rather than simple twitches. As we will see shortly, muscles must contract this way because the nerve fibers to a muscle usually do not conduct isolated nerve impulses but, instead, send volleys of impulses—one impulse following another quickly enough to force muscle to yield summation of contractions.

Under normal bodily conditions many muscles are not completely relaxed but are said to exhibit *muscle tone*. This may be characterized as a state of partial contraction resulting from alternating contractions of different groups of muscle fibers within one muscle.

CHAPTER X

The Nervous System

ALL CELLS are irritable. But even relatively early in the course of evolution some became more irritable than others. Among these cells certain ones called *receptors* became especially sensitive to stimuli. Others were especially adapted to conducting impulses and formed a network of nerve cells or *neurons*, the first nervous "system". This crude system enabled the lowly organisms in which it arose to achieve a grade of integration somewhat above that of the one-celled Amoeba.

When worms evolved from the lower forms of animal life, *ganglia* or clusters of nerve cell bodies made their first appearance. These acted as primitive centers of *coördination* of activities. Each body segment contained one or two ganglia. The neurons of the ganglia served as intermediaries between *afferent neurons*, which conducted nerve impulses into the ganglia from *receptors*, and *efferent neurons*, which relayed impulses to *effectors* (muscles or glands). In this way simple *reflex circuits* were established. In time, connections between ganglia developed and chains of ganglia came into being. Such interconnected ganglia became the first real "message center" for nerve impulses or, in other words, a *central nervous system* was developing. At this stage the central nervous system reminds one most of the *spinal cord* of higher animals. Even in man the latter retains its segmental pattern.

At the worm stage of evolution the *head* was beginning to assume dominance over the rest of the body. Since the head end was the first to encounter stimuli as the animal moved, the more important sense organs (eyes, ears, etc.) developed in this region. Coupled with this development, the ganglia of the head segments began to fuse with one another. The larger nerve cell centers resulting were the fore-runners of the *brain*. The oldest—in an evolutionary sense—parts of the brain in higher animals retain traces of primitive segmentation, although to a lesser degree than the spinal cord.

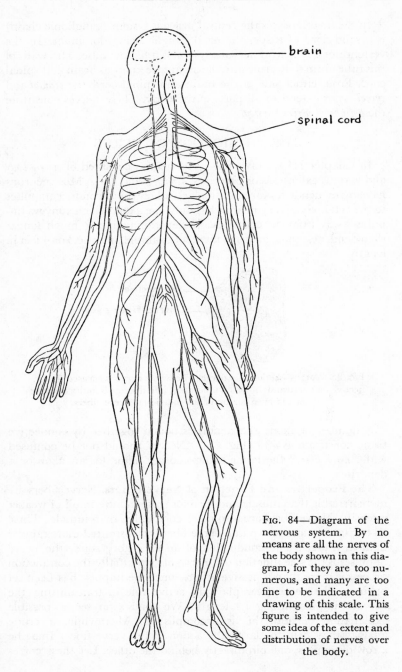

brain

spinal cord

Fig. 84—Diagram of the nervous system. By no means are all the nerves of the body shown in this diagram, for they are too numerous, and many are too fine to be indicated in a drawing of this scale. This figure is intended to give some idea of the extent and distribution of nerves over the body.

In the invertebrates the central nervous system (ganglionic chain) is a solid cord of tissue, the head ganglia being dominant. In the vertebrates the central nervous system is a hollow tube. The walls of this tube ultimately grow into the organs we know as brain and spinal cord. From either side of the brain and spinal cord the *cranial* and *spinal nerves* extend to all parts of the body. These nerves constitute the *peripheral nervous system*.

THE PHYSIOLOGY OF NERVE

In Chapter III we saw that every neuron consisted of a *cell body* and various extensions or processes, *dendrites* and *axons*. Most neurons have many dendrites (are multipolar), all of which conduct impulses to the cell body. Every neuron has only one axon, which conveys impulses away from the cell body. In general, axons are much longer than dendrites; some axons in man, for example, may be 3 or 4 feet in length.

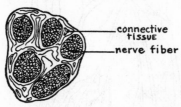

Fig. 85—A cross-section of a nerve. The whole nerve is encased in connective tissue, strands of which separate it into discrete bundles of nerve fibers and even surround the individual nerve fibers.

A number of axons and dendrites bound together by connective tissue constitute a *nerve* (Fig. 85). "Nerve" should not be confused with "*nerve fiber*," the latter being another name for an axon or a dendrite.

The Properties and Function of Nerve Fibers. Nerve fibers are more irritable than muscle and therefore respond to stimuli of weaker intensity. Nerve fibers are also more conductive than muscle. Thus, an excitatory state set up in a nerve fiber is transmitted more rapidly than in muscle. The conduction of an excitatory state (the nerve impulse) is the sole function of a nerve fiber. Actually the conduction process is more than a passive affair—once the impulse has been set up in it, the nerve fiber plays an active role in transmitting the nervous impulse along its length. We shall soon see a possible explanation of how this is accomplished. Meanwhile, a crude analogy may help to clarify the action of the nerve fiber. Imagine a row of tenpins, one pin directly behind the other. Let these correspond to successive points on a nerve fiber. A ball is bowled at the first pin and its impact (the stimulus) knocks over the pin. The first pin in falling causes the second to fall, the second hits the third, and so on. The continuous wave of motion created by the pins falling in series (Fig. 86) would correspond to the nerve impulse (actually much like a wave of electricity). And each pin, in turn, is necessary for the propagation of the wave.

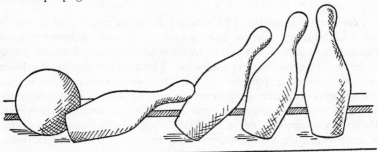

Fig. 86—The wave of motion created by the falling tenpins roughly corresponds to the passage of a nerve impulse from segment to segment along a nerve fiber.

The Stimulation of Nerve. In the body, nervous impulses are generally set up at one end of a nerve fiber. The axon of a neuron (for instance) receives a nervous impulse at its point of exit from the cell body. The impulse then travels in one direction only. But, if a nerve is exposed or a long segment of one removed from an experimental animal, it can be stimulated effectively at any point. The nervous impulse so produced will travel in both directions along the nerve fibers.

Under experimental or natural conditions, nerve, like muscle, can respond to a variety of stimuli. For experimental purposes, electrical stimuli are most widely used since, compared to other types, they are most easily and accurately controlled and measured and also do less harm to tissue. Under physiological conditions in the body, a combination of chemical and electric changes is most often the initiator of an impulse. Let us remember that a stimulus, to be effective, must fulfill the conditions noted in the discussion of Excitation of Muscle (Chapter IX).

An active nerve appears no different to our eyes than a resting nerve. To study its activity, one must record some kind of change. An older, indirect method of study was to record the muscular contractions resulting from nervous stimulation. While much information can be gleaned by comparing the differences in results when different sequences and patterns of stimulation are employed, we have had available since the 1930's a much better, direct recording method. Using sensitive electronic apparatus—stimulators, amplifiers, cathode ray oscilloscopes—one can detect, amplify, and even visualize the minute and fleeting pulses of electricity occuring in a nerve or even in a single nerve fiber. The visualization on the screen of an oscilloscope can be photographed and studied accurately at a later time.

The Nerve Impulse. The analogy between a nerve fiber and a series of tenpins is, as we saw, a very crude one. Structurally, of course, there is no resemblance at all, and the kinds of action going on in the two cases are very dissimilar. The analogy also breaks down in another very important respect. In order to repeat the tenpin phenomenon it is necessary to set the pins up again. They obviously have no recovery power of their own. The nerve fiber, however, after the passage of a nerve impulse, brings about its own recovery. A short time after it has conducted one impulse it is once again ready to conduct another.

What follows is an explanation of how a nerve impulse begins in and then moves along a nerve fiber, and how the fiber makes itself ready again to conduct another impulse. Our discussion will explain equally well the similar phenomenon in muscle fibers, since nerve and muscle impulses differ from one another only quantitatively.

THE NERVE FIBER AT REST. A nerve fiber at rest has a *selectively permeable cell membrane;* that is, there are certain materials which the membrane does not permit to penetrate it. Sodium ions (positively charged) and some organic—probably protein—ions (negatively charged) cannot pass through the membrane easily. The negative organic ions inside the fiber, which cannot get out, tend to line up on the inner side of the membrane; the positive sodium ions, present in the extra-cellular fluid in much greater concentration than in the interior of the fiber, tend to line up on the outer side of the membrane. What is more, those sodium ions that may enter tend to be extruded from the fiber by an active mechanism (which we will discuss later on). The over-all result is a layering of oppositely charged ions on either side of the membrane (see Fig. 87); the membrane is thus said to be *polarized* (it has an electrical potential difference across it and exhibits a *resting potential*).

Do not be misled by Fig. 87 into the belief that only negative ions are present inside and only positive outside the fiber. This would be a physical impossibility. In any ionic system at equilibrium there are always equal numbers of positive and negative ions. What we are saying in the preceding paragraph is only that the membrane, because of the unique properties conferred upon it by the metabolism of the nerve cell, becomes differentially charged on its inner and outer surfaces.

Note that not every factor is in equilibrium between the inside and the outside of the fiber. The total electrical charge outside may be said to equal that inside; but sodium ions are much more concentrated outside than inside, and negative organic ions are more

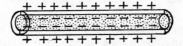

Fig. 87—A polarized nerve fiber. The positive and negative charges do not exist as such but are present because of the accumulation of positively and negatively charged ions in the appropriate places.

concentrated inside than outside. It is not surprising, then, to discover that other ions also show imbalance of concentrations: potassium ions (positive) are more greatly concentrated inside than out, and chloride ions (negative) more concentrated outside than in.

The polarization and permeability of the membrane are interdependent: each helps to maintain the other, and, if one varies, the other varies with it. If permeability increases, polarization decreases (more ions can freely penetrate, and the charge across the membrane decreases). If polarization increases, permeability decreases (the greater charge across the membrane seems to decrease the penetrability of ions).

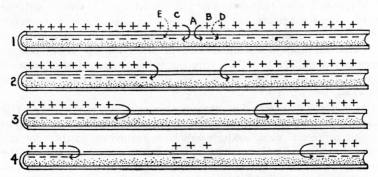

Fig. 88—When a nerve fiber is adequately stimulated at one point, a nerve impulse is propagated in both directions along the nerve fiber. Here, four stages in the conduction of the impulse are shown. In stage 4, the membrane is already repolarizing at the region where the impulse began, although the latter is still traveling along more distant regions.

IMPULSE INITIATION AND CONDUCTION. When a nerve fiber is adequately stimulated at one point, the membrane at that point suddenly becomes more permeable, and *depolarization* occurs (the charge at that point disappears, as at A in Fig. 88). To be even more specific than the diagram in Fig. 88 indicates, the membrane now becomes permeable to sodium ions and, since many more of these are present outside than inside, they rush in. This takes place to such a degree that the interior becomes positive with respect to the exterior; in other words, to be more accurate, stimulation causes not simply a disappearance of charge but rather a momentary reversal of polarization.

As a consequence, point A is now negative with respect to adjacent points B and C. The sodium ions (positive) at B and C are attracted to A (because unlike charges attract one another), and they move through the more permeable membrane at A. This changes the polarization at B and C so that ions at D and E are now attracted to B and C, etc. This progressive discharge of one region into the next accomplishes the conduction of the impulse from the point of activation to the ends of the fiber.

To summarize: at rest, each point on the membrane is a minute "battery" and exhibits a resting potential. When one point becomes "active," the permeability increases, ions move, and the potential reverses (this new voltage reading is called the *action potential*). Now, however, a potential difference exists between adjacent active and resting points; and as a resting point discharges into an active point, a current (the *action current*) flows between them. Successive discharges constitute a current or "impulse" along the whole fiber.

We note further that once one point is adequately stimulated, the nerve fiber itself takes over the complete activity. Each active point serves as a stimulus for the next resting point and no additional external stimulation is needed. Passage of the impulse is not passive conduction of current as in a wire but is better spoken of as *propagation;* that is, the nerve fiber actively participates in the conduction process.

REFRACTORY PERIOD. Let us turn to a consideration of what else happens at an active region. The resting equilibrium of that region is now quite distorted: sodium ions have rushed in, so that, for the moment, at that point the interior is positive with respect to the exterior. For the very short time that this condition exists, it is impossible to re-excite the fiber at that point; it is *refractory*. The refractory period persists only briefly. In those nerve fibers that are most excitable—that is, those that have the lowest thresholds—its duration is 0.0005 second, or ten times shorter than for the most excitable muscle fiber. However brief, its existence prevents *continuous* excitation of a nerve fiber.

RECOVERY. How can the nerve fiber be re-excited? Shortly after sodium ions have come in, potassium ions (also positive) start going out (they were more concentrated inside than out), and they continue to diffuse outward until the resting potential is restored. The fiber is then ready to be re-excited, even though it is not completely in the same state as the original resting fiber. Although it has the same resting potential, it now has somewhat more sodium and less potassium inside than before. Recall that we said previously that a nerve fiber has an active mechanism for extruding sodium, the *sodium "pump."* This mechanism comes into play; for every sodium ion pushed out, a potassium ion is brought back in. Nerve fibers have remarkable powers of propagating a message and then repolarizing themselves and instituting processes for complete recovery.

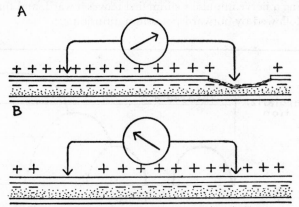

Fig. 89—When one electrode is placed on an injured region of a nerve fiber and another on an intact region (*A*), an injury current can be recorded by a current-recording instrument. An action current can be recorded when one electrode is placed on a depolarized region of an intact nerve fiber and another on a polarized region (*B*). See text for further description.

EXPERIMENTAL EVIDENCE. Is the preceding explanation simply a hypothesis or is there proof of it? While we cannot account for every aspect of the phenomena just described (as, for example, just what is responsible for the permeability changes), there is some very pertinent evidence.

If a portion of a nerve is crushed and one electrode is placed on it and a second electrode on an intact region, a potential difference, the *injury potential,* can be measured. The injured region always is negative in relation to the uninjured. This is presumptive evidence that the interior of the fiber is negative to the exterior (Fig. 89).

There is also very direct evidence to support this point. In a number of invertebrates (squid, lobster, earthworm, etc.) can be found giant nerve fibers, much larger in diameter than any vertebrate fiber. It is possible without too great damage to introduce an electrode into a giant fiber and measure potentials across the membrane. Whenever this has been done, a measurable resting potential has been found with outside positive with respect to inside; and action potentials have been recorded with these charges reversed.

Additionally, we are now certain from chemical analysis and measurement that sodium, potassium, and chloride concentrations are unequal on either side of the membrane in the ways previously mentioned. By the use of radioactive sodium and potassium, whose presences in a particular region can be detected by instruments sensitive to the particles they discharge, it has been demonstrated that during a nerve impulse sodium first moves inward, and that this event is followed by outward potassium diffusion.

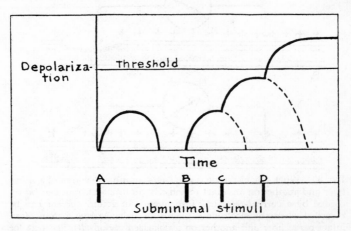

Fig. 90—A single subminimal stimulus to a nerve fiber will cause a certain amount of depolarization which will shortly disappear without having caused an impulse to be set up (A). When a few subminimal stimuli (B, C, D) are sent in rapidly enough so that the depolarization set up by the preceding one has not had time to disappear, the depolarizations caused by each can sum sufficiently to yield a threshold amount of depolarization. In the latter case an impulse will be initiated due to the summation of effects caused by the stimuli. The dotted lines indicate the course the depolarization would have taken if another stimulus had not been received.

SUMMATION OF STIMULI. Not only must the nerve fiber have an adequate degree of polarization, but there must be a definite amount of depolarization occurring before an impulse will be set up. It is an experimental fact that one *subminimal* stimulus (one below threshold strength) will not excite a nerve fiber but that a series of such stimuli sent in rapidly enough will cause a response. This phenomenon is known as *summation of stimuli*—a series of stimuli none of which is adequate by itself can add up to produce a response.

One subminimal stimulus obviously cannot cause an adequate depolarization of the nerve fiber membrane. It does cause some depolarization, however. Since it takes time for ions to move back and
completely repolarize the membrane, a second subminimal stimulus
coming soon enough after the first can add the depolarization it
causes to that still remaining from the first stimulus. Enough of these
stimuli at a sufficiently rapid rate will depolarize the membrane
adequately and an impulse will arise (see Fig. 90).

ALL-OR-NONE RESPONSE. A *nerve fiber* obeys the all-or-none "law." A
nerve does not, since it is made up of many nerve fibers which have
different thresholds of excitability. Therefore, stimulating a nerve
with electric shocks of increasing intensity will provoke larger and
larger action potentials until all the nerve fibers are activated. The
response of nerve is very similar to that of muscle in this respect.

Every point on a single nerve fiber will respond to the maximal
amount of which it is capable at the moment or will not respond at
all. A striking illustration of this can be shown by depressing the
irritability of one section of a nerve by exposing it to ether vapor (see
Fig. 91). When the nerve is stimulated by a maximal stimulus at A,

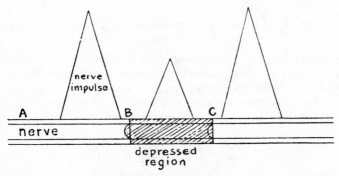

FIG. 91—A diagrammatic representation of the all-or-none character
of the nerve impulse. See text for description.

an impulse is set up which travels the length of the nerve. From A
to B the action potential is maximal but suddenly decreases and
remains smaller in traveling from B to C (the depressed region). At
C it emerges from the depressed area at its initial height and continues at that height to the end of the nerve. The action potential is,
then, maximal for the condition of the nerve at every point.

The Velocity of the Nerve Impulse. The speed at which a nerve
impulse travels depends upon the electrical resistance of the nerve
fiber and the amount of polarization of the nerve fiber in its resting state. Just as wires of large diameter have less resistance to the
passage of a current than smaller ones, large nerve fibers have less

resistance than small ones. The former generally conduct impulses at faster rates. The polarization of the nerve fiber membrane is the driving power behind the impulse; the greater it is, the faster the impulse travels. If the polarization is decreased (as by etherization), the velocity as well as the amplitude of the impulse (action current) is decreased.

Another factor is of importance in large fibers. All peripheral nerve fibers (those outside the central nervous system) are invested with an outer sheath of cells, the *neurilemma*. Nerve fibers when of large

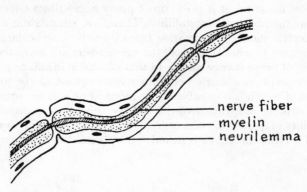

nerve fiber
myelin
neurilemma

FIG. 92—A peripheral nerve fiber with myelin and neurilemmal sheaths.

enough diameter also are encased in a *myelin sheath;* a layer of myelin (a fatty substance) is deposited beneath the neurilemma. When both sheaths are present, the myelin sheath is broken at intervals into segments (Fig. 92). Nerve impulses in the latter type of nerve fibers have

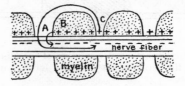

FIG. 93—In a myelinated nerve fiber the impulse jumps from node to node (see text).

the highest velocity of all. The explanation for this is based on the fact that myelin, as a fatty substance, is a poor conductor of electricity and insulates the nerve fiber in whichever region it is present. Since the current meets a greater resistance in flowing through myelin (B to A in Fig. 93), it will preferentially follow the path of lesser resistance (C to A) through the salt solution bathing the nerve fiber.

The nerve impulse in such fibers thus jumps from node to node (a node being a region at which the myelin sheath is broken) and travels more quickly than by going from one segment to its neighbor.

The velocity of the nerve impulse in man varies in different nerve fibers according to their size and myelination. The speeds of conduction range from about 1 to over 100 meters per second. (100 m. per sec. is equivalent to about 200 miles per hour.) The pilot of a plane moving faster than 200 miles an hour would have difficulty, then, in avoiding a collision with another object if his movements depended on a split-second decision.

It is interesting to note that velocity of conduction is also dependent upon temperature. Frog nerve at room temperature (about 70° F.) has a maximal nerve impulse velocity of about 30 m. per sec. When the temperature is raised to the body temperature of man (98.6° F), the maximal velocity of the impulse borders on 100 m. per sec.

The Effects of Activity on Nerve. We know much less about the chemical reactions that occur in nerve than in muscle. Nonetheless it is apparent that they are responsible for the changes which accompany and follow upon even a short burst of activity. Electrical fluctuations in the polarization of the membrane occur which are correlated with changes in irritability. These changes, plus an increased oxygen consumption and the elaboration of heat, may continue for 15 to 30 minutes after activity that lasts only for seconds. A nerve fiber does not return to its original resting condition until long after its active period has ended.

It is puzzling, therefore, to find that a nerve can continue to conduct impulses over long periods of time without completely fatiguing. The refractory period does limit the number of impulses that a nerve can conduct per second. Since the nerve cannot respond to a second stimulus until 0.0005 sec. has passed, it can conduct a maximum of 2000 impulses per second. Actually this rate of activity can be maintained for only a short time. However, the nerve does not cease responding. Instead, the refractory period begins to lengthen and the frequency of impulses decreases. With continued stimulation the frequency of impulses conducted declines quite a bit until, when the processes of activity and recovery are going on at the same rates, it levels off and remains fairly constant. Nerve cannot be completely fatigued under normal circumstances.

Degeneration and Regeneration of Nerve. When a peripheral nerve is severed, the portions of the nerve fibers separated from the cell bodies degenerate completely in two to three weeks. The nerve fibers themselves disintegrate, the myelin decomposes, and both disappear. The neurilemmal sheath alone remains. On the other side of the cut some reversible minor changes may occur unless the cut is too close to the cell body. In the latter case the whole neuron will degenerate; once this happens it cannot be replaced.

In the peripheral nervous system there will be complete functional and anatomical regeneration of nerves provided that the neurilemmal sheath is intact. The central ends of the nerve fibers grow out into the neurilemmal sheath (Fig. 94 B) and are guided by it to their

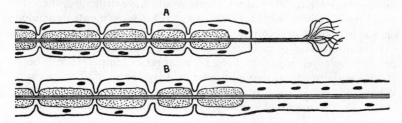

Fig. 94—Regeneration in peripheral nerve fibers (see text).

eventual termination. Surgeons generally sew the two ends of a cut nerve together so that the growing nerve fibers will be properly directed. If the neurilemma is absent or the gap too great between the ends of a nerve, the nerve fibers will still grow but will tend to curl up into a tangled mass (Fig. 94 A). This can prove a very painful growth and may have to be removed surgically if allowed to develop.

Nerve fibers within the central nervous system have no neurilemmal sheaths and are said to be incapable of regenerating successfully for that reason. In recent years experiments on animals have attempted to show that, given directional aid, such nerve fibers can regenerate. Some of these experiments appear to have been successful. But much work remains to be done to prove conclusively that this can be of value in cases of human injury.

THE SPINAL CORD AND REFLEX ACTION

Having discussed the propagation of a nerve impulse within a single nerve fiber, we are now ready to examine the effect of an impulse in one nerve cell upon a second nerve cell and, further, to trace the paths impulses take from peripheral receptors to the central nervous system and outward again to peripheral effectors.

We have already noted many reflexes in discussing the control of various systems of the body. To understand reflex action in greater detail, let us turn our attention to the simplest reflexes, those centered in the spinal cord.

The Structure of the Spinal Cord. The *spinal cord* is securely encased by the bony vertebrae. In vertebrates with tails (cat, dog, etc.) the spinal cord extends virtually the whole length of the vertebral column; in those without tails (frog, ape, man, etc.) it is shortened somewhat. In man it ends at about the second lumbar vertebra (the second vertebra below the thoracic region). At its upper end the spinal cord merges with the brain.

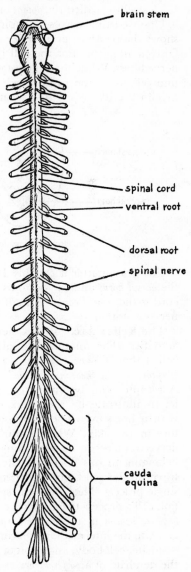

If removed from the body or exposed, the spinal cord is revealed as a longish white "cylinder" (Fig. 95) which is oval in cross-section. Evidence of its primitive segmental arrangement is seen in the nerves which extend from it on either side. There are 31 pairs of spinal nerves, each pair arising in one spinal "segment." The "segments" of the cord are not distinguishable internally, however. Although the cord is shortened, each spinal nerve still exists at the level of the vertebra with which it was associated during evolution. This means that nerves from the lower segments of the cord must travel for a considerable distance within the vertebral canal before leaving it. Below the spinal cord, then, a number of nerves are seen descending. They somewhat resemble a horse's tail, which is the meaning of the name *cauda equina* given to the region.

On closer inspection it can be seen that each spinal nerve arises from the spinal cord in two bundles (see Fig. 95), the *dorsal* (towards the back) and *ventral* (towards the belly) *roots*. For over a hundred years it has been known that the dorsal root contains *afferent* or *sensory nerve fibers* (those coming in-

Fig. 95—The spinal cord and its nerves.

to the central nervous system) and the ventral root *efferent* or *motor nerve fibers* (those leaving the central nervous system). Thus, each spinal nerve contains a mixture of sensory and motor fibers. Note, for the moment, that each dorsal root has a swelling called the *dorsal* or *spinal ganglion*.

Upon cutting across the spinal cord, the cross-section (Fig. 96) shows the presence of an outer *white matter* and an inner *gray matter*. Gray matter contains the cell bodies of neurons and unmyelinated nerve fibers. White matter contains only nerve fibers, myelinated and unmyelinated; the myelinated ones give it its white coloring since myelin is milky-white in appearance.

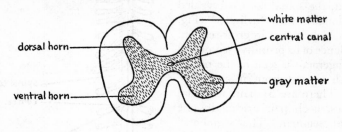

FIG. 96—A cross-section of the spinal cord.

The gray matter is roughly H-shaped, the tops of the "H" being the *dorsal horns* and the bottoms the *ventral horns*. In the center of the cord is the *central canal*, a small remnant of the cavity in the central nervous system.

The Reflex Arc. Reflex acts are the basis of many nervous activities. The anatomical unit which makes a reflex possible is called the *reflex arc* (Fig. 97). This consists of five essential parts— *receptor, afferent neuron, intermediate neuron, efferent neuron*, and *effector*. A receptor can be any sense organ. For the sake of convenience let us illustrate by the reflex withdrawl of a finger from contact with a hot stove. The receptors concerned will be the heat receptors in the skin. When stimulated by the heat, a *receptor* causes nerve impulses to be sent along an *afferent nerve fiber*. The cell body belonging to this fiber is located in a *dorsal ganglion*. The impulses travel to the cell body and then leave along the other branch of its single process. They enter the spinal cord via a *dorsal root*. The ganglion cell's process there makes contact with the dendrites of an *intermediate neuron* in the *dorsal horn* of the gray matter. The impulses activate the intermediate neuron, and new impulses travel along the dendrite, cell body, and axon of this neuron. These impulses activate the dendrite of an *efferent neuron* in the *ventral horn* to set up new impulses which travel along its cell body and axon and leave the spinal cord via this *efferent nerve fiber*. The latter extends through a *ventral root* and spinal nerve to a muscle. The impulses activate myoneural junctions (as described in Chapter IX) and cause the *effector* (muscle) cells to contract. The finger is withdrawn. The result of the stimulation of a receptor is a reflex response from some effector organ.

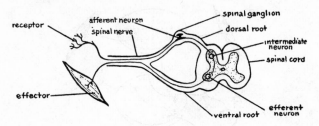

FIG. 97—A typical spinal reflex arc.

One aspect of the preceding description requires more elaboration. As you might suspect from our discussion of the myoneural junction, neurons, similarly, are not anatomically continuous with one another. Where the axon of one neuron approaches a second neuron, the fine axonal ending usually terminates in a small bulbous enlargement or *endfoot*. The membrane of the endfoot is separated from the membrane of the second neuron by a gap which, though exceedingly small, is nonetheless a true separation. The small region of membrane in the second neuron just opposite the endfoot has special properties, unlike those of the membrane in general. The combination of endfoot and special portion of membrane, the region of "contact" between two neurons, is referred to as a *synapse*. One axon can branch repeatedly and make a number of synaptic connections with a second neuron and with other neurons as well. We shall presently describe the differences between the activity at synapses and that at myoneural junctions, but first we will examine the different types of reflexes and the way in which reflexes differ from nerve impulses.

Types of Reflexes. The reflex arc described above is a simple one. Most reflexes involve more complex arcs, complexity being due to the inclusion of more than one intermediate neuron between afferent and efferent neurons. Instead of being limited to one side of one segment of the spinal cord, the reflex may then include both sides of the spinal cord and more than one level. A number of muscles can, therefore, be involved in a reflex response and a complicated pattern of muscular contractions results from stimulation of a few receptors. For some varieties of possible reflex arcs note Fig. 98.

We can classify reflexes in various ways, and one of these is in point of complexity. A *simple reflex* is that in which a single muscle gives a response to a single stimulus. The *knee jerk* is an example: when one leg is crossed over the other and the *patellar* (kneecap) tendon of the upper leg is struck, that leg jerks upward. This knee jerk results from the stimulation by stretching of receptors in the muscle that extends the lower leg.

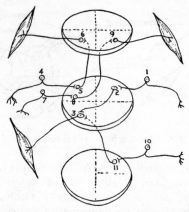

Fig. 98—A sketch of three different levels of the spinal cord and some of the varieties of possible reflex arcs. Neurons *1*, *2* and *3* comprise a reflex arc which is centered at one level of the spinal cord but which ends on the opposite side from which it began. A similar arc to this but involving two levels of the cord is illustrated by neurons *7*, *8* and *9*. The arc containing neurons *4*, *5* and *6* involves two levels of the cord but ends on the same side on which it began. Stimulation of the receptor leading to neuron *1* may not be strong enough to cause a discharge of neuron *3*. Simultaneous stimulation of the receptors leading to neurons *10* and *1* can bring about summation at *3* of the effects caused by impulses from neurons *11* and *2*, and *3* can thus be activated. This is an example of spatial summation (see page 168).

The majority of reflexes, however, involve more than one muscle and are known as *coördinated reflexes*. The *flexion reflex*, resulting from painful stimulation of the skin, illustrates this type: your response to stepping on a tack—the flexing of your leg in order to withdraw from the painful stimulus—would in part be accomplished by the contraction of a flexor muscle or muscles (which bend the leg at the knee). In most cases there will be several flexor muscles acting together as *synergists*. In addition, there will always be a simultaneous relaxation of an extensor muscle or muscles (which straighten the leg at the knee). We say that, with respect to each other, the flexors of the knee and the extensors of the knee are operating as *antagonists*. In any coördinated reflex, if one muscle contracts, its antagonist must relax. To accomplish this, the muscles involved are *reciprocally innervated*. Thus, not only does reflex *excitation* occur here in the activation of the flexor muscles; but reflex *inhibition* must also occur in the relaxation of the extensor muscles. We shall soon have more to say about excitatory and inhibitory states when we discuss synaptic events.

The flexion reflex is usually accompanied by another coördinated reflex, *the crossed extension reflex*. For example, painful stimulation of one foot does not result merely in the coordinated flexion of the same leg but also in the coordinated extension of the other leg. We will return to related flexor and extensor reflexes after having examined synaptic events.

Still more complex, *chain* reflexes are coördinated ones but are compound in nature—a series of reflexes in which one acts as the stimulus for the next. The rhythmic series of movements that make up walking is, in part, a chain reflex. Many extended instinctive acts, such as the homing instincts of bees and birds, are also reflexes in this category.

Reflexes are also classified according to the types of receptors that initiate them. Stimulation of *exteroceptors* (receptors in the surface regions of the body) gives rise to *exteroceptive* reflexes, such as the flexion reflex initiated by painful stimulation of the skin of the foot. Receptors in the viscera, *enteroceptors*, initiate *enteroceptive* reflexes. Circulatory, respiratory, etc. reflexes are examples of this kind. Another class of receptors located in muscles, tendons, joints, and some parts of the inner ear, *proprioceptors*, set up *proprioceptive* reflexes. The knee jerk is this kind of reflex.

The reflexes we have mentioned so far are examples of *inherited* reflexes. The pathways for them have been established in the course of evolution, and all of them can be demonstrated in an experimental animal after its brain has been destroyed. There are also acquired or *conditioned* reflexes, which we learn by repetition of performance. Since they are dependent upon the highest levels of the brain, we shall discuss them later in connection with learning.

Properties of Reflexes and Nerve Impulses Contrasted. The reflex arc, with its receptor, afferent neuron, intermediate neuron, efferent neuron, and effector, is of course an aggregation of cells, and it behaves differently, in certain important respects, from the way in which a single nerve fiber behaves when it is stimulated. The reasons for some of these differences will be obvious to the reader; the reasons for others will become clearer after he has acquainted himself with the section explaining synaptic events.

CONDUCTION. We have already seen that the nerve impulse can be conducted in either direction along a nerve fiber. But in the reflex arc, conduction of impulses proceeds in one direction only. This is due to the synapses and myoneural junctions which in this respect act like one-way valves; they allow impulses to flow only in the one direction previously indicated.

LATENT PERIOD. In muscle the time between application of a stimulus and the beginning of a response is comparatively short (0.01 sec.). Nerve has an even shorter latent period. But reflexes have much longer ones. In part this is due to the longer path impulses must travel (the whole reflex arc) before the response is forthcoming. Also, the phenomenon of *central delay* is a factor; that is, the synaptic regions are more resistant to passage of impulses than the other parts of the reflex circuit, and additional time is needed to overcome that resistance. The latent period of a reflex response is usually measured in seconds, sometimes many seconds. If you have a dog, you can observe this in the *scratch reflex*. Scratching the belly of a dog generally elicits scratching movements of the hind leg, but a fairly long latent period may intervene.

AFTER-DISCHARGE. When a nerve fiber is activated, an impulse flashes along the fiber and the activity is soon over. A reflex response may, however, continue for some time after stimulation has stopped. This phenomenon is what is called *after-discharge*. The scratch reflex, as you may be able to observe, is especially likely to exhibit a long after-discharge.

SUMMATION OF STIMULI. Summation of stimuli does occur in nerves, as we have noted. The same kind of summation can occur in the reflex arc. Summation of this type is called *temporal summation*—subminimal stimuli sent rapidly into one nerve fiber can add up to activate it. There is one difference between reflex and nerve responses with respect to temporal summation. In the case of nerve, if the first few stimuli do not activate the nerve, later ones will not. A reflex response, however, can be elicted by additional subminimal stimuli, even though the first few do not initiate the response. It seems that there is some region in the reflex arc where effects of stimuli can accumulate and be preserved to a much greater extent than in nerve.

Another kind of summation can occur in the reflex arc—*spatial summation*. In temporal summation, stimuli impinge upon one fiber and are separated by a time interval; in spatial summation stimuli are separated in space, being sent into different nerve fibers. Impulses thus set up may eventually terminate upon the same neuron and their effects add up at that point in the reflex arc. A reflex arc permitting this phenomenon is shown in Fig. 98.

GRADATION OF RESPONSE. Adequate stimuli of unequal strength elicit responses of unvarying amplitude in a nerve fiber, provided conditions are the same at all times. A nerve, though, does not follow this all-or-none pattern of response. Nor does a reflex. Stimuli of graded intensity produce responses of graded intensity. The stronger the initial stimulus, the greater the response. The prime reason for this is that a receptor responds to a single stimulus by setting up a volley of nerve impulses in the afferent nerve fiber. When this barrage of impulses is finally relayed to the muscle at the end of the reflex circuit, a tetanic contraction results. The latter, you will remember, is of greater intensity than the corresponding single twitch and will vary in amplitude with the intensity and frequency of stimuli. A strong stimulus to a receptor increases the rate of discharge of the receptor and makes for greater tetanization of the muscle than a weaker stimulus.

RHYTHM OF RESPONSE. Stimulation of nerve with a number of adequate stimuli yields a one-to-one response. This is rarely true of a reflex response. First of all, a receptor responds to a single stimulus by discharging a volley of impulses. Eventually the efferent neuron may discharge still a different volley over the efferent axon leading from it. The net result of a single reflex stimulus is a variable number of impulses in the efferent neuron—depending upon the physiological state and the specific properties of the particular reflex arc—and a correspondingly variable tetanic contraction of muscle.

METABOLIC EFFECTS. Central nervous tissue has a much higher rate of metabolism than nerve. This is in all probability due to the greater requirements of nutrients and oxygen and faster turnover of materials in the cell bodies and synaptic regions. As evidence for this, it is known that gray matter has a higher metabolic rate, greater oxygen consumption, and larger blood supply than white matter.

On this basis it is understandable that reflexes fatigue more quickly, succumb to *asphyxia* (lack of oxygen), anesthetics, and other drugs more rapidly than nerve fibers do. The higher the metabolic rate in general, the greater the tendency to fatigue. After a comparatively small number of repeated stimuli, a reflex response may temporarily be completely fatigued.

Stopping the blood flow to parts of the central nervous system (thus depriving them of oxygen) kills them rather rapidly. The highest levels of the brain, the cerebral cortex and cerebellar cortex, will never regain their functions if deprived of blood for more than five minutes; lower centers of the brain may withstand as much as thirty minutes of asphyxia and the spinal cord about sixty minutes' worth.

Peripheral nerve may recover after several hours of asphyxiation. The ability to withstand oxygen lack would thus vary inversely with the metabolic rate.

Anesthesia abolishes reflexes rather rapidly. On the other hand, in an animal killed by an overdose of an anesthetic, nerves are still able to conduct impulses in a fairly normal fashion. Of course, if the concentration of the anesthetic gets sufficiently high, even nerve will be incapacitated—the direct application of ether, for instance, to a nerve will abolish its excitability.

The site in the central nervous system most quickly attacked by fatigue, asphyxia, etc. is the synapse or the cell body of the neuron. In the peripheral neuromuscular apparatus the myoneural junction most readily succumbs to adverse conditions.

Synaptic Events and their Explanation. We have already mentioned that synapses have properties somewhat similar to those of myoneural junctions. The situation is, however, more complex at the synapses. At myoneural junctions only excitatory events take place, but at synapses it has long been known that both excitatory and inhibitory events occur.

NEW TECHNIQUES OF STUDY. For many years a physiological controversy "raged" over the question of what mechanism best explains synaptic transmission. Is it essentially electrical or chemical in nature? Much evidence was adduced in support of both hypotheses, but it was necessarily indirect, since the structures studied are very small and difficult to get at. Here, again, technical advances in instrumentation have considerably aided the resolution of conflicting ideas. In this case, the development of microelectrodes, and the techniques to make proper use of them, give us a better idea, although not complete knowledge, of what goes on in synaptic transmission.

Motor neurons have been studied especially, since their cell bodies are somewhat larger than those of other neurons. Insertion of the very fine tip of an electrode into the cell body of a neuron, with placement of another electrode just outside the membrane, make possible the recording of potentials across the membrane. The membrane of the cell body exhibits a resting potential, just as the membrane of an axon does. Microelectrode recordings show us what happens after impulses from other neurons arrive at synapses.

SYNAPTIC TRANSMISSION. As mentioned before, the terminal ending of an axon comes close to but does not make actual contact with the membrane of the next neuron. Some agency must bridge the small gap between the two. When excitatory impulses arrive at a synaptic region, recordings show that a depolarization occurs in the membrane of the next neuron (the resting potential is decreased at that point); this is called an *excitatory post-synaptic potential* (EPSP). On the other hand, when inhibitory impulses arrive at a synaptic region, the membrane of the next neuron exhibits an overpolarization (its resting potential is increased at that point); this is called an *inhibitory post-synaptic potential* (IPSP).

Note that, when EPSP results, the outside of the membrane of the next neuron becomes more negative. Theoretically, at least, the impulse in the presynaptic fiber, which is a wave of negativity, might have acted as an electrical stimulus to set up the EPSP. Can we, however, say the same for the IPSP? The impulse in the presynaptic fiber is once again a wave of negativity. How could this, as an electrical stimulus, set up a more positive change in the next membrane? Since this seems an impossibility, most people now accept the idea that a chemical substance must be released at the synaptic ending and diffuse to the membrane of the next neuron in order to change its permeability. There must be at least two such chemical transmitters, one increasing the permeability of the membrane and producing an EPSP, one decreasing permeability and producing an IPSP. (It is possible that more than two chemicals are involved: there may be different ones in different regions of the central nervous system.) It also seems necessary to assume that a neuron that produces an excitatory influence on another neuron always produces that same kind of influence; other neurons would always have inhibitory influences. It would be quite improbable that one neuron would at one moment secrete an excitatory chemical and at another, an inhibitory chemical.

PROPERTIES OF EPSP AND IPSP. EPSP and IPSP are opposite in sign and produce opposite effects in a neuron, but they have somewhat similar properties in other respects. Both achieve a sufficiently effective intensity only when at least several incoming impulses arrive at a synapse; in other words, summation of stimuli is essential for EPSP or IPSP to achieve threshold intensity. Neither of these potentials is all-or-none in character, and each can remain at threshold or above for a time (this is usually the result of recurrent circuits of neurons keeping impulses arriving at the same synapses). Thus, when EPSP arrives at threshold and remains there or above for a while, a number of impulses may be successively set up in that neuron. This will account for discharges of volleys of impulses by central nervous neurons, for the height of the reflex response, and also, when it persists, for after-discharge. For as long as IPSP persists at threshold or higher, a neuron will be prevented from discharging impulses.

Related Flexor and Extensor Reflexes. Fig. 99 shows a simplified scheme for the setting up of two related reflexes. (To be more accurate, more intermediate neurons should be shown.) In A, the pattern of taking a step forward with the left foot is represented: contraction of the extensor and relaxation of the flexor muscles in the left leg and the reverse in the right leg. As the left foot comes down, it steps on a sharp object. The painful stimulus institutes impulses in afferent and intermediate neurons; these impulses reverse the EPSP and IPSP at the appropriate efferent neurons. The outcome is marked flexion of the left leg and extension of the right.

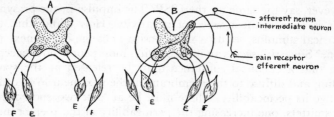

FIG. 99—Production of the flexion and crossed extension reflexes. E = extensor muscle; F = flexor muscle. In A is shown the pattern of muscular responses when a step forward with the left foot is taken. In B, pain impulses cause a reversal of these responses by changing the IPSP and EPSP at the appropriate efferent neurons (see text).

All motor neurons do not have the same thresholds. In the above reaction, note these differences: the flexor motor neurons have lower thresholds and shorter after-discharges than the extensor neurons. The evolution of such differences is advantageous to the individual. It is important that flexor reflexes provide as rapid as possible withdrawal of a part of the body in order to avoid its injury; speed of response is of less importance in extensor reflexes, whose longer duration provides better support for the body.

Stretch Reflexes and Posture. There are some reflex acts that come into play still more rapidly than any of the above. These are known as *stretch reflexes*, since they are set in motion by receptors sensitive to stretching. When a portion of a muscle or the whole muscle is lengthened, sensory impulses are initiated by stretch receptors within the muscle. Sensory neurons convey these impulses to the spinal cord and make synaptic contacts with motor neurons directly (no intermediate neurons are involved, which accounts, at least in part, for the greater speed of the reaction). When a sufficient EPSP is achieved, the motor neuron discharges impulses back to the very portion of the muscle that was stretched and causes a partial contraction of short duration. The knee jerk is an example of such a reflex, although it serves no useful function in the body.

A longer-lasting stretch can provoke a longer-lasting response. If the stretch lasts for a considerable time, a response can continue; under these circumstances, however, we know that the same muscle fibers do not contract continuously. Rather, adjacent groups of fibers alternately contract and relax (this obviates fatigue).

In skeletal muscles that exhibit *tone*, stretch reflexes may very well provide the basis for it and, further, be responsible for the contractions resulting in a given posture. While this may hold true in a number of animals, it is less clear that stretch reflexes maintain the muscle tone and posture of man. In us, evidence seems to indicate that the pull of gravity is not a strong enough stretching stimulus to induce postural reflex contraction. Instead, the standing posture is probably maintained by the "locking" characteristics of our skeletal joints aided by slight voluntary contractions of muscles.

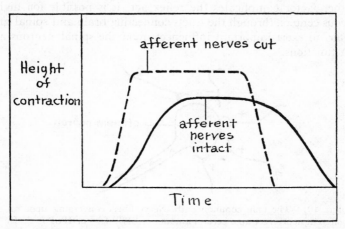

Fig. 100—The contraction of an extensor muscle with its afferent nerves intact and then after they are cut (see text).

The preceding does not mean that stretch reflexes have no significance in man; it means simply that a stronger stimulus than ordinary gravitation is necessary to elicit them. Stretch reflexes, and certain inhibitory influences set up by stretch of receptors in muscle tendons, may have importance in the smoothing of muscular responses. Note in Fig. 100 the more abrupt contraction and relaxation in a muscle when no sensory impulses from that muscle or its tendons can influence its reactions.

Functions of the Spinal Cord. We have just discussed the spinal cord mainly in its role as a central nervous system "interpreter" of spinal reflex impulses. In the gray matter of each "segment" of the cord there are at least several special collections of neurons (either intermediate or efferent), each of which is the *center* for some reflex. A center receives impulses from receptors in skin, viscera, or muscles and tendons; "interprets" this information; and brings about appropriate action or inaction in specific motor units.

It must be kept in mind, however, that the white matter of the spinal cord, which consists solely of nerve fibers, enables the spinal cord to function in addition as a *conduction pathway*. The nerve fibers are organized into specific *tracts*, each of which runs from one part of the central nervous system to another. Some tracts are concerned with intercommunication among the different segments of the cord itself. Others convey sensory information upward to various regions of the brain. Still others descend from the brain into the spinal cord; at various levels in the cord, nerve fibers leave these tracts, pass into the gray matter, and synapse with certain neurons there. Thus, still another factor complicates the reflex act: it is possible for higher nervous centers, through the tracts connecting brain and spinal gray matter, to exert important influences upon the spinal neurons and their functions.

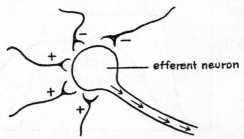

Fig. 101—The final common path. Nerve fibers converging upon an efferent neuron set up a certain amount of EPSP (+) or IPSP (−). In this case EPSP is predominant and the neuron discharges impulses (arrows).

Eventually, a host of influences—from the brain and from spinal and peripheral neurons—can play upon any given efferent or motor neuron. The latter, since it communicates in turn only with the muscle fibers it innervates, is often called the *final common path*. Whether or not impulses go out along a motor neuron depends upon the resultant (the algebraic sum, so to speak) of the many impulses that can converge upon that neuron. A schematic, simplified (many, many more synaptic connections exist than are shown) version of this principle is illustrated in Fig. 101.

Spinal Shock. The extent to which impulses from the brain can influence spinal reflexes is dramatically demonstrated in cases in which the spinal cord is severed. Brain influences can no longer reach the portion of the cord below the cut. Although the reflex pathways are still completely intact below the level of the cut, in most species of animals a temporary cessation of all reflex activity occurs in this area. In the frog this condition of *spinal shock* lasts but a few minutes, in a cat or dog perhaps half an hour, and in a monkey a few days. In man, when the spinal cord is accidentally severed, spinal shock may last from one to three weeks. Thus, the higher the animal is in the evolutionary scale, the more profound the shock and the greater the dependence of the spinal cord on higher centers. We deduce that there must normally be impulses descending from the brain which permit spinal reflexes to occur. We shall see other examples of the dominance of higher levels of the nervous system over lower levels as we proceed.

THE AUTONOMIC NERVOUS SYSTEM

Anatomically, the *autonomic nervous system* is a special portion of the peripheral nervous system. This system, concerned with the automatic control of activities of *visceral* organs, can be contrasted with the reflex system controlling *somatic* organs (primarily skeletal muscles) just described above.

Structure of the Autonomic System. The autonomic nervous system is a dual system, structurally and functionally. Its two subdivisions are called the *sympathetic* and *parasympathetic systems*. Each system is based upon a reflex network which shows some modification of that for somatic organs.

The *afferent neurons* are very similar to those we have dealt with before. They begin in receptors in various visceral regions and have their cell bodies in a spinal ganglion or a ganglion lying near the brain. They then continue into the brain via cranial nerves or into the spinal cord via dorsal roots. The exact pathways of many autonomic reflexes within the central nervous system are not very clear. The afferent neurons, either directly or through some intermediate neurons, make connections with autonomic *efferent neurons*. Differing from the other reflexes we have studied, there are *two* efferent neurons in the autonomic reflex arc. The first of these is found in the central nervous system and sends its axon to a ganglion outside the cord or brain. For this reason it is called a *preganglionic neuron*. The preganglionic axon synapses with a neuron in the ganglion which sends its axon to the effector organ—smooth or cardiac muscle, or a gland. This second efferent neuron is the *postganglionic neuron*. An autonomic reflex arc is sketched in Fig. 102.

THE SYMPATHETIC SYSTEM. The sympathetic system is sometimes referred to as the *thoracico-lumbar division* because its preganglionic neurons arise in the lateral horns (see Fig. 102) of the gray matter of the thoracic and lumbar segments of the spinal cord. The preganglionic axons leave the cord by the ventral root and then leave the root. They may now terminate in one of three places.

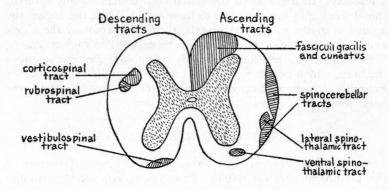

Descending tracts

Ascending tracts

corticospinal tract

rubrospinal tract

vestibulospinal tract

fasciculi gracilis and cuneatus

spinocerebellar tracts

lateral spino-thalamic tract

ventral spino-thalamic tract

FIG. 102—An autonomic reflex arc. Preganglionic neurons in the lateral horn of the gray matter of the spinal cord may send their fibers to a post-ganglionic neuron in a ganglion of the sympathetic chain (————), to a postganglionic neuron in a collateral ganglion (— — —) or to a post-ganglionic neuron in a terminal ganglion (— · — ·).

Along either side of the spinal cord is a chain of ganglia—the *sympathetic chain*. Some preganglionic axons synapse with cells in these ganglia. The postganglionic axons from these ganglion cells join the spinal nerves and are then distributed to smooth muscle and glands in the superficial regions of the body, such as the skin. (Some postganglionic axons do not rejoin the spinal nerves but go to organs of the head and thoracic cavity.) Other preganglionic axons pass through ganglia of the sympathetic chain without synapsing and terminate in ganglia lying free in the abdominal cavity—*collateral ganglia*. Postganglionic axons from these ganglia then pass to smooth muscle and glands in the abdominal organs. Still other, but comparatively few, preganglionic axons synapse with cells in *terminal ganglia* which lie in the walls of the organs innervated. Postganglionic axons then travel the very short distance to the effectors of that organ.

THE PARASYMPATHETIC SYSTEM. Another name for the parasympathetic system is the *cranio-sacral division* because its preganglionic nerve cells are found in the brain and sacral segments of the spinal cord. The preganglionic axons then proceed to *terminal ganglia* which lie in the walls of the organs innervated. Postganglionic axons have to travel only a very short distance before reaching the effectors they control.

There is not the same variety of ganglia in the parasympathetic system. Note also that in the sympathetic system the preganglionic axons are relatively short and the postganglionic generally long, while the opposite holds true for the parasympathetic system.

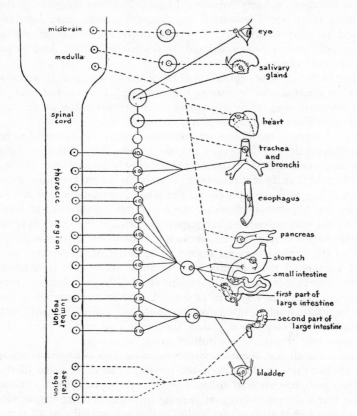

Fig. 103—The organs innervated by the autonomic nervous system. Parasympathetic (cranio-sacral) fibers are indicated by dotted lines, sympathetic (thoracico-lumbar) by solid lines. Parasympathetic impulses constrict the pupil of the eye; promote a profuse, watery secretion of saliva; slow the heart rate; constrict the trachea and bronchi; promote peristalsis in the esophagus; provoke secretion of pancreatic juice; tend to augment peristalsis and secretory activity in the stomach and intestines; cause contraction of the bladder. Sympathetic impulses dilate the pupil of the eye; promote a scanty, viscous secretion of saliva; speed the heart rate; dilate the trachea and bronchi; tend to inhibit peristalsis and secretory activity in the stomach and intestines; cause relaxation of the bladder.

Functions of the Autonomic System. A glance at Fig. 103 will show that almost every visceral organ receives a double innervation

—both sympathetic and parasympathetic systems send nerve fibers to it. In general the fibers from each system have antagonistic actions on the various organs.

The heart rate is accelerated by sympathetic impulses, slowed by parasympathetic (vagal) impulses. The motility and secretion of the digestive tract are augmented by parasympathetic impulses, inhibited by sympathetic ones. The pupil of the eye is constricted by parasympathetic impulses, dilated by sympathetic ones. And so on for the many viscera.

Most of the nervous regulation of the various systems that we have discussed is autonomic in nature, the autonomic system thus being a most essential integrating apparatus in the preservation of the dynamic equilibria involved in living.

For a long time the autonomic nervous system was believed to be quite independent of the central nervous system. Recent studies show more and more that the two systems are closely interrelated. It may even be said that these divisions of the nervous system are quite arbitrary and are so named purely for the sake of convenience. It is now known that afferents from either the autonomic or the central nervous system may initiate reflex responses through the other system. Centers for the control of the autonomic system are located at every level of the central nervous system. The respiratory, cardiac, and other centers of the medulla are certainly autonomic in nature. Other centers are located in the midbrain, hypothalamus (very important ones), cerebellum, and cerebral cortex. Evidence is becoming increasingly impressive for the close correlation of both systems in the coördination and integration of bodily parts and processes that constitute the unified living organism.

The transmitting agents between neurons and between neurons and effectors are in the autonomic system, as in other areas of the nervous system, chemical substances. Acetylcholine, already noted as the transmitter substance at skeletal myoneural junctions, is also the transmitter at all synapses within autonomic ganglia, at all parasympathetic postganglionic endings, and at some sympathetic postganglionic endings. At most sympathetic postganglionic terminals, *noradrenaline* is the chemical transmitter.

THE STRUCTURE OF THE BRAIN

The brain is, of course, the most complex and most advanced portion of the nervous system.

Major Areas of the Brain. The brain is the continuation of the spinal cord. The older portion, the *brain stem*, is vaguely similar to the cord in appearance, though of larger bulk and more irregular contour. Like the cord, the stem consists of inner gray matter surrounded by outer white matter as a general rule, but these distinctions are less reliable than in the cord. There is some mixture of gray and white matter with the result that certain portions of the gray matter stand out. These clumps of gray matter are known as *centers* or *nuclei* (collections of nerve cell bodies).

As it develops, the brain stem can be seen to consist of three main divisions (Fig. 104), the *hindbrain*, *midbrain*, and *forebrain*. These retain faint traces of their original segmental character and give rise to the twelve pairs of *cranial nerves*. By the time the brain is fully formed, two large regions have been added. The *cerebellum* grows out of the hindbrain, and the *cerebral hemispheres* grow out of the forebrain.

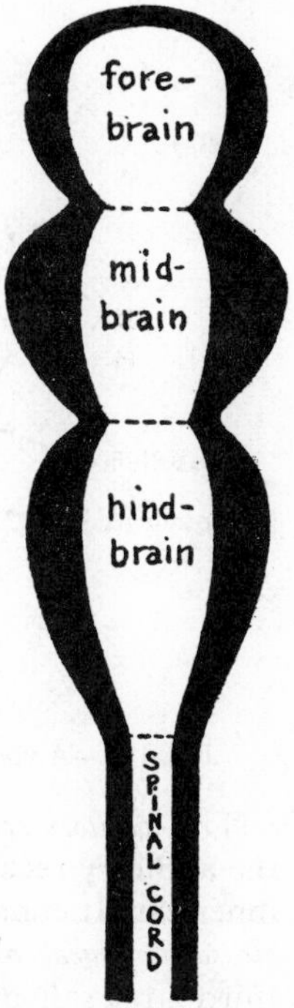

In Fig. 105 is a diagram of the brain cut in half down its midline. The brain stem portion of the hindbrain consists of the *medulla* and *pons*. Dorsal to the latter is the *cerebellum*. Next is the midbrain. The forebrain consists of the *thalamus*, *hypothalamus*, and *cerebral hemispheres*. Suspended by a stalk under the hypothalamus hangs the *pituitary gland*.

The Cranial Nerves. The twelve cranial nerves innervate a great many structures in the head and in other parts of the body. Cranial nerve I, the *olfactory nerve*, is entirely sensory in function; its fibers run from the smell receptors in the nose to the cerebral hemispheres. Cranial nerve II, the *optic nerve*, is also a completely sensory one; it travels from the visual receptors in the eyeball to the thalamus.

Fig. 104 — The developing brain stem and spinal cord.

Cranial nerve III, the *oculo-motor nerve*, is a purely motor nerve. As its name implies, it has to do with movements of the eyes. It sends fibers to four of the six muscles of the eyeball. It also innervates muscles which control the size of the pupil of the eye and the curvature of the lens. The third nerve originates in the midbrain. Cranial nerves IV and VI, the *trochlear* and *abducens nerves*, arise in the midbrain and pons respectively and innervate the other two muscles of the eyeball.

The *trigeminal nerve*, V, is the main general sensory nerve of the head region. Its sensory fibers bring impulses from the skin of the head, the teeth, and mucous membrane of the mouth into the pons.

It also is a motor nerve to the muscles which move the lower jaw. The *facial nerve*, VII, is mainly motor in nature. Its fibers go from the pons to the muscles of the face and also to two of the three large salivary glands. Some sensory fibers from the taste receptors on the front two-thirds of the tongue are also found in this nerve.

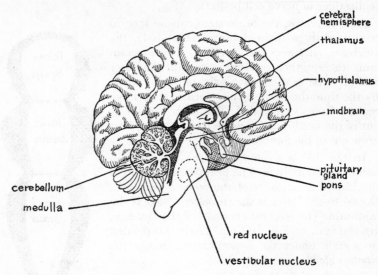

cerebral hemisphere
thalamus
hypothalamus
midbrain
pituitary gland
pons
cerebellum
medulla
red nucleus
vestibular nucleus

Fig. 105—A view of the inner surface of the brain cut down the midline.

The *auditory nerve*, VIII, is purely sensory. It contains fibers from the auditory receptors and from those for equilibrium located in the inner ear. It conducts impulses into the pons. Cranial nerve IX, the *glossopharyngeal nerve*, sends motor fibers from the medulla to the third large salivary gland and to the muscles of the pharynx that are involved in the swallowing process. On the sensory side it conveys impulses in from the rest of the taste receptors of the tongue, from the mucous membrane of the pharynx, and from the carotid sinus.

We have frequently encountered the *vagus nerve*, X, in preceding chapters. It well deserves its name which means "wanderer." On the efferent side its fibers run from the medulla to muscle in the esophagus, stomach, intestines, heart, and larynx; to glands in the stomach, small intestine, and pancreas. On the afferent side its fibers come from the alveoli of the lungs, mucous membrane of the larynx and stomach, and from the arch of the aorta.

The *spinal accessory nerve*, XI, and the *hypoglossal nerve*, XII, are purely motor nerves. Both arise in the medulla, the former innervating the shoulder muscles and the latter the tongue muscles.

Strictly speaking, the "purely" motor nerves are not solely motor.

They also contain afferent fibers from the muscles they innervate which bring proprioceptive information into the brain.

The efferent fibers of the cranial nerves arise in neurons within the brain stem (in the nuclei of the cranial nerves). The afferent fibers originate in receptors, of course, and with the exception of the optic and olfactory nerve fibers, have their cell bodies in ganglia lying outside of, but close by, the brain. They are fairly similar to the spinal nerves in this respect.

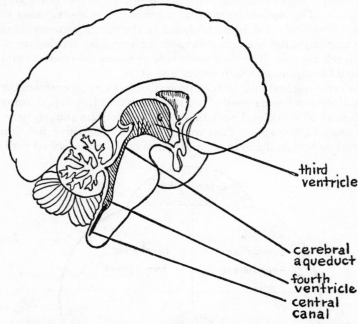

FIG. 106—View of the inner surface of the brain, showing ventricles. The first and second ventricles are within the cerebral hemispheres and cannot be seen.

The Ventricles and Cerebrospinal Fluid. The central nervous system originates as a hollow tube and retains a cavity even in the mature brain, although the cavity is much smaller than in the embryonic brain. In the spinal cord the remnant of the cavity is the *central canal*. The continuation of this canal into the hindbrain is called the *fourth ventricle*. The latter has a thin membranous roof which is very vascular. The fourth ventricle continues as the very narrow *cerebral aqueduct* in the midbrain. The *third ventricle* in the thalamic region has a similar roof to that of the fourth. The third ventricle communicates with the *first* and *second ventricles*, one in each cerebral hemisphere (see Fig. 106).

These cavities are filled with the *cerebrospinal fluid*, a fluid derived from the blood and fairly like protein-free plasma. The cerebrospinal fluid is formed partly by filtration from the blood vessels in the roofs of the third and fourth ventricles, partly by the secretory action of the cells of those membranous structures.

The brain and cord are surrounded by three protective membranes or *meninges*. (Inflammation of these produces the disease called *meningitis*.) The outermost is a tough coat of connective tissue. The innermost, a thin membrane, covers the surface of the brain very intimately. The middle membrane consists of a web-like mass of fibers. Cerebrospinal fluid is also found in the spaces between these fibers and circulates between them and the ventricles via tiny openings in the medulla. The fluid eventually re-enters the blood stream through blood sinuses which empty into veins.

The cerebrospinal fluid serves a protective function. It cushions the central nervous system against sudden shocks and jars, liquid being much more able to absorb such blows than the delicate and soft nervous tissue. Cerebrospinal fluid may also serve a nutritive function and be involved in the over-all metabolism of brain and spinal cord.

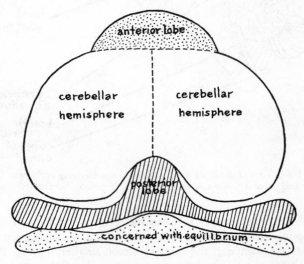

FIG. 107—A diagrammatic representation of the parts of the cerebellum.

The Cerebellum and the Cerebral Hemispheres. As we have mentioned, the cerebellum and the cerebral hemispheres are both outgrowths of the more primitive brain stem, which became more highly developed during vertebrate evolution. They also have in common the facts that their gray matter is concentrated in a thin layer (*cortex*) on their surfaces, and, with the exception of some additional gray centers deep within, their internal bulk is composed of white matter.

The cerebellum consists of a primitive portion (the dotted section at the bottom of Fig. 107) and the newer *anterior* and *posterior lobes* and *cerebellar hemispheres.*

The cerebral hemispheres become the most prominent parts of the brain in later evolution. In the frog they are small parts of the anterior end of the brain; in the cat they have grown enough to cover over the midbrain; in man their size is such that, from the dorsal view, they are the only visible portions of the brain (Fig. 108).

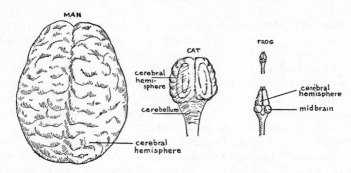

Fig. 108—The brains of man, cat and frog contrasted. The smaller figure of the frog brain gives its true size in proportion to the other brains.

The surface of each cerebral hemisphere is marked by many grooves or *sulci;* the protruding areas between sulci are called *gyri.* The reason for the infoldings of the surface tissue is that it grows at a faster rate than the interior tissue. Some of the clefts are quite deep; these *fissures* are useful landmarks in dividing each hemisphere into four lobes (Fig. 109): *frontal, parietal, temporal,* and *occipital.*

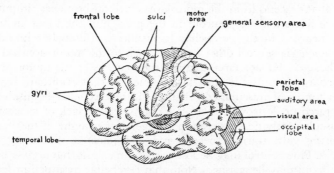

Fig. 109—The external surface of a cerebral hemisphere.

The cerebral cortex is the site of the most complex nervous functions. Through painstaking histological study it has been divided into more than two hundred areas differing from one another with respect to arrangement and size of neurons. For the moment, let us note (Fig. 109) that a *motor area* and various *sensory areas* can be singled out in each hemisphere.

THE BRAIN AND MOTOR ACTIVITIES

By motor activities is meant all kinds of muscular activities—voluntary and reflex—and also glandular activities under nervous control.

Voluntary Movements. All voluntary movements are initiated by discharge of neurons in the motor areas of the cerebral cortices. (There is more than one motor area in each hemisphere, which may account for the fact that destruction of a motor area by accident or disease does not invariably result in permanent loss of voluntary movement.) Impulses from these neurons traverse a pathway which, for most of the nerve fibers concerned, crosses to the other side of the brain. The axons from the motor areas synapse with intermediate neurons and these in turn synapse with motor neurons of the brain stem and spinal cord. Almost all voluntary movements of the right side of the body are initiated by the left cerebral cortex, and vice versa.

The parts of the body are represented in the motor areas in an upside-down fashion. Stimulation of upper regions causes movements of the legs; middle regions, the trunk and arms; lower regions, the neck and head. Representation is not in terms of the size of the body region but rather in terms of the complexity of motion possible. The hand, for instance, occupies more space in the motor areas than the arm, and the thumb more than the fingers.

Voluntary movements are well coördinated because of connections between the motor areas and the cerebellar hemispheres. The nerve fibers that descend from the motor areas give off branches; impulses in these fibers activate neurons in the pons, and the latter in turn excite neurons in the cerebellar hemispheres. Cerebellar impulses are relayed via several other neurons back to the motor areas. This complicated feedback circuit causes the neurons of the motor areas to discharge impulses in just those sequences that eventuate in the proper timing of muscular contractions. If the cerebellar hemispheres are injured or destroyed, there is a characteristic lack of synergism in muscular activities—as seen in exaggerated swaying of the body, staggering gait, slurred speech, and disconnected movement sequences. Fine control may be lost to such an extent that a glass held in the hand may be crushed. Note that cerebellar dysfunction leads to no actual muscular paralysis, whereas cerebral damage usually results in at least temporary paralysis of voluntary motion. Reflex movements are still possible, since other sites and pathways are responsible for these.

Reflex Movements. Both somatic and visceral responses are here included. Let us first consider somatic reflex movements.

Every time the head moves or remains in some position other than the erect one, receptors in the sense organs of equilibrium are activated. Consequently, impulses proceed to the *vestibular nuclei* (Fig. 105) of the medulla and pons; these centers send impulses to motor neurons in the brain stem and spinal cord. The resulting contractions of skeletal muscles will be those best calculated to maintain the equilibrium of the body in relation to the movement or position of the head. Since the head is rarely immobile, a variable but continual stream of impulses will be playing upon somatic motor neurons. The over-all vestibular influence is excitatory, tending to keep motor neurons in readiness to discharge impulses. In fact, both experimental and clinical evidence indicates that when systems that normally counterbalance the vestibular effect are not operating, many skeletal muscles are maintained in a state of continual contraction or *rigidity*.

Another important mechanism involves the cerebellum. Whenever skeletal muscles change their activity (again, this is practically continual), receptors within the muscles or their tendons activate sensory neurons. Impulses from the sensory neurons are relayed to the anterior and posterior lobes of the cerebellum and thence to the *red nucleus* (Fig. 105). This center sends impulses, by a relay system, to motor neurons of the brain stem and spinal cord. The predominant effect of this system is inhibitory, exerting a modulating influence on somatic reflexes.

Similar impulses from muscles and tendons can ascend to the cerebral cortex and be relayed to motor areas. Therefore, voluntary movements, although consciously initiated, soon become influenced by other parts of the nervous system and are reflexly modified.

The motor areas are also the source of an inhibitory influence on motor neurons that counteracts the effects of lower excitatory centers. Deprivation of this higher influence characteristically results in muscular *spasticity*, as seen in some cases of *cerebral palsy* or of gunshot wounds of the cerebrum or its connections.

Still other somatic reflex centers are present in the midbrain. These are prominent in *righting reactions* (reflex turning in spiral fashion from the supine to the normal position, best seen in dogs or cats placed involuntarily on their backs), and in *startle reactions* to visual and auditory stimuli.

Visceral reflex activities, like somatic reflexes, are controlled by various levels of the brain. Here, too, higher levels tend to dominate lower ones.

The lowest level of the brain, the medulla, contains many important visceral reflex centers: *inspiratory* and *expiratory*, *cardio-acceleratory* and *cardio-inhibitory*, *vasoconstrictor*, *swallowing*, *salivary*, and *vomiting centers*. By regulating the rate of activity of cardiac or smooth muscle, or of gland cells, these centers reflexly control the individual activities that their names indicate.

While there is some interplay between centers at this level, permitting some coördination of the systems involved, the more important regulatory influences emanate from the higher levels of the brain, especially the hypothalamus and the cerebral cortex. Thus, when afferent impulses reach medullary centers, heart rate *or* breathing *or* digestive activity may be varied. However, when afferent impulses reach hypothalamic or cortical centers, impulses may be sent out that simultaneously influence heart rate *and* breathing *and* digestive activity and other activities, producing an over-all effect distinctly advantageous to the individual at a certain time.

Another important feature of motor organization is that not only are there pyramids of control centers for both somatic and visceral activities, but also there is increasing coördination of somatic and visceral activity the higher the level of the nervous system. At the higher levels, activity of one center can produce synchronized somatic and visceral effects.

THE SENSES

Man is equipped with *receptors* for receiving a great variety of stimuli. These respond to changes in both the internal and external environment. To be activated each receptor must be stimulated with a minimal amount of energy. Every receptor is especially sensitive to a particular form of energy and has a lower threshold for it than for any other kind. When activated, the receptor responds by initiating a volley of nerve impulses in the afferent nerve fiber that leads from it.

There are many varieties of sensations. Man not only has a "sixth" sense but a "seventh", "eighth," and so on. There are receptors sensitive to light, sound, smell, and taste; to pain, touch, heat, cold, pressure, and tickle; to rotation and changes in balance; to muscle, tendon, and joint sense. For most of these sensations we know the receptors involved. For some other sensations—like hunger, thirst, and sexual sensations—we know comparatively little about the receptors involved and the mechanisms of perception.

We have already classified receptors into *exteroceptors*, *entero-ceptors*, and *proprioceptors*. They can also be classified in other ways.

For some receptors the stimuli must actually make contact with the body—touch, tickle, some kinds of pain and pressure, etc. Others can sense stimuli coming from a distance—visual and auditory receptors. Still others are best stimulated by chemicals in solution—taste and smell receptors.

Sense organs vary in structure from simple nerve endings to rather complex organs like the eye and ear.

VISION

Vision is the sense upon which man places most reliance. The eyes are very complicated sense organs, as they must be to fulfill their functions. Vision is an intricate process involving sensitivity to light rays and the perception of form, color, depth, and distance. To understand the functions of the eyes we must first know their structure.

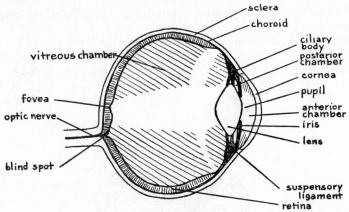

FIG. 110—A section through the eyeball.

Structure of the Eye. The eye is protected on three sides by projecting bones of the skull and furthermore by the eyelids and by the secretion of tears. The *wink reflex* is evoked whenever some object approaches too close to or actually touches the eyeball. The blinking of the lids that goes on normally also serves a good purpose in that it prevents excessive fatigue of the eyes. Try staring at a line of printed words without blinking. Fairly soon the words will blur. Now blink your lids once and note that the short rest has cleared your vision very perceptibly. Tear secretion, which goes on continually, keeps the front of the sensitive eyeball moistened and also washes away foreign particles or irritants. The *tear* or *lachrymal gland* lies just above the eyeball and can be reflexly stimulated to excess tear secretion by the contact of a foreign particle with the eyeball. The tears are spread over the surface of the eyeball by the blinking of the lids and drain into the nasal cavity through a duct.

The globular eyeball has a three-layered wall (see Fig. 110). The outer *sclera* is tough and fibrous (it is seen as the "white of the eye"), and is modified in the front of the eyeball into the transparent *cornea*. The middle coat is the pigmented and vascular *choroid* layer which continues, in the front of the eyeball, as the *ciliary body* and the *iris*, the ring of colored tissue. The hole in the center of the iris is the *pupil;* the blackness of the pupil is due to the fact that one looking at it sees the dark interior of the eyeball. The innermost layer is the *retina* which contains the receptors for vision, the *rods* and *cones*, and from which the optic nerve begins.

Between the cornea and iris is the *anterior chamber* and between the iris and *crystalline lens* the *posterior chamber*. Both chambers contain a watery fluid, the *aqueous humor*. The largest cavity of the eyeball is the *vitreous chamber* which contains a viscous fluid, the *vitreous humor*.

Perception of Form. In order to understand the ability of the eye to perceive form, it is necessary to be familiar with the principle of refraction of light and with the method of image formation.

Fig. 111—A stick appears bent when placed in water due to the refraction of the light rays when passing from a lighter (air) to a denser (water) medium.

REFRACTION OF LIGHT RAYS. Light rays are bent (*refracted*) in passing from one medium into another of different density. For this reason a straight stick, partly in water and partly in air, appears bent (Fig. 111). A glass *lens*, which is a transparent piece of glass ground to a certain curvature, has the property of refracting light rays. Any ray of light which strikes a lens perpendicular to its surface, however, will not be refracted (a in Fig. 112). Rays striking a lens at an angle are refracted; the greater the angle, the greater the refraction (b and c in Fig. 112). A convex lens (Fig. 112) will focus parallel rays of light to a single point behind it. The distance between the *nodal point* of

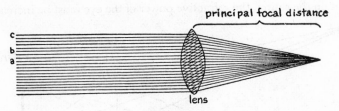

FIG. 112—A convex lens focuses parallel rays of light to a single point behind it.

the lens (its optical center, through which rays pass without being refracted) and the point of focus of parallel rays is called the *principal focal distance*. This distance is used as a measure of the focusing strength of a lens. The greater the curvature of the surface of the lens, the greater its refractive power and the shorter its principal focal distance.

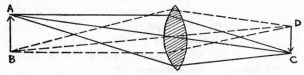

FIG. 113—Formation of an inverted, smaller image of an object by a convex lens.

FORMATION OF AN IMAGE. An image of an object is formed by a lens in the manner diagrammed in Fig. 113. All the light rays from point A are brought to a focus at C and all those from other points on A B at corresponding points behind the lens. Thus, an inverted, smaller image of the object is formed.

A similar method of image formation occurs in the eye (Fig. 114). Actually the process is more complicated because there are more refractive surfaces in the eyeball, but the principle involved and the end result are the same as with a simple lens system. A small, inverted image of an object in the field of vision is formed upon the retina. Most of the refractive power of the relaxed eye is in the cornea, the lens not being as important for viewing distant objects (20 or more feet away) in the normal eye. For all practical purposes light rays from such objects are parallel when they strike the cornea.

IMPORTANCE OF THE LENS. If the lens is relatively unimportant in the image formation of distant objects, of what use is it? In order to see distant objects clearly, the principal focus of the refracting system of the eye must lie on the retina. But what happens when the object viewed is less than twenty feet distant? The rays of light coming from it will be divergent when they strike the cornea and would tend to focus behind the retina (Fig. 115). In order to bring these rays to a focus on the retina, the refractive power of the eye must be increased.

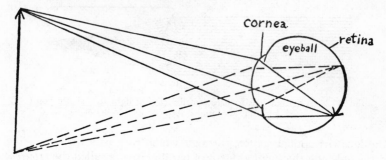

Fig. 114—Formation of an inverted, smaller image of an object on the retina by the refractive system of the eye (only the cornea is shown here).

At this point the lens becomes important. The lens is an elastic body whose thickness can be varied. The thicker it becomes, the more curved its surface is and the greater its refractive power. The nearer the object to be viewed, the more the lens is made to bulge. This process is called *accommodation*. It is effected by the contraction of the *ciliary muscles* of the ciliary body. Contraction of these muscles slackens the tension in the *suspensory ligaments* which hold the lens taut in the relaxed eye. When the tension drops, the lens bulges forward because of its elasticity.

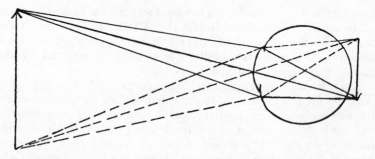

Fig. 115—A blurred image will result if a normal, relaxed eye views an object nearer than 20 feet from it (see text).

Accommodation can proceed only to a certain extent; that is, an object closer than a certain minimal distance cannot be focused

clearly. For every eye there is, therefore, a *near point* of distinct vision.
For a twelve-year-old with normal vision this point is about two and
one-half inches in front of the eye. With increasing age the lens
gradually loses its elasticity and is unable to accommodate as
strongly. This condition is called *presbyopia* or old-sightedness. Since
at sixty years of age the near point has generally receded so that it is
then a yard or more distant from the eye, older people may in the
normal course of events have to resort to wearing glasses for seeing
near objects.

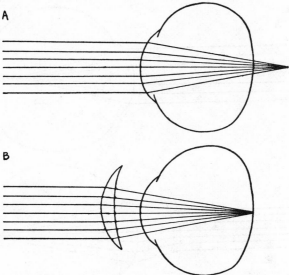

Fig. 116—Parallel rays of light will tend to come to a focus behind the
retina of a farsighted eye (*A*) and the image will, therefore, be blurred.
Use of an appropriate convex lens corrects the condition (*B*).

ERRORS OF REFRACTION. Normal eyes sharply focus parallel rays of
light on the retina; but many eyes have some error of refraction.

Farsightedness or *hyperopia* generally results from an eyeball that is
too short for its refractive power. Parallel rays of light tend to focus
behind the retina and a blurred image is seen (Fig. 116 A). By accommodating, the farsighted person can focus distant objects clearly.
This will result in considerable eye strain if allowed to go uncor-
rected. By using a convex lens (one thicker in the middle than at the
periphery) parallel light rays are sufficiently converged before reaching the cornea to be focused properly (Fig. 116 B). The more far-
sighed a person is, of course, the more convex his glasses must be.

Nearsightedness or *myopia* generally results from an eyeball that is
too long. Parallel rays of light are focused in front of the retina and

the image is blurred (Fig. 117 A). By accommodating for such rays a nearsighted person would only aggravate the condition and must resort to concave glasses (thicker at the periphery than in the middle) for relief. Such lenses diverge rays before they reach the cornea and thus allow them to be focused (Fig. 117 B). Unlike the normal or farsighted eye which has no definite *far point* of vision (stars millions of miles away can be seen, for instance), the myopic eye has a finite far point beyond which it cannot see objects clearly.

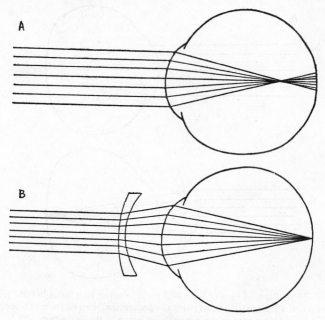

Fig. 117—Parallel rays of light will come to a focus in front of the retina of a nearsighted eye (*A*) and the image will, therefore, be blurred. Use of an appropriate concave lens corrects the condition (*B*).

An even more common refractive error is *astigmatism*. This results from the cornea having disproportioned curvatures in one or more planes. Light rays in one plane are properly focused while those in another are not. An astigmatic person whose vision is defective for rays in the vertical plane will see a cross as pictured in Fig. 118 B. For this type of defect cylindrical lenses are prescribed as corrective.

PUPILLARY REFLEXES. The iris has two sets of smooth muscle in it. One circles about the pupil and will constrict the pupil when it contracts. The other is arranged like the spokes of a wheel and will dilate the pupil when it contracts.

In bright light the pupil reflexly constricts; in dim light it dilates.

A   B

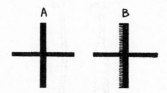

Fig. 118—A cross as seen by a person with normal sight (*A*) and by one with astigmatism for the vertical plane (*B*).

The amount of light reaching the retina initiates these reflexes and the reflexes in turn regulate the amount of light which can enter the eye. The pupil is also reflexly constricted when accommodation occurs.

These reflexes serve a dual function. In dim light or when looking at distant objects, dilation of the pupil allows more light to fall upon the retina, making for better vision in either case. In looking at near objects constriction of the pupil permits sharper focus of light rays. All lenses, including the eye's, have a defect known as *spherical aberration*—rays passing through the periphery of the lens are brought to a focus sooner than those passing through the center (Fig. 119), a partially blurred image resulting. Constriction of the pupil eliminates the marginal rays and thus aids visual acuity or keenness.

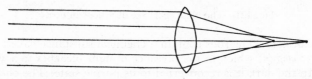

Fig. 119—Spherical aberration. Rays of light passing through the periphery of a lens are brought to a focus closer to the lens (exaggerated here) than those passing through the center.

The Rods and Cones.   The light-sensitive elements of the retina are the *rods* and *cones* (Fig. 120). All protoplasm seems to be somewhat sensitive to light, but specialized cells like these receptors are much more sensitive.

In the center of the retina there is a small pit, the *fovea* (Fig. 110), which contains only cones. On either side of the fovea the concentration of cones decreases, and that of rods increases as distance from the fovea increases. At the extremes of the retina only rods are found. To one side of the fovea is the place of exit of the optic nerve. This region is called the *blind spot* because light rays falling upon it are not perceived. Light rays, therefore, can only be seen if they fall upon rods or cones and not if they fall upon nerve fibers. To demonstrate the presence of the blind spot, hold Fig. 121 in front of you. Close

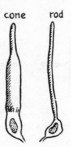

Fig. 120—A rod and a cone.

the right eye and focus on the X with your left. Shift the book backward or forward until the circle is no longer visible. At this point light rays from the circle fall on the optic nerve fibers and are not seen.

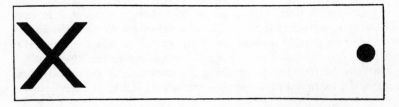

Fig. 121—The blind spot. See directions in text.

VISUAL PURPLE. The rods contain a chemical substance called *visual purple (rhodopsin)* which in the presence of light bleaches to a yellow color. In the dark it is reconverted to its purple state. The chemical change induced in the visual purple initiates the nerve impulses arising in the rods. A similar photochemical process probably occurs in cones but its chemistry is not as yet clearly elucidated.

CENTRAL VS. PERIPHERAL VISION. When vision initiated at the fovea (central vision) is compared with that initiated at the extremes of the retina (peripheral vision), it is observed that central vision is very acute, colorful, is at its best in bright light, and adapts itself to dim light poorly; peripheral vision is less acute, colorless, is at its best in and adapts very well to dim light. Since the fovea contains only cones, the characteristics of central vision are attributable to them, and peripheral vision must be mediated by the rods.

The ability of the rods to adapt themselves to dim light makes them more sensitive to light of low intensity than are the cones. For best vision in dim light, then, it is wise not to focus directly upon the object you are looking at, for its light rays would then fall upon the fovea. It is preferable to look slightly off center at the object so that the light rays will fall where the concentration of rods is thickest. Some night first try looking at a dim star directly and then shift your gaze slightly; note the improvement in visual clarity.

It may take the rods as much as thirty minutes to adapt completely to dim light. This may mean that it takes this long for enough visual purple to be re-formed to achieve maximal sensitivity to such light.

PERCEPTION OF COLOR. Most theories of color vision attribute color perception to three different types of cones, each being sensitive to one of the three primary spectral colors. In the visible spectrum red, green, and blue are these three colors. Combination of the three produces white—and stimulation of all three simultaneously is believed to cause white to be perceived. Other combinations of stimuli produce the other colors we see.

The problems of color vision are complex and, as yet, very inadequately answered. No one theory has been able to explain all the known facts. We must await some future solution for this extremely interesting and perplexing process.

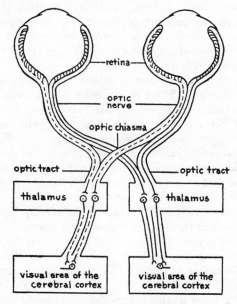

FIG. 122—The visual pathway.

Perception of Depth and Distance. The adequate perception of a three-dimensional world is largely due to the fact that man has *binocular vision*—sees with two eyes which are widely enough separated to get slightly different views of the same object. The construction of the visual pathway to the brain then makes possible the fusion of these two images into a single one in our mind's eye.

THE VISUAL PATHWAY (see Fig. 122). The *rods* and *cones* synapse with some *intermediary neurons* in the retina which in turn give rise to the *optic nerve fibers*. Each *optic nerve* runs to the brain where the fibers from the inner half of each retina cross to the other side of the brain. Nerve fibers from the right half of each retina now proceed together as the *optic tract* to the *thalamus*. From the thalamus new fibers are sent to the right *visual area* of the cerebral cortex. The fibers from the left half of each retina follow a similar route to the left visual area.

CORRESPONDING-POINT VISION. Each point on one retina has a *corresponding point* on the other. Because of the arrangement of the visual pathway, nerve impulses from corresponding points are relayed to the *same* point in one visual area; so although two images are formed on the retinas, only one image sensation results.

Any images which do not fall on corresponding points will give rise to two image sensations. Actually all other objects in the field of vision but the one being focused on are seen doubly. Ordinarily we take no cognizance of these images in our concentration upon the one object. To observe these double images, hold up two pencils, one behind the other and about a foot apart. When you focus on one of the two, the other will appear double.

These are normal occurrences. Double image vision can, however, be abnormal. If one of the six eye muscles which control the movement of the eyeball is weakened, the two eyes will not be able to move synchronously. Since one eye will not focus properly, light rays from objects will fall upon non-corresponding points and two images will be seen. A person with this disability generally learns through experience to disregard the false image created. This may lead to overwork of the good eye and eye strain. It can be corrected by special glasses, exercise, or even by surgery on the muscle.

PERCEPTION OF DISTANCE. The visual fields overlap in animals with binocular vision and this with corresponding-point vision makes for superior distance vision. Animals whose eyes are on the sides of their heads or people with one eye have only monocular vision, and their perception of distance is inferior. They still can judge distance to some extent by clues such as the clearness of an object, the intensity of light coming from it, the interposition of nearer objects, or the purity of its color.

The clues for distance vision that a man with two eyes has are the *degree of convergence* of the eyes, the *degree of accommodation*, and *parallax*. The first two depend upon learning through experience to judge at what distance an object is by the amount of contraction of the muscles involved in convergence and accommodation. Parallax is the apparent displacement of an object when viewed from two separate points. It applies here in that the two eyes are separated enough for each to give a slightly different view of an object with respect to the background behind it. For instance, hold up one finger, focus on it and then alternately close your eyes. Note the apparent shift in position of the finger with respect to the background.

DEPTH PERCEPTION. Because the left eye views more of the left side of an object and the right more of the right side, and because we learn to recognize that one part of an object is farther away than another, we interpret images on the retinas that possess these differences as coming from an object possessing depth. Three-dimensional or *stereoscopic* vision gives the world a far different appearance from that which it would have if we were to view it without the stereoscopic effect.

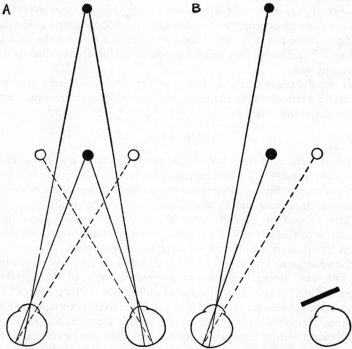

FIG. 123—Projection. Focusing on the far object causes the near one to appear double (the light rays from the latter fall upon non-corresponding points on the two retinas). Closing one eye, we think the opposite of the double images disappears (see text).

INTERPRETATION BY THE CORTEX. You will note that many of the aspects of vision that we take for granted are the results of learning through experience. The clues for distance and depth perception are in this category. There is also the phenomenon of *projection*. We learn to associate rays falling on one half of the retina with objects in the opposite part of the field of vision. Thus, if we hold two pencils up behind one another as before and focus on the far one, we see two images of the near pencil (Fig. 123 A). Now close the right eye and note that the left image of the double image disappears (Fig. 123 B). Even though the rays going to the right eye are the ones shut off, we think the left image disappears. This occurs because the rays cut off had fallen on the outer half of the right retina, and through experience we have learned to project objects to the left part of the field of vision when light rays impinge upon that part of the retina.

We also interpret the inverted images falling upon the retina as right-side-up sensations. That this is actually learned is proved by the following experiment. A scientist put on a pair of glasses that made images appear right side up on the retina. He then saw everything upside down. Keeping them on for some days, he learned to get used to an "upside-down world." Then after he had learned, he took the glasses off and found that he had to relearn to interpret things as they normally were.

It is no exaggeration to say that the eyes and visual pathway merely furnish the raw material which enables our cerebral cortex to do the actual "seeing."

HEARING

While light rays may travel through a vacuum, sound waves require the presence of some physical medium. A light ray is a pure form of energy but a sound wave results from some source of energy emission imparting energy to the molecules in the medium.

The process of hearing may be divided into two parts: first, *conduction* of vibrations to the inner ear and, second, *reception* of vibrations by the *cochlea* followed by interpretive processes.

Conduction. The *ear* (Fig. 124) consists of three parts—outer, middle, and inner. The *pinna* or external portion of the outer ear directs sound waves into the canal called the *auditory meatus*. The somewhat funnel-like shape of a pinna helps to direct sound into the meatus. Pinnae are of greater service in this function for other animals than for man because, in the former, they can be moved in the direction of the source of sound. Some of us can "wiggle" our ears, but this is about as much as we can maneuver them. Even so, the pinnae are useful to some degree.

Sound waves travel through the meatus to the *eardrum* (also called the *tympanic membrane*). They set the eardrum into vibration, and the vibrations are transmitted through the middle ear by a bridge of three small bones—the *hammer*, *anvil*, and *stirrup* (so called because of their shapes).

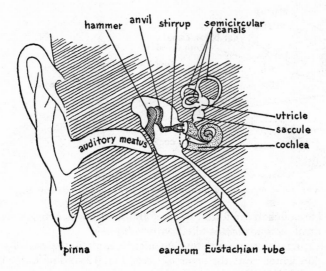

Fig. 124—A section through the head showing the outer, middle and inner ear.

The middle ear is filled with air which must be kept at the same pressure as that on the other side of the eardrum in order not to damage that membrane. If you have ever climbed mountains or flown (or even taken a fast elevator ride in a tall building), you may have experienced a feeling of pressure in your ears. Then suddenly a "click"—and the pressure is relieved. This is what happens. There is a drop in atmospheric pressure as you ascend which disturbs the balance of pressure on either side of the eardrum, the pressure being higher now in the middle ear. Connecting the middle ear with the pharynx is the *Eustachian tube*. Most of the time this remains closed. When you swallow, it opens. The pressure being greater in the middle ear than in the pharynx, air now leaves the middle ear by the Eustachian tube until the pressure is equalized. The click is probably the snapping back of the eardrum which had been bulging outward because of the higher pressure inside.

Vibrations are transmitted by the middle ear bones to the *oval window*, a membrane separating the middle from the inner ear. Before we can continue this account, we must become acquainted with the structure of the cochlea.

Structure of the Cochlea. The cochlea of the inner ear is a spirally coiled organ embedded in the temporal bone of the skull. When uncoiled, it is seen to be a cone composed of three canals (Fig. 125). The *vestibular* and *tympanic canals* are filled with a fluid called *perilymph* and communicate with one another at the apex of the cochlea.

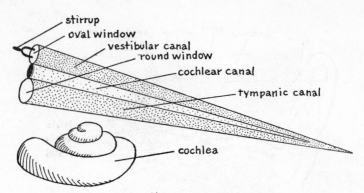

FIG. 125—A sketch of the cochlea uncoiled to show its canals.

At the base of each are found the *oval* and *round windows* respectively. The central *cochlear canal* is filled with *endolymph*.

Separating the tympanic and cochlear canals is the *basilar membrane* upon which rests the *organ of Corti* (Fig. 126). The latter contains "*hair*" *cells* (ciliated cells) which are the auditory receptors and from which the auditory nerve fibers arise. The cilia of the hair cells are in contact with (or may actually be imbedded in) the *tectorial membrane* which overhangs the organ of Corti.

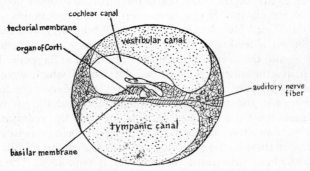

FIG. 126—A cross-section through the cochlea.

Reception and Interpretation of Sound. When the oval window is set into vibration by movements of the stirrup, vibrations in the perilymph are set up and transmitted throughout the fluid system in the cochlea. The movements of the fluid set the basilar membrane into vibration, whereupon the hair cells bob up and down. As they do, the cilia bend against the tectorial membrane. The bending of the cilia is probably adequate stimulus for setting up nerve impulses in the auditory nerve fibers.

DETERMINATION OF PITCH. A good theory of hearing must account for the discrimination of different pitches or tones. The resonance theory of hearing stresses the importance of the basilar membrane. This membrane is composed of fibers of varying lengths, arranged somewhat like the strings of a piano. Although the cochlea is wider at its base than at its apex, the basilar membrane (in the dimension perpendicular to and going from front to back of the page) is wider at the apex of the cochlea than at the base. Thus, the longer fibers are at the apex, the shorter at the base.

The long strings of a piano produce sounds of low pitch (bass notes) and short strings high tones (treble notes). Low frequency sounds (low tones), are believed to set into vibration the fibers of the basilar membrane at the apex of the cochlea; high tones those at the base. The cilia of the hair cells on these fibers are bent and nerve impulses are sent along the nerve fibers involved to the auditory area of the cerebral cortex. Here the sensations of low or high tones are actually perceived.

There has been experimental confirmation of this theory. Destruction of the organ of Corti at the apex produces deafness to low tones, and destruction of it at the base, deafness to high tones. Workers in factories where high-pitched sounds of great intensity are frequent develop a deafness to those sounds (*boiler-maker's deafness*). Examinination of their cochleas after death has shown degeneration of the organ of Corti at the base of the cochlea.

DETERMINATION OF LOUDNESS. A given sound may be interpreted as "softer" or "louder" with respect to another. In part, at least, this may be explained by the following example. If a particular sound is presented to the ear first at one intensity and then at a greater intensity, in both instances the same portions of the basilar membrane are caused to vibrate especially hard and, therefore, the same receptors and the same nerve fibers will tend to be activated. However, although the same pattern of receptors is excited, in the second instance the greater intensity of the sound waves eventually causes more violent vibration of the basilar membrane than in the first case; a greater number of impulses reaches the auditory area and this is interpreted as "louder" than the first sound.

DETERMINATION OF TIMBRE. We recognize not only pitch but also the quality of a given sound. The same musical tone played on a piano and on a violin (and even on a viola and a cello) is recognizably and identifiably different in quality. It is assumed that the overtones produced by each instrument differ somewhat from each other and cause somewhat different (although basically similar) patterns of vibrations in the ear. This is eventually interpreted by the cerebral cortex as differences in timbre.

Deafness. *Conduction deafness* is usually quite amenable to treatment. Such deafness can occur from accumulation of wax in the ear and can then be remedied by removal of the wax. A more serious conduction disturbance results from immobilization of the middle ear bones or perforation of the eardrums. If these occasion permanent impairment of natural hearing, advantage can be taken of the fact that the bones of the skull conduct sound waves. Hearing aids that convert sound waves into vibrations which are transmitted to the cochlea via bone are used. You can demonstrate bone conduction of sound on yourself. Plug both ears and place a ticking watch between your teeth. The ticking should be heard very plainly.

If deafness is due to some affection of the auditory nerve or of the organ of Corti, it may be incurable.

EQUILIBRIUM

Besides the cochlea in the inner ear there are the *utricle, saccule,* and *semicircular canals* (see Figs. 124 and 127). These organs contain the receptors for equilibrium.

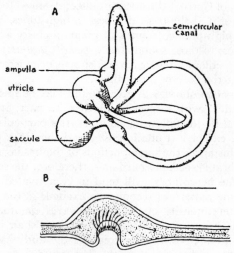

FIG. 127—The sense organs of equilibrium (*A*). In *B* are shown the hair cell receptors in an ampulla of a semicircular canal. When the head moves in the direction of the long arrow, the endolymph within the canal lags behind and thus tends to move in the opposite direction. The movement of the fluid bends the hairs and sets up impulses in the nerve fibers (not shown) leading from the hair cells.

Static Reflexes. The utricle and saccule are filled with endolymph. Each utricle and saccule contains a group of hair cells upon whose cilia rests a "stone" made up of calcium carbonate. Pull is exerted on the stones by the force of gravity, and the bending or lack of bending of the hairs (depending upon the position of the head) is believed to be sufficient cause for stimulating fibers of the *vestibular nerve*, a branch of the auditory nerve, which lead from the hair cells.

Whenever the position of the head is changed with respect to gravity, nerve impulses are initiated especially from the utricle which are relayed through the vestibular nuclei to efferent neurons and muscles. These impulses serve to change the pattern of muscle tone and preserve the *static equilibrium* of the body.

The functions of the saccules are still rather obscure. The utricular reflexes, however, are of great importance in maintaining the normal position of the head despite changes in the position of the body. These can be more easily demonstrated on lower animals than on man, because in man even awkward positions can be voluntarily maintained if he wishes them to be.

Righting Reflexes. When an animal such as a frog, bird, or cat is placed on its back, it quickly turns over to its normal position. A succession of movements is involved which you can see for yourself by holding a cat upside down in the air and then dropping it. If you observe it closely as it turns in the air to land on its feet, you will see that it rights itself in a spiral fashion—first the head, next the fore part of the body and finally the hind part. These movements are reflex in nature and are called *righting reflexes.*

When on its back, stimuli arising in the utricle cause the neck muscles to contract in such a way as to right the head. The twisting of the neck muscles initiates proprioceptive impulses from those muscles which set up reflex responses of the limb and body muscles. These reflexes right the limbs and body.

If the utricles are removed, it is very difficult for animals to right themselves. The head especially hangs limply. In animals with good vision, however, there are accessory *visual righting reflexes* which can operate in place of the utricular reflexes. If an animal without utricles is blindfolded, it is practically unable to maintain its static equilibrium.

Dynamic Reflexes. There are three semicircular canals in each inner ear, each canal being at right angles to the other two (Fig. 127). These canals are likewise filled with endolymph and contain hair cell receptors. These receptors initiate reflexes in response to *movements* of the head whereas utricular receptors respond to changes in *position* of the head.

Each canal joins the utricle at two points. At one of these points is a swelling, an *ampulla*, which contains hair cells. When the head moves, the endolymph in the canals tends to lag behind because of its inertia and thus to build up pressure in the direction opposite the movement of the head. Increased pressure of the endolymph stimulates the hair cells which in turn set up nerve impulses in the vestibular nerve fibers that lead from the hair cells.

Responses to rotation are especially well marked. If the head is rotated in one direction, stimulation of the hair cells in the ampullae give rise (via impulses relayed to the cerebral cortex) to the sensation of dizziness and also initiate reflex responses of the head and eyes. During the rotation, movements of the head and eyes are in the opposite direction. When the rotation stops, the endolymph pressure increases in the direction opposite to its prior build-up (again because of its inertia) and the head and eyes now move in the same direction as that of the rotation.

Another example of reflex response to semicircular canal stimulation is the shooting out of your hands when you trip and begin to fall. Movements of the head, then, initiate reflex responses through the semicircular canals. Maintenance of the new position of the head is brought about by utricular reflexes. All of these reflexes serve to maintain the normal position of the head and eyes and to preserve the equilibrium of the body.

Evidence seems to implicate the utricles in the production of sea sickness or other forms of motion sickness, although just how the symptoms are produced is not clear. Drugs of the *dramamine* type have proven quite effective in protecting against the result of equilibratory disturbance; these drugs apparently act to tone down the activity of the vestibular nuclei.

Taste and Smell

Although taste often seems dependent upon smell, it has been difficult to establish how these two senses are correlated. They have in common the fact that taste and smell receptors are both especially stimulated by chemicals in solution. The receptors are not alike anatomically nor do these senses have similar pathways to the cerebral cortex or similar areas of representation in the latter. In terms of pathway and cortical representation there is much more similarity between taste and other types of sensation arising in the mouth (touch and temperature) than between taste and smell.

Smell. Man is not as dependent upon the sense of smell as are certain other animals. The cerebral hemispheres in the beginning of their evolution were, in fact, largely smell centers. Despite its primitiveness and seeming simplicity, the sense of smell is far less well understood than are more complex senses.

The *olfactory receptors* (Fig. 128) are located in the nasal mucosa above the respiratory passageway to the interior. Sniffing is advantageous in getting the odor of something because it carries the air-borne chemicals up to the region of the smell receptors; in ordinary breathing, air may mostly pass by them in its journey to the lungs.

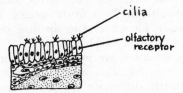

Fig. 128—Smell receptors.

There has been no satisfactory classification of odors, so that we characteristically say that such and such has an odor like some other well-known substance. For as many different odors as there are, there seem to be as many different kinds of smell receptors. Some indication of this is afforded by the ease with which smell receptors are fatigued. Within a couple of minutes of continual stimulation of an odor, we can completely lose the ability to recognize it. But, if we immediately smell another odor, the fatigue to the first one seems in no way to impair our sensing the second. On the other hand, there do not appear to be sufficient numbers of receptors to account for all odors recognized.

The olfactory receptors also seem to adapt themselves rather rapidly. You are probably familiar with the fact that you can accustom yourself to an unpleasant odor quite quickly and soon not even recognize its presence.

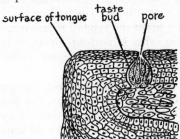

Fig. 129—A taste bud of the tongue.

Taste. Despite an apparently large variety of tastes, there are only four distinct taste sensations that are accepted—salt, sweet, sour, and bitter. For each of these there is a distinct type of *taste bud* or receptor (Fig. 129). These receptors are most abundant on the tongue, but some are also present in the mucosa of the mouth and pharynx.

The taste buds for the different taste sensations are not equally distributed over the surface of the tongue. Those sensitive to sweet and salt substances are predominantly localized at the tip of the tongue, those to acid materials along the sides of the tongue, and those to bitter substances towards the back of the tongue. We seem to grasp this fact unconsciously, for we tend to sip wine yet gulp beer; and children's licking of sweets is another instance.

Varieties of taste sensation are produced by combinations of the four fundamental ones, by other sensations that these substances arouse in the mouth (the difference in "taste" between hot and cold food or liquid, for instance), or by the simultaneous stimulation of smell receptors by the odors arising from the substance.

OTHER SENSES

Impulses set up in *proprioceptors*, receptors present in muscles, tendons, and joints, inform us about the position of parts of our body and the degree of tensing of muscles. Even with your eyes closed, you undoubtedly can tell in what position your feet are, whether your arms are flexed or extended, etc.

The *cutaneous*, or *skin*, *senses* are touch, pressure, heat, cold, and pain. Each arises in its own type of receptor (in some cases, in more than one type of receptor) and, as with taste buds, these receptors are not distributed uniformly over the surface of the body. The fingertips are more sensitive to touch and pressure than are the back of the hand or the forearm; the cornea of the eyeball has only pain receptors; and so on. The various skin receptors can rather easily be mapped by applying a fine-pointed instrument to the skin. It is then found that a certain spot will give rise to only touch or pain or heat sensations, depending upon the type of receptor that happens to be located there. Certain other sensations (tickle, vibration) may arise from stimulation of combinations of receptors rather than of a single receptor.

We adapt ourselves quite rapidly to touch and temperature sensations within moderate ranges of stimulation. For instance, we are not very often aware of the touch of the clothes we wear. Or, put one finger in luke-warm water and another in cold water; now put both into water at room temperature. The finger that was in the warmer water now feels cool and the other feels warmer. The temperature receptors have adapted themselves to the warm and cold temperatures to which they had been exposed and room temperature then acts as a stimulus to each finger, one finding it cool and the other warm.

We do not easily adapt to painful stimulation—which is very useful since pain acts as a warning that some harm is being done to or will be done to the body if a response is not made.

SPECIFICITY OF SENSATIONS

No matter what type of stimulus is applied to a receptor, the eventual sensation produced is that typically associated with the receptor concerned. If one gets hit in the eye and sees "flashes of light," it is because the retinal receptors were stimulated, even though mechanically. In the same way, with a fine probe one can stimulate all the skin receptors by mechanical stimuli yet get temperature and pain as well as touch sensations.

What this means is that the nerve impulses in different sensory fibers are not different in themselves but terminate in different regions of the brain. It is only at the end of the sensory pathway that perception and interpretation of sensation occurs, and these terminal connections determine the specificity of sensations. If we could connect the rods and cones to the auditory nerve, and the hair cells of the cochlea to the optic nerve (the endings of these nerves in the brain being unchanged), then a sound would be interpreted as a visual image and a light ray as a sound.

All sensory pathways involved in conscious sensation, except that for smell, have a way station in the thalamus (Fig. 105). Here the sensory fibers are regrouped before each pathway continues. From the thalamus, appropriate groups of fibers proceed to various areas of the cerebral cortex (Fig. 109): *visual area, auditory area* (hearing and equilibrium), and *general sensory area* (muscle and tendon sense, most skin senses, taste). In recent years, multiple areas for most of the preceding have been located in the cerebral cortex, but the significance of this finding is not yet clear. There are also *olfactory* (smell) *areas* in the cerebral cortex, but in regions not visible in Fig. 109.

It is only when impulses reach these cortical areas that we become aware of being stimulated—that we perceive a sensation. An exception to this last statement is the sense of *pain*, which has its site of consciousness in the thalamus itself. No area of the cerebral cortex when stimulated has been found to give rise to painful sensation. Injury, though, to certain thalamic regions in disease or by accidents may cause the severest pain that humans experience.

We are by no means consciously aware of all sensory information received by the thalamus and cortex. One should remember that sensory impulses arriving even at these highest levels of the nervous system may eventuate in reflex action rather than in conscious appreciation. Such impulses may activate sensory area neurons to discharge impulses to motor areas, and thence on down to motor neurons and effectors. It is very probable that our voluntary activities are reflexly modified in this fashion; and it is possible that some activities that we classify as voluntary may, instead, be complicated reflexes of this sort.

THE HIGHER MENTAL FUNCTIONS

The more "advanced" in evolution an animal is, the more dependent it is upon the cerebral cortex for the performance of complex activities and for life itself. A frog deprived of its cerebral hemispheres can perform most of its normal activities; it is distinguished from a truly normal frog mainly by its apathy to what goes on about it. A decorticated bird can fly and a decorticated dog can walk; both can swallow food and continue to live for many months if given proper treatment. Such animals move about, however, only when impelled to by hunger, thirst, or other unpleasant but persistent stimuli. They do not recognize or feed upon food placed before them, but must be fed in order to survive.

It sometimes happens that human infants, because of some defect in their embryological development, are born without a cerebral cortex. No matter how long they may live, they have no true capacity for learning. Widespread destruction of the cortex in adult man is usually fatal.

Techniques of Study. To analyze the functions of different parts of the cerebral cortex, various methods of study have been employed. Small or large areas of cortex can be destroyed in experimental animals and the effects of such operations observed and tested. Disease of or accident to the cortex in man yields like information. Under anesthesia, localized stimulation of the cortex can help determine whether an area is motor or sensory. With local anesthesia (since the cortex "feels" no pain) and with permission of the patient, the human cortex has been directly stimulated during brain operations; the patient can immediately report what is perceived under these circumstances.

Another kind of study makes use of "brain waves." Neurons are continually active at all times and generate electrical energy as one result of their activity. The difference in electrical energy levels between cells or regions can be led off, even from the intact skull, as *brain potentials*. A record of brain potentials is called an *electroencephalogram* (EEG). Brain potentials vary and are characteristic for different cortical areas. Some of our knowledge of cortical function is derived from noting changes in the EEG when sensory conditions change; for an example, see Fig. 130, which records the effect when visual impulses reach the cortex. Data have also been gained from EEG records when other parts of the nervous system are stimulated, or when chemicals (including drugs) are applied to the brain or administered to the body. The EEG has, moreover, been useful in the study and diagnosis of *brain tumors* and *injuries* and of *epilepsy*. (For some further discussion of the EEG, see Chapter XIX.)

In recent years there has been renewed interest in brain chemistry. The *biochemical* approach is beginning to yield valuable information about the metabolism of central neurons and the roles of a variety of compounds in health and disease. The use of drugs, both experimentally and clinically, has increased tremendously, and *pharmacological* and *psychopharmacological* information is also expanding our knowledge of the brain in general and the cerebral cortex in particular. Among other possible benefits, there is hope that still more effective chemical treatments for psychoses may be forthcoming.

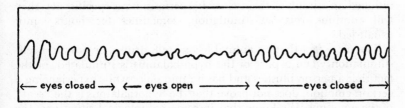

Fig. 130—Record of brain potentials ("brain waves").

Association Areas. Almost all of the cerebral cortex that is not specifically designated in Fig. 109 as a motor or a sensory area is composed of *association areas*. These areas are necessary for interpretation of sensory information, for meaningful action, and, in general, for all higher mental functions.

Experimental stimulation of a motor area gives rise to movement, it is true, but not to movement of real purposiveness. It is believed that motor performance in everyday life results from *patterned* stimulation of motor areas by surrounding association areas.

Similarly, we believe that only the raw data of perception result from the activation of a sensory area through its sensory pathway from receptors. A "roundish, colored object" perceived by the visual sensory area becomes an "orange" only after the work of the visual association areas has been added.

It is important to realize how imperfectly at this time we understand the association areas of the cortex, which are devoted to discriminative and correlative functions so vital to our lives.

Emotion, Memory, Learning. The *emotions* are complexly controlled by a number of centers in the *hypothalamus* (Fig. 109) together with portions of the cerebral cortex and deeper-lying centers within the cerebral hemispheres collectively called the *limbic system*. Other portions of cerebral cortex may also be involved.

Much recent attention has been given to hypothalamic centers.

We know that these centers control widespread visceral activities and a number of kinds of behavioral manifestations such as eating and drinking behavior. Many interesting studies have made use of *implanted electrodes*. Tiny electrodes with wire leads to the outside are surgically placed in regions of the brains of anesthetized animals; the animals are then sewn up and allowed to recover. Stimulation through long wires attached to the electrodes permits observation of the animals under quite normal conditions. In one hypothalamic location, stimulation results in maintained feeding activities; in another, drinking activities. When some animals are stimulated in certain hypothalamic (or some other) regions and are then conditioned to stimulate themselves by performing a specific act they will continue this self-stimulation, sometimes for hours, until exhausted.

The mere fact that an animal feeds itself, drinks, or practices self-stimulation when a part of the hypothalamus is stimulated, or the fact that a person blushes and has a rapid pulse while experiencing a certain emotion, does not prove that the hypothalamus is the "seat" of the emotions. We know that in some pathological situations, the motor acts accompanying emotions and the mental states themselves become dissociated. The mental states are, of course, much more difficult to study than the motor acts, and we know little about their physiology. Current data make it seem more probable that emotional states originate in the cerebral cortex and are funneled through the limbic structures and hypothalamus which then instigate the motor or behavioral activity that accompanies a particular mental attitude.

Just as we cannot ascribe particular cortical areas to specific emotions, we cannot point out fixed cortical sites for the higher rational functions of *memory*, *learning*, or "*thinking*." Instead, it appears that a variety, or perpaps all, of the association areas are involved with these higher functions, in a shifting pattern. Since there are millions of neurons in cortical tissue, it would not be at all surprising if large numbers of them were concerned with a single "memory" or "thought." Once the memory or thought is acquired, however, it might not be necessary for all these neurons to be active at a given moment in order that a particular mental activity rise to the level of consciousness.

Some evidence indicates that the activity of neurons leads to physical changes at synaptic regions, changes which may persist over long periods of time. These may be the physical and physiological basis of memory and, perhaps, of some aspects of the learning process.

It is believed that *conditioned reflexes* are relatively simple examples of learning. How do these differ from the reflexes to which we have repeatedly referred in preceding pages? A dog will salivate when food is placed in its mouth. This is the kind of reflex we have noted earlier—an unconditioned, inherited one. If shortly before or at the same time that food is placed in the dog's mouth a bell is rung, and this procedure is repeated a few times, the dog will learn to salivate in response to the sound, even when food is not presented. This learned salivation response is a conditioned reflex. Similar or more complicated conditioning processes lie behind many of our "habits." We, too, can respond to a dinner bell by salivating. The finger movements learned in typing or playing muscial instruments are other examples of conditioned reflexes; many more could be cited.

As yet, there are only hypothetical explanations of the way that neurons, reacting to a conditioning stimulus, make connections with the neurons in an inherited reflex circuit and, thus, open up a new reflex circuit. For more complicated learning processes, such as learning by "insight," we have even less information as to the physiological process involved.

There is little doubt, however, that it is the association areas that are responsible for higher mental functions. It is these areas which integrate the continual influx of sensory impressions into meaningful concepts and ideas. It is these areas which enable us to comprehend abstractions and to utilize the symbols of language.

The defects resulting from their damage or destruction furnish the most forceful illustrations of the functions of the association areas. When sensory recognition is impaired, a condition of *agnosia* is said to exist: visual agnosia (loss of recognition of objects seen although vision itself is unimpaired), auditory agnosia, or tactile agnosia. Impairment of motor performance is called *apraxia* (individuals are not paralyzed but cannot execute certain meaningful acts). When more complicated defects are seen, such as impairment of ability to use symbols, the individual suffers from *aphasia*. Aphasias are of several varieties: sensory (ability to see but not read language, ability to hear but not understand speech), motor (ability to vocalize but not speak words properly), intellectual (partial or complete loss of understanding of symbolic usage), or combinations of these.

In the thin layer of gray matter covering the cerebral hemispheres reside the factors and mechanisms which differentiate man from all other known living things. The great extent and complexity of his cerebral cortex grant him greater powers of intellect and reason than are possessed by any other animals. These intellectual powers have enabled man to dominate the world today, although in many instances he has not acted most wisely. Let us hope that they will lead him to a better, more rational life in the future.

CHAPTER XI

The Endocrine System

IF WE can designate one system as the most important coördinating and integrating agent of the body, that system will be the nervous system. Without it the organism would be only a loosely knit composite of organs and tissues whose activities would not be well correlated. There are, however, chemical as well as nervous coördinating agents in the body. We have already noted the activities of carbon dioxide as such an agent, for example. There are still other chemical agents produced by many of the glands of the body. Most glands secrete the chemical products they manufacture for some rather localized region or function; such products are delivered from the gland by way of its duct.

GENERAL DISCUSSION OF THE ENDOCRINE GLANDS

Certain glands became ductless during the course of evolution, and secreted chemical substances directly into the blood that flowed through them. The *ductless* or *endocrine glands* (glands of internal secretion) do not form a well-unified system in a structural sense, scattered as they are throughout many parts of the body. But the substances they secrete, the *hormones*, do exert a considerable welding influence on many vital activities.

A hormone is a chemical substance which is specific to the gland that secretes it and is distributed through the blood to regions far from or near to its place of origin. Such a substance must also exert a specific influence on some part or activity of the body if it is to be considered a hormone. An organ of the body is considered to have an endocrine function only if it contains a specific chemical substance which, after secretion into the blood, has a specific function.

These criteria are met only by the *thyroid, parathyroid, adrenal,* and *pituitary glands* and by the *pancreas, gonads* (the primary sex organs),

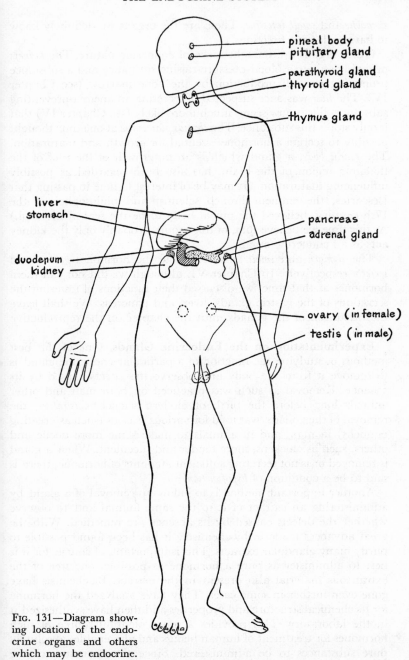

pineal body
pituitary gland
parathyroid gland
thyroid gland
thymus gland
liver
stomach
pancreas
adrenal gland
duodenum
kidney
ovary (in female)
testis (in male)

Fig. 131—Diagram showing location of the endocrine organs and others which may be endocrine.

stomach, and *small intestine*. These are the organs we definitely know to have endocrine functions.

Other organs are thought to be of endocrine nature. The *kidneys* probably secrete a blood-pressure-raising substance and a substance promoting red-cell production by the bone marrow (see Chapter IV). The *liver* was once suspected of secreting an anemia-preventing substance, but it now seems much more likely (see Chapter IV) that it only stores this substance. The *thymus gland* was at one time thought possibly to secrete a hormone essential for growth and maturation. The *pineal body*, a gland which is an outgrowth of the roof of the thalamic region of the brain, has also been regarded as possibly influencing maturation. (It may be of interest to note in passing that Descartes, the eminent French scientist and philosopher of the 17th century, believed the pineal body to be the seat of the soul.) At this time we believe that, of this group, probably only the kidney acts as an endocrine organ.

The *stomach* and *small intestine* secrete the hormones *gastrin* and *secretin* respectively. In Chapter VI, although we did not call them hormones at that time, we discussed their functions of fostering the secretions of the gastric glands, liver, and pancreas. We shall leave the discussion of the gonads until the chapter on the reproductive system.

Experimentation on the Endocrine Glands. One of the best methods of studying the function of a particular endocrine gland is to remove it from the body and observe the effects caused by its absence. Removal as such was practiced on both man and other animals long before the birth of modern science. *Castration*, the removal of the gonads, was used for various reasons (such as creating eunuchs) in man, and in animals to make some more docile and others, such as chickens, more tender and succulent. When a gland is removed or is not secreting sufficient amounts of hormone, there is said to be a condition of *hypofunction*.

Another important method is to follow up removal of a gland by administering an extract of it to the same animal and to observe whether the defects caused by its absence are remedied. With the great advances made in biochemistry it has been found possible to purify many glandular extracts. This is important, of course, for it is best to administer as pure a hormone as possible, one free of the extraneous material also present in the extract. Biochemists have gone even further in some cases. They have analyzed the hormone for its chemical structure and properties and then have synthesized it in the laboratory. This provides a more plentiful source of such hormones for treatment of human beings and also enables absolutely pure substances to be administered. Since the hormones of the endocrine glands are alike in all the vertebrates, it is usually safe to administer glandular extracts from lower animals to man.

Hormones or gland extracts can also be injected into normal animals to simulate the action of an overactive endocrine gland. When a gland secretes too much hormone, there is said to be a condition of *hyperfunction*.

Paralleling these types of experimental study have been studies on human beings suffering from endocrine diseases. Much has been learned about the functions and activities of the endocrine glands by observation and treatment of human patients.

THE THYROID GLAND

The *thyroid gland* is a bi-lobed structure lying on either side of the upper part of the trachea (Fig. 131). The two lobes are connected by an isthmus of tissue crossing the ventral surface of the trachea.

The Thyroid Gland in Health. The thyroid gland has a marked influence on the normal functioning of the body. The thyroid hormone helps to regulate the metabolism of every cell in the body. As we shall see below, this hormone apparently exerts its effects by controlling the rate at which oxidations occur. Since oxidative reactions are the means by which the body is furnished with energy, it is evident that the thyroid gland indirectly controls a great variety of bodily activities.

One means of determining the state of health of the thyroid gland is by measuring the *basal metabolism* of a person. By basal metabolism is meant the heat production of the body under certain standard conditions of inactivity. (The concept of basal metabolism will be developed in Chapter XIV.) Although this is the most important criterion, other observations must be made in conjunction with it in order to confirm or reject the opinion to which the state of the basal metabolism would lead us. Determining the iodine level of blood is now a more sensitive index of thyroid activity.

It is extremely difficult to study the normal function of the thyroid gland in the normal individual. We can best understand its function (and the same approach will be made in our study of the other endocrine glands) by observing the defects produced when it is not functioning properly or when it is actually absent from the body.

Cretinism and Experimental Hypofunction. When the thyroid gland is removed from an immature experimental animal, hypofunction results. If hypofunction of the thyroid spontaneously occurs in a human child, the condition is known as *cretinism*. In either case the defects that result are strikingly similar.

The *basal metabolic rate* (B.M.R.)—the rate at which the body produces heat under certain standard conditions—is markedly reduced. Bone growth is stunted and the bones may be deformed. The sexual maturation of the individual is slowed or stopped. The skin is dry and the hair tends to fall out. The heart rate is slowed. The muscles are weak and fatigue can be quickly induced. There may be anemia, subnormal temperature, and increased susceptibility to infection. Intelligence is definitely impaired. Degenerative changes appear in all other endocrine glands except the pancreas. There may be a lower than normal concentration of sugar in the blood.

Myxedema. Hypofunction in the human adult is called *myxedema* or *Gull's disease.* The symptoms are again quite similar to those in an adult experimental animal whose thyroid has been removed. Most of the symptoms are just like those in cretinism. But there are some differences. The name myxedema is derived from the fact that there is an accumulation of fluid under the skin which resembles an edemalike state. It is not the same as edema however. And, of course, since an adult has already attained full growth, there can be no retardation of physical development. There is, often, a tendency to put on weight. Otherwise the symptoms parallel those of cretinism.

In reading over the defects produced by hypothyroidism, it becomes evident that the thyroid must influence all the cells of the body. Since a deficiency of the thyroid hormone slows up so many of the body's activities (the lowered B.M.R. is especially significant), it may be stated that the thyroid hormone markedly influences the oxidation reactions going on in all the cells of the body. The effects on growth, intelligence, and sexual development in hypothyroidism are probably consequences of this basic metabolic disturbance, although the hormone may have some more specific functions with regard to these processes.

Experimental and Human Hyperthyroidism. We might expect, in a case of spontaneous hyperthyroidism in man, that the symptoms would be exactly the opposite of those for hypothyroidism. Our expectations are almost completely fulfilled. The B.M.R. is greatly increased. The heart rate may reach 150 beats per minute. Despite a ravenous appetite and huge amounts of food eaten, the patient tends to become quite emaciated. The individual has tremendous drive and seemingly limitless energy, but is also extremely nervous. The skin is moist. There may be a slight rise in body temperature and also a somewhat higher than normal concentration of glucose in the blood.

We are surer that these symptoms result from an excess of thyroid hormone when we learn that almost all of these symptoms can be reproduced by administering thyroid extract to a normal experimental animal. Another symptom that frequently is found in human hyperthyroid cases—protrusion of the eyeballs—cannot be produced by injection of thyroid hormone. It is doubtful, therefore, that this symptom is due directly to an overactive thyroid.

Goiter. An enlarged thyroid gland is called a *goiter*. It is rather puzzling when we hear for the first time that a goiter may signify either a hyperactive, hypoactive, or a normally functioning gland. Perhaps we can clarify somewhat this queer phenomenon.

At the time when the existence of a goiter denotes a hyperactive gland, it is believed that the enlargement of the gland is the cause of the hyperthyroidism. That is, the enlarged gland has a greater number of cells secreting thyroid hormone and, consequently, more hormone is passed into the blood. Hyperthyroidism results. But we have no answer to the question, "What causes the enlargement of the gland?"

At other times goiter signifies a hypoactive gland. The explanation for this assumes that for some reason the gland is not producing enough hormone for normal functioning. The gland responds to the decreased hormonal output by increasing in size. Although each cell produces a subnormal amount of hormone, the increased number of cells secreting may produce enough to add up to a normal amount from the whole gland. Unfortunately, if the condition causing the initial hypothyroidism persists at the same intensity, the compensatory efforts of the gland are to no avail—there is still hypothyroidism. The gland seems at times to exhaust itself in its attempt to compensate for the deficiency.

At still other times, when the initial cause of hypothyroidism is not too drastic, the compensatory efforts of the gland are crowned with success. The increased number of cells secrete adequate amounts of hormone. In such cases—*simple goiter*—although the gland may be considerably enlarged, there are no symptoms of hormonal deficiency or excess.

Goiter may, then, accompany hypo- or hyperthyroidism, although it is not an invariable symptom of either condition.

Iodine and the Thyroid Hormone. In the 19th century there were large inland areas of the world known as *goiter belts* because the incidence of simple and hypothyroid goiter was very high in the inhabitants. The Great Lakes area in the United States was such a region. It took many years to correlate the high incidence of goiter with the lack of *iodine* in the soil and water of these belts, even though it was learned in that century that iodine feeding was of help in treating goiter. During the present century, however, in most places the situation has been taken in hand by the use of iodized table salt or the inclusion of small amounts of iodine in the drinking water.

The true significance of the remedial action of iodine came forth somewhat later in studies upon the chemical structure of the thyroid hormone. Iodine was found to be an essential part of the hormone.

Treatment of Thyroid Defects. The isolation and identification of the thyroid hormone was delayed in part by the lack of incentive. It had been found that feeding hypothyroid individuals with thyroid gland relieved their malady. Since use of the gland itself was effective, there seemed no great need to isolate its hormone.

However, upon further investigation a substance called *thyroglobulin* was isolated. Once thought to be the true hormone, thyroglobulin is now believed to be the form in which the hormone is stored in the gland. Two iodine-containing amino acids can be released from thyroglobulin into the blood. One of these, *thyroxine*, seems to be the major circulating form of the hormone. The other amino acid, *triiodothyronine*, is present in the blood to a very small extent. Thyroxine, by partial deiodination, can be transformed into triiodothyronine and the latter utilized by the cells of the body.

Most hormones are destroyed by digestive enzymes and cannot be orally administered. Since thyroid hormone is resistant to this action, it can be taken orally—in the form of thyroxine, thyroglobulin, or the glandular tissue itself—to relieve hypothyroidism. Daily dosages may be required.

Hyperthyroidism can be combatted by surgery, X-irradiation, administration of *radioactive iodine* or of *antithyroid substances*. All of these methods can reduce the secretion of thyroid hormone. Care must be taken not to remove or destroy the whole gland nor to inhibit its function completely, for a swing to hypothyroidism might result. If the gland regenerates or increases its secretion sufficiently, retreatment of the hyperthyroid state may be necessary.

THE PARATHYROID GLANDS

The *parathyroid glands* are quite small ($\frac{1}{4}$ inch long) bits of glandular tissue which either lie very close to or are embedded in the thyroid gland (see Fig. 131). Their number varies from two to four in man.

The ovoid-shaped parathyroids, composed of densely packed cells within a connective tissue framework of reticular fibers, are the smallest endocrine glands. Although they differ from the thyroid glands in structure and function, they have the same nervous innervations, supply of arteries, and venous and lymph drainage.

The Parathyroid Glands in Health. The tiny parathyroid glands have a profound influence on the maintenance of a normal level of calcium ions in the blood and the tissue fluid. We have frequently noted the many functions that calcium ions serve in many bodily activities. The most important of these is the role that calcium plays in the maintenance of healthy cellular activity. Especially significant is the control of muscular and nervous irritability. Nerve and muscle cells require a certain concentration of calcium ions in their environment if they are to respond to normal stimuli in a healthy way. The importance of the parathyroid hormone is in the maintenance of the proper distribution of calcium in "storage depots" like bone and in the body fluids.

Experimental Removal of the Glands. In the course of experimentation on hypothyroidism in dogs, it was found that removal of the thyroid resulted in death of the animals in a short time. The question at once arose whether in dogs, unlike other animals, the thyroid was essential for life. Removal of the thyroid, as we have seen, does not lead to a fatal end in other animals. The reason for this difference was soon discovered. In dogs the parathyroid glands lie in the thyroid gland, unlike their location in other experimental animals, and it was actually the removal of the tiny parathyroids which led to death.

After removal of the parathyroids in an experimental animal there is prompt loss of appetite accompanied by extreme thirst. The animal is unable, however, to hold either food or water in its stomach. Soon muscular twitchings appear which grow more and more violent and become convulsive in nature. Over the next few days the convulsions grow stronger, the muscles going into tetanic spasms. When one of these spasms lasts a little too long, the animal dies of asphyxiation because, along with the other skeletal muscles, the respiratory muscles are involved. These muscular symptoms are collectively referred to as *parathyroid tetany*.

Hypofunction in Man. Proof of spontaneous hypofunction of the parathyroids in man is still lacking. Some convulsive conditions have been ascribed to hypoparathyroidism, but the evidence for the involvement of the parathyroids in these cases is only indicative at best. Hypofunction does occur at times when some parathyroid tissue is accidentally removed during an operation upon the thyroid gland. It may also develop when a tumor of the parathyroid tissue is removed and along with it too much of the glands. The condition is generally quite mild in man (since at least some parathyroid tissue is present) and can be promptly relieved.

The Cause of Parathyroid Tetany. In searching for the reason behind the muscular twitchings and spasms that occur in parathyroid tetany, investigators noticed that when the glands were removed the irritability of both muscles and nerves was significantly increased —they would respond to weaker stimuli than are normally effective. Thus, stimuli within the body which would ordinarily be ineffective in eliciting muscular contractions are now adequate.

But why should the irritability be increased? It was also discovered that the concentration of calcium ions in the blood was decreased. This factor accounts for the increased irritability. Normally the irritability of muscle and nerve is controlled by a balance between the concentrations of sodium, potassium, and calcium ions. A lowered concentration of calcium ions unhinges the balance and favors greater sensitivity.

The parathyroid hormone evidently regulates the amount of calcium ion in the blood and by this action indirectly controls the irritability of muscle and nerve.

The Treatment of Parathyroid Tetany. Since a lowered blood calcium brings on tetany, the logical treatment would seem to be the administration of calcium. When this was tried in cases of experimental parathyroid tetany, the treatment was a marked success. Calcium salts can be given by mouth (if the condition is not too acute) and will then be absorbed into the blood in the small intestine. When it is imperative to get the calcium into the blood more quickly, a solution of calcium salts can be injected intramuscularly or, as a last resort, into a vein. Any of these methods of treatment can be applied to man, but since hypofunction is usually mild, calcium is usually safely given orally.

Another method is also possible. An extract of the parathyroids, *parathormone*, can be injected. This extract undoubtedly contains the parathyroid hormone but the latter has not as yet been isolated in a very pure form. Parathormone cannot be administered orally. Care must also be taken in using it, for too much of it can raise the concentration of calcium ions in the blood, an undesirable condition.

Hyperparathyroidism. Injections of parathormone into a normal experimental animal can simulate hyperfunction of the parathyroids in man. This condition does occur, though infrequently, and was known as *von Recklinghausen's disease* before it was ascribed to hypersecretion of parathyroid hormone. It is generally associated with tumor and enlargement of the parathyroids.

Hyperfunction of the parathyroids causes a decreased phosphate but an increased calcium ion concentration in the blood. Increased calcium ion concentration results in decreased muscular and nervous irritability and lowered muscle tone. Other symptoms of especial interest are a high excretion of calcium in the urine and a drawing of calcium out of the bones. The loss of phosphate and calcium from the bones weakens them and they may be deformed. They also tend to fracture very easily and to heal slowly.

Hyperparathyroidism can only be treated by removal of parathyroid tissue, an operation which may successfully relieve the condition. However, if the calcium concentration of the blood has risen too high, there is no known remedy for lowering it.

The parathyroid hormone, as we can see now, is essential for life because of its regulation of the calcium balance of the body; this hormone also regulates the phosphate ion concentration in the blood through its control of excretion of this ion by the kidneys. If the hormone concentration is too low, blood calcium drops and may result in death if unchecked. An excess of parathyroid hormone draws calcium from the bones, raises its concentration in the blood, and increases its rate of excretion.

THE ADRENAL GLANDS

Resting atop each kidney like a cap is an *adrenal gland* (see Fig. 131). Both structurally and functionally each adrenal gland is really a double gland. It consists of different glandular tissues, one forming the outer layer or *adrenal cortex*, the other the inner *adrenal medulla*.

The Adrenal Glands in Health. There has been no definite interpretation of the normal role of the hormone of the adrenal medulla. A rather extensive theory of its importance has been proposed, but as yet it lacks complete confirmation. It is known that this hormone can in sufficient concentration produce the same effects that stimulation of the sympathetic nervous system would effect. The crucial evidence which is now awaited is whether the adrenal medulla produces significant amounts of the hormone under normal conditions.

The hormones of the adrenal cortex, on the other hand, are known to be extremely important in the normal economy of the body. These hormones help to regulate the salt and water balance of the body fluids (especially the sodium and potassium balance) and also the level of carbohydrates, proteins, and fats throughout the body. Adrenocortical hormones are also critical for maintaining normal reactions of the body to stress.

The Adrenal Medulla. The hormone of the adrenal medulla has been known since the turn of the century. An extract of the adrenal medulla was first obtained in 1895. It was found that this extract, when injected into an experimental animal, caused, among many other effects, a notable rise in blood pressure. From this extract a substance called *adrenaline* was isolated.

THE EFFECTS CAUSED BY ADRENALINE. After its discovery adrenaline became the most studied hormone of all. Its chemical formula was soon discovered and it was also synthesized. The effects caused by adrenaline on injection into the blood are a steep rise in arterial blood pressure, a faster heart rate, constriction of the arterioles in the abdominal viscera, release of extra glucose into the blood, and inhibition of motility in the digestive tract.

THE "EMERGENCY THEORY." You may have noticed that the effects brought about by adrenaline are the same as can be produced by widespread activation of the sympathetic nervous system. Dr. Cannon of Harvard University used this observation as the basis for his *emergency theory of adrenal function.*

According to Cannon, in times of great stress—such as during flight, fright, or a fight—the sympathetic system aided by the adrenal medulla sets up reactions in the body which enable an animal to meet the emergency effectively. The faster heart rate assures a greater cardiac output per minute. The constriction of the abdominal arterioles diverts blood from the abdominal viscera to the skeletal muscles (whose arterioles are dilated) and also helps to raise the blood pressure by increasing the peripheral resistance (the faster heart rate also contributes to the rise in blood pressure). The resultant of these changes is to deliver more blood at a faster rate and under a greater pressure to the skeletal muscles. The latter obviously must have an increased blood supply to bring them the greater amounts of oxygen and fuel necessary for vigorous activity.

The oxygen capacity of the blood is increased somewhat by the discharge of stored red blood cells from the spleen. The respiratory rate is accelerated and the bronchioles are dilated so that the ventilation of the lungs is increased. These factors plus the faster circulation time make oxygen transport to the active muscles as great as possible. The release of extra glucose into the blood provides a greater supply of fuel substance for the muscles. The muscles are also enabled to work longer without fatiguing.

Certain accessory phenomena help to point up the theory. Adrenaline has the property of increasing the coagulating power of the blood. So the argument continues that if the animal is wounded the danger to it from hemorrhage is lessened. The emotions that accompany emergency situations are marked by many physical manifestations—dilation of the pupils, erection of the hairs, bulging of the eyeballs, sweating, etc. And all of these manifestations can be produced by sympathetic stimulation or by the presence of adrenaline in the blood.

SIGNIFICANCE OF THE ADRENAL MEDULLA. The acceptance of this most attractive theory hinges on a very important question, namely whether or not the adrenal medulla secretes enough adrenaline into the blood to bring about the effects described above. Comparatively large amounts of adrenaline are usually injected into an experimental animal to get its effects.

The claim by Cannon and his co-workers that the adrenal medulla secretes a significant amount of adrenaline in conditions of stress has been contested by other physiologists. The latter say that they have been unable to obtain that much adrenaline under physiological conditions. It is not possible in the light of available evidence to make a final decision in favor of either one of these schools of thought.

There is no doubt that the adrenal medulla does secrete adrenaline continuously, although at a very low concentration. Of what significance this is in the daily activities of the organism is not clear.

The adrenal medulla is not essential to life. Both medullas can be removed and the animal will survive with no observable adverse effects.

Adrenaline, as a drug, has proved very useful both in experimental and medical practice. It is very often used as a heart stimulant, even though its effects are very short-lived. Because of its property of dilating the bronchioles, it is also used to ease breathing in patients suffering from *asthma* (in which condition the bronchioles may be chronically or spasmodically constricted).

The Adrenal Cortex. In contradistinction to the neighboring adrenal medulla, the *adrenal cortex* has been found to be essential for life. Although it was a long time before its functions were recognized, we are now at least on the way to an understanding of them.

HYPOFUNCTION OF THE ADRENAL CORTEX. Upon removal of both adrenal glands most experimental animals exhibit a loss of appetite, extreme muscular weakness, and marked depression of activity and interest. They then usually lapse into coma and die within ten days following the operation.

Addison's disease, the comparable condition in man, was recognized long before it was associated with hypofunction of the adrenal cortex. A frequent cause of the disease is tuberculosis of the adrenal gland. The symptoms in man are similar to those in animals but milder, for the disease runs a longer course. One symptom not found in experimental animals is a peculiar bronzing of the skin because of the presence of excess amounts of normal pigment. If not treated, those having Addison's disease die from one to three years after it starts.

THE DEFECTS CAUSED BY HYPOFUNCTION. By looking behind the external symptoms of hypofunction, a number of other symptoms have been noted by many scientists. There is a fall in the concentration of sodium ions and a rise in the concentration of potassium ions in the blood. Accompanying this is a decrease in blood volume due to loss of water from the blood and a lowered blood pressure. There may also be a significant drop in blood glucose.

The changes in sodium and potassium ions have a serious effect upon physiological functions. In cases of cortical insufficiency, the kidneys excessively excrete sodium ions and retain too many potassium ions. It is believed that inadequate secretion of the hormone also makes the capillary walls more permeable and thus allows greater seepage of fluid out of the blood.

Another point of great importance is that adrenalectomized

animals or cortically-deficient humans much more easily succumb to conditions of stress (surgical operations, trauma, cold, oxygen depletion, etc.) than do normal creatures.

THE HORMONES OF THE ADRENAL CORTEX. A number of pure compounds have been obtained from cortical tissue, some of which have also been synthesized in the laboratory. It still has not been completely established whether the cortex secretes one or several hormones. At present there appear to be two main types of compounds that are significant: *mineralocorticoids* and *glucocorticoids*. The former is exemplified by the compound, *aldosterone*, and the latter by the compound, *cortisone*.

THE TREATMENT OF ADRENAL HYPOFUNCTION. Two methods of treatment have been used, but neither is successful in all cases of adrenal insufficiency. One method is to inject either a mineralocorticoid or a glucocorticoid, depending upon which deficiency symptoms are the more serious. The other is to feed the patient on a high sodium diet. Probably the best treatment yet devised is a combination of these methods. It should be stated that treatment is more often successful than not. In the cases in which it is not, no completely satisfactory reasons have come forth. Since we are not at all certain that we have isolated the true hormone or hormones, it may be that some important defect will not be remedied unless the exact hormone is administered.

HYPERFUNCTION OF THE ADRENAL CORTEX. Injection of large amounts of cortical extract or compounds into normal animals or humans produces effects opposite to those seen in hypofunction. There is no disease in man which is the opposite of Addison's disease.

There are, however, cases of adrenal tumor (the enlarged gland presumably secreting excessive amounts of hormones) in women in which the main effects are a change in secondary sex characteristics toward the male type. The breasts atrophy, hair tends to take a masculine distribution, and the disposition becomes more mannish. Cases of adrenal tumor in men are rarer but some cases of feminism resulting from it are reported. In children such tumors can lead to precocious sexual maturation. In any of these cases surgical removal of the tumor may correct the condition.

IMPORTANCE OF THE ADRENAL CORTEX. The adrenal cortex exercises a pervasive influence throughout the body by its regulation of salt and water balance on the one hand and of carbohydrate, fat, and protein metabolism on the other.

Aldosterone directly influences the kidney tubules to excrete normal quantities of sodium and potassium, favoring retention of sodium at the expense of potassium. Preserving the normal salt con-

centration in the body fluids greatly influences the retention of appropriate volumes of water in the fluids and also is of paramount
importance in the normal functioning of every body cell.

No less important is the role of cortisone in helping to maintain
beneficial concentrations of fat, protein, and carbohydrate products
in tissues and fluids. Of special significance is its ability to promote
conversion of amino acids into carbohydrates, a process which
normally aids the maintenance of an adequate blood sugar level.

The ability of the normal organism, having normal amounts of
adrenocortical hormones, to withstand a variety of stresses is dependent not only upon the functions outlined just above, but also
upon cortisone's ability to modify connective tissue throughout the
body. Since connective tissue is so widespread, it is not surprising
that cortisone assumes even more importance both in normal physiology and in medical treatments.

It is evident that adrenocortical hormones impinge upon many
bodily processes, including sexual ones. This latter relationship,
although by no means clear, might have been predicted, for adreno-
cortical and sex hormones have very similar chemical structures.

THE PANCREAS

We know the *pancreas* (Fig. 131) as a gland secreting digestive
juices. But it, too, is a double gland. Interspersed among the more
numerous cells for the secretion of pancreatic juice are little islets of
tissue—the *islets of Langerhans*—which are endocrine in nature.

The Pancreas in Health. The endocrine portion of the pancreas
secretes a hormone, *insulin*, which is the most important single
regulator of the balance and utilization of carbohydrates in the tissues. The pancreatic hormone aids in the preservation of a normal
level of blood sugar, of adequate stores of glycogen ("animal starch")
in the liver and muscles, and, perhaps, in the oxidation of carbohydrate substances by the tissues. Since carbohydrates are our
primary energy-yielding substances, it becomes obvious that the
pancreas is a potent factor in the scheme of healthy bodily activity.

Diabetes Mellitus or Pancreatic Diabetes. *Diabetes mellitus* or
sugar diabetes has been known as a disease for many centuries. Until
late in the 19th century, however, there was no knowledge of its
cause or of how to treat it. Even then it was an accidental discovery
that opened the way to a better understanding of the condition.

The pancreas was removed from dogs by von Mering and Min-
kowski who wanted to observe the digestive upsets that lack of
pancreatic enzymes would induce. But, in addition to digestive

malfunction, they discovered that such dogs developed symptoms very similar to those seen in human beings with sugar diabetes.

These symptoms are a large amount of sugar (glucose) excreted in the urine and a high blood sugar concentration. Incomplete products of fat oxidation are found in the blood and urine. The daily urine output is greatly increased. Acidosis, a state of too much acid in the blood, also occurs.

The high concentrations of sugar and fat products in the blood account for their presence in the urine. Glucose, you will remember, is normally filtered into the kidney tubules and then completely reabsorbed into the blood. But when its concentration reaches a high enough level in the blood, the tubules are not able to absorb the excess. Incomplete oxidation of fats indicates that something has upset the normal metabolism of fat.

Because of the increased concentration of substances in the tubular urine, more water is held in the tubules and the volume of urine is thereby increased. Since the incomplete products of fat oxidation are acid in nature, acidosis results.

If pancreatic diabetes is not treated in experimental animals, the animals die within a few weeks. In man the condition is a much more prolonged one since not all of the islet tissue is destroyed or ceases functioning at the same time.

Insulin and Treatment of Diabetes Mellitus. After the initial experiments on pancreatic diabetes, careful research showed that the diabetic state resulted from the absence of the islet tissue of the pancreas. Many workers then tried unsuccessfully to isolate a hormone from a pancreatic extract. Their difficulty may have been that they attempted to isolate a hormone from an extract of the entire pancreas. The pancreatic enzymes secreted by the digestive portion of the gland in all probability destroyed the hormone. Then in 1922 Drs. Banting, Best, McLeod, and Collip of the University of Toronto, using only islet tissue, reported an extract which relieved the symptoms of diabetic dogs.

Upon purification, the extract, which they named insulin, was tried in human cases with the same favorable results. Insulin has since been crystallized and is now obtainable in a very pure form.

Insulin must be injected since it is not effective by mouth. Upon injection it promptly corrects the diabetic condition. But it does have to be injected at least once daily to prevent a recurrence of diabetic symptoms. Diabetic patients, even children, have learned to calculate and inject the daily doses they require. Milder diabetic cases can often be ameliorated solely by dietary precautions; these latter should be prescribed by a physician. Some cases respond favorably to the administration of such substances as *orinase*, which can be taken by mouth. Orinase is unrelated to insulin and it acts to lower the blood sugar level in a different manner.

The Functions of Insulin. Insulin is believed to function in the following ways: it promotes the conversion of glucose (blood sugar) to glycogen in the liver and in skeletal and cardiac muscle; it accelerates the utilization of glucose by other tissues (probably, for this and the preceding function, by accelerating the passage of glucose through cell membranes); it slows the breakdown of fats by the liver; and, by keeping carbohydrate levels high, it also slows conversion of amino acids to carbohydrates. All these activities combine to lower the blood glucose level, thus tending to counteract the influence of most of the other major hormones of the body.

It should be mentioned here that evidence is accumulating to indicate that the pancreatic islets secrete a second hormone, *glucagon*, which tends to raise blood sugar level.

The Effects of Excess Amounts of Insulin. Injection of insulin into a normal animal or of too much of it into a diabetic one results in a profound fall in blood sugar concentration. If the blood sugar content drops below a certain minimal level, very serious symptoms develop—convulsions, coma, and death. The best emergency treatment is the injection of a glucose solution to raise the blood sugar concentration. The brain cells apparently require a certain minimal level of sugar in the blood coming to them; if this is not maintained, they become much more irritable than they normally are and initiate the convulsions.

Spontaneous production of too much insulin does occur at times, and, if persistent, can best be relieved by removal of some pancreatic islet tissue. Certain types of poisoning and also liver damage may produce the same end effects as hypersecretion of insulin, but the causes are, of course, dissimilar.

THE PITUITARY GLAND

Hanging from a stalk at the ventral surface of the hypothalamus is the *pituitary gland* or *hypophysis* (Figs. 105 and 131). It, too, is a double gland in structure and function. The part nearest the brain, the *posterior lobe*, is derived from embryonic brain tissue, while the *anterior lobe* is an outgrowth of the tissue in the roof of the embryonic mouth.

Although quite a small structure, the pituitary gland secretes more hormones than any other endocrine gland. Since among these hormones are at least some which control the activity of other endocrine glands, it has been called the "master gland." Whether or not it deserves this appellation, this gland has a variety of very important influences.

The Pituitary Gland in Health. The pituitary hormones serve many functions in the normal person. They regulate growth, sexual activities, and the amount of water excreted by the kidneys. They serve as important aids in the control and use of carbohydrates, proteins, and fats in the body. As just mentioned, they are important coördinators of endocrine activity since they control the secretion of hormones by a number of other endocrine organs. The widespread importance of normal levels of pituitary hormones will become more and more evident in the later sections of this book.

The Functions of the Posterior Lobe. The posterior pituitary lobe retains its connection to the brain and, unlike most other endocrine organs, is under nervous control. A nerve tract passes from the hypothalamus through the pituitary stalk to the cells of the posterior lobe. To be more accurate, it is now known that the hormone (or hormones) once believed to be secreted by the posterior lobe is (or are), in truth, secreted by nerve cells in certain hypothalamic centers. From these sites one or more substances make their way through the stalk to the posterior lobe. Here they can be stored until released as the result of nervous stimulation.

A number of functions have been ascribed to posterior lobe hormones. In 1894 an extract called *pituitrin* was obtained from the pituitary which was remarkable for its blood pressure-raising properties when experimentally injected. A few years later it was ascertained that the substance responsible was to be found only in the posterior lobe of the gland. Subsequent work on this extract showed that it could be divided into at least two important fractions. One of these, *pitressin*, retained the property of raising blood pressure. The other, *pitocin*, had a marked excitant effect on the smooth muscle of many viscera but especially on that of the uterus.

The blood pressure-raising fraction of pituitrin is of some value as a drug, though it is not now believed to exert any hormonal effect on blood pressure. There is evidence that in some animals pitocin, or something like it, controls the contractions of the uterus during labor. Whether this occurs in the human female is not known. Pitocin is beneficially used by doctors, however, to stimulate uterine contractions if they do not occur normally, or to strengthen weak normal contractions.

Also recently, posterior lobe extract has been found to possess an *anti-diuretic effect*. Its injection, for instance, considerably delays the increase in urine excretion that follows ingestion of large quantities of water. Much more important is its action in relieving the disease called *diabetes insipidus*. This disease is marked by the excretion of very large volumes of urine containing very little solid material. There is no glucose present. The condition can be brought on by removal of the posterior lobe or by cutting the nerve tract to it (the latter procedure results in degeneration of posterior lobe cells). Since posterior lobe extract relieves the condition, we must conclude that the posterior lobe contains an *anti-diuretic hormone*, ADH, secreted by hypothalamic cells (as indicated above). ADH partially regulates the reabsorption of water by the kidney tubules. In its absence, more water is excreted than under normal conditions (see Chapter VII).

The Functions of the Anterior Lobe. At one time or another a great many hormones have been said to be located in the anterior pituitary lobe on the basis of the very many effects produced by injections of anterior pituitary extract. Whether each effect signifies the presence of a distinct hormone is not known. The tendency lately has been to reduce the number of hormones with the idea that some have more than one effect. There are, nevertheless, some hormones of whose existence we can be quite certain.

THE GROWTH HORMONE. Removal of the anterior lobe causes marked stunting of the growth of experimental animals. Such dwarfed animals can be stimulated to renewed growth by anterior lobe extract if too much time does not elapse between the removal and injection. On the other hand, injection of this extract into young normal animals promotes their growth to abnormal size. The increase in size is due to true growth of bones and other tissues and is not just increased adiposity. The hormone derived from this extract has now been isolated and purified; it is named *somatotropin* or *somatotropic hormone* (STH). STH increases growth by promoting protein synthesis in cells.

THE GONADOTROPIC HORMONES. There are two hormones which definitely stimulate the secretion of sex hormones. When the anterior lobe is removed, the gonads degenerate. We shall discuss the pituitary-gonadal interrelationship at greater length in the next chapter.

THE LACTOGENIC HORMONE. We shall have more to say about this later on, too. We may just mention here that an anterior lobe hormone is concerned in the secretion of milk by the mammary glands.

OTHER "TROPIC" HORMONES. When the anterior lobe is removed, not only the gonads degenerate but the thyroid and the adrenal cortex do also. From anterior lobe extracts have been isolated both a *thyrotropic hormone* and an *adrenocorticotropic hormone* (ACTH), either of which, when administered to an animal deprived of its anterior lobe, brings about regeneration of its respective "target" gland.

Each target gland has a specific interrelationship with the anterior lobe. For example, the thyroid gland cannot maintain its normal size nor secrete normal amounts of its hormone unless a certain level of thyrotropic hormone is released from the anterior pituitary lobe.

If, however, thyrotropic hormone causes the secretion of excess thyroid hormone, the blood level of the latter depresses the secretory activity of the anterior lobe with respect to thyrotropic hormone. The fall in thyrotropic hormone decreases thyroid stimulation, and eventually the level of thyroid hormone falls. If thyroid hormone concentration is sufficiently decreased, this change can act as a stimulus to renewed secretion of thyrotropic hormone, which, in turn, causes more thyroid hormone to be secreted, etc. The interaction of the two glands promotes the maintenance of as beneficial a level of target gland hormone as possible.

Note the application of some of what has just been said to the use of an antithyroid substance. The latter acts as a chemical deterrent to thyroid hormone synthesis (hence its utility in treatment of hyperthyroidism). If the substance is administered excessively, however, it can depress thyroid hormone level to such an extent that thyrotropic hormone secretion is markedly increased. This latter increase cannot cause increased thyroid hormone secretion (because of the interference of the antithyroid compound) but it will cause growth of the thyroid gland; if this situation remains in effect, the net result is eventually a goitrous gland incapable of much hormone synthesis.

Pituitary Diseases in Man. When certain cells of the anterior lobe degenerate or secrete insufficient quantities of growth hormone in children, *dwarfism* results. These dwarfs are generally not deformed, but may be sexually underdeveloped. Some success has been achieved by treatment with growth hormone. Tumor of these anterior lobe cells in children causes *giantism*. A pituitary dwarf may be only 3 or 4 feet tall while a pituitary giant often grows to a height of 7 or 8 feet. If the growth-hormone cells are affected after full growth has been achieved, there is no further increase in height but *acromegaly* follows. This consists of overgrowth of the bones of the face, feet and hands, and of the viscera. Degeneration of the gonads is another prominent effect.

Simmond's disease results in adults from degeneration of the anterior lobe. It is best described as premature senility—graying and loss of hair, wrinkling of the skin, reduction in the size of the body and its parts, atrophy of the gonads, mental deterioration, muscular weakness, and early death in coma. This disease in man is the equivalent of removing the anterior lobe in an experimental animal.

Cushing's disease is due to oversecretion of some of the anterior lobe cells. It is marked by great adiposity of the trunk and face but not of the limbs. There is often an increase in size of the adrenal glands and atrophy of the gonads. Other secondary effects may be due to the involvement of other endocrine glands.

It has been extremely difficult to treat pituitary disease. In cases of

hyperpituitarism, surgery is especially difficult and dangerous because of the location of the gland. Even if an operation is feasible,
the removal of just the right part of so small a structure without
damaging some other essential part makes the job no easier. There
have been limited successes with surgery, laser surgery, and radiation
techniques. Purification of pituitary hormones is proceeding to such
an extent that they are being used with some success in treatment of
cases of hypopituitarism.

CHAPTER XII

The Reproductive System

REPRODUCTION of the individual may be considered a form of growth —a discontinuous growth which perpetuates the species. Methods of reproduction have evolved along with other aspects of animal life. In general, the less specialized an animal is, the simpler its reproductive behavior.

Evolutionary Development of Reproduction. In Amoeba and many other one-celled animals, reproduction is a simple *splitting* of the one cell into two portions, each daughter cell receiving an equal share of the nuclear and cytoplasmic materials.

In somewhat more advanced animals the reproductive process takes the form of *budding* or splitting off of a part of the parent organism, the part then reproducing a complete new individual. In this way animals like the jellyfish are able, under certain favorable conditions, to reproduce their own kind.

Sexual reproduction is common to a great many animals, notably all the higher kinds. The essential process in sexual reproduction is the union of two cells to form one which then grows into a new individual. One of the two sex cells, the *sperm*, usually comes from a male individual; the other, the *egg* or *ovum*, from a female. This is not always true, for, in some animals, both sperm and egg cells are produced in the same individual.

In vertebrates like fish and frogs the union of sperm and ovum (*fertilization*) takes place outside the body. Egg and sperm cells are extruded into the water in which the animal lives and the sperm swim to and enter the eggs. For land vertebrates this method is, of course, not feasible. In these animals sperm cells must be introduced into the body of the female (copulation occurs), fertilization thus taking place internally.

Internal fertilization demands a more complicated organ system. This is certainly the case in animals which do not lay eggs but bear their young, and nourish them by their own milk (*mammals*—dog, rat, whale, man). This system we commonly think of as the *reproductive system.*

THE MALE REPRODUCTIVE SYSTEM

In the human male the reproductive system (Fig. 132) is constructed in a rather simple fashion. The male gonads are the *testes* which are found outside the body in a sac, the *scrotum.*

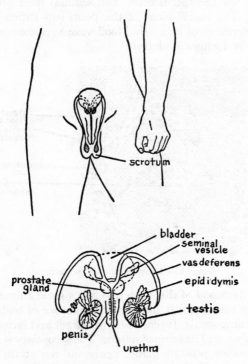

FIG. 132—The male reproductive system.

Internally, each testis consists of a number of *seminiferous tubules*, (Fig. 133) in which the sperm cells are produced and mature. Scattered among the elements of tubular tissue are other cells which comprise the *interstitial tissue.*

Normal Activities of the Male Reproductive System. The normal function of the testes is to produce mature sperm cells and the male sex hormone. The male sex hormone is responsible for the production of the bodily characteristics of the male and also for the maintenance of the accessory sexual organs. The latter are important in providing the proper medium for the sperm cells so that they may continue to live and be active in their passage out of the male and into the female during the process of copulation.

The mature sperm cells pass from the cavities of the tubules into the much-coiled *epididymis* where they are temporarily stored. At the times when copulation takes place, sperms pass up the *vas deferens* into the *urethra* which conducts them out through the *penis*. Along this route the *seminal vesicles, prostate*, and *bulbourethral glands* pour *seminal fluid* into the tubes. This fluid serves as a carrier and preservative medium for the sperm cells. The seminal fluid plus sperm is called *semen*. The *erectile tissue* of the penis can stiffen that organ by the engorgement of its many blood vessels. Semen is ejaculated from the penis during copulation.

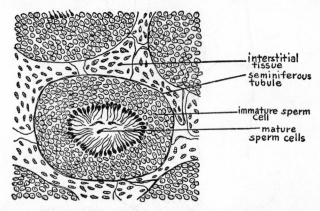

FIG. 133—Cross-section of the testis.

Effects of Removal of the Testes. When a male animal is *castrated* (has its testes removed), it undergoes a number of bodily changes besides becoming sterile. It tends to grow larger and fatter and to become less active, and its temper softens. The secondary sex structures —seminal vesicles, prostate gland, penis—do not attain maturity if castration is performed on an immature male; and they atrophy and lose their function in a castrated adult.

The *secondary sex characteristics* do not appear if the immature male is castrated. Castration of the young rooster, for instance, prevents the normal development of the comb, wattles, and plumage. In the immature human castrate, hair does not grow on the face and body as it normally would and the quality of the voice does not change. The castrated adult, however, retains his male characteristics.

The sex urge is abolished by castration in many animals. This does not hold for man.

The Testicular Hormone. Even if the sperm-producing cells have degenerated, an extract of the testis is potent in combatting the effects of castration. The secondary sex characteristics will appear and the secondary sex structures grow to maturity if testicular extract is administered to the immature castrate. Retrogressive changes can be prevented by injecting it into the adult castrate.

Evidently some part of the testis must produce a hormone and, since the seminiferous tissue does not, the interstitial tissue must be responsible. The testicular hormone has been found in blood and is excreted in the urine. It has been isolated from testicular extracts, crystallized, and even synthesized. Although a group of compounds is now known to possess at least some of the properties of the testicular hormone, the most potent of these (which has been isolated from the testis) is believed to be the hormone itself. This substance is called *testosterone*.

Pituitary Control of the Testis. Removal of the anterior lobe of the pituitary can prevent maturation of the testes and accessory sex structures or cause them to degenerate, depending upon their state of development at the time of the operation. It also abolishes the sex urge. Administration of anterior lobe extract to an animal in this condition reverses the effects of the operation.

The pituitary hormones (there are two) responsible for the maintenance of the testis and its hormone are the *gonadotropic hormones*. The first of these is necessary for *spermatogenesis*, the production of sperm cells. The second stimulates the interstitial tissue to produce testosterone.

We might also mention here that temperature is a factor in the control of spermatogenesis. The temperature within the scrotum is several degrees below body temperature. If the testes are kept at body temperature, the seminiferous tubules (but not the interstitial tissue) degenerate within a few days' time. It sometimes happens that the testes (which originate within the abdominal cavity) do not descend into the scrotal sac but remain in the body cavity. The seminiferous tubules do not develop in such cases, and the individual will be sterile if the condition is not corrected.

The Sequence of Sex Changes in the Male. Before *puberty* (sexual maturity) is attained, neither sperm cells nor the male sex hormone is produced. The onset of puberty is believed to be caused by the liberation of gonadotropic hormones. (What brings about the release of these hormones at that time is not known.) The first of these hormones stimulates the maturation of sperm cells, and the second, the production of testosterone. Testosterone in turn promotes the maturation of the secondary sex structures and brings on the secondary sex characteristics. The production of all three hormones can apparently continue to a ripe old age since old men have been reported to beget children. While testosterone may influence sex urge in man, it seems that the gonadotropic hormones are mainly responsible for its maintenance.

THE FEMALE REPRODUCTIVE SYSTEM

The female gonads are the *ovaries* (Fig. 134), the egg-producing organs. Eggs are released from the ovaries into the abdominal cavity but soon enter the *Fallopian tubes* or *oviducts*. The latter are extensions of the *uterus*, the organ in which fertilized eggs grow and remain until childbirth. The narrow neck (*cervix*) of the uterus projects into the *vagina* which opens into the *vestibule*.

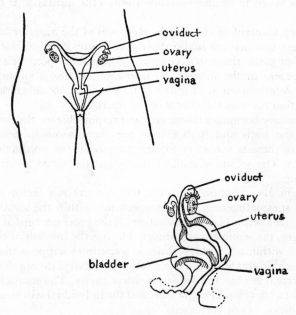

FIG. 134—The female reproductive system.

In the female mammals there are periodic changes during sexual life. Once puberty has been reached there are periodic *breeding* or *mating seasons* when the female is receptive to the male. During each mating season there occur one or more (depending on the species) *estrous cycles*, in which ovarian and uterine changes can be observed.

There is no one mating season in human beings, although statistics seem to show that fertility is greater in the spring. There is, however, a series of changes comparable to the estrous cycle of lower mammals. This is the *menstrual cycle*.

The testes of the male produce sperm continually but the ovaries of the female release eggs only periodically. An elaborate series of cyclical changes in the ovaries and uterus make the physiology of the human female much more intricate than that of the male.

Normal Activities of the Female Reproductive System. The ovaries produce mature egg cells and the female sex hormones. The latter are responsible for the maintenance of female bodily characteristics and of the accessory sexual organs. As we shall see, the ovarian hormones play a major role in the regulation of the sequence of changes that comprise the mentrual cycle. The menstrual *flow*, commonly considered to begin the cycle, actually denotes the completion of the cycle.

OVARIAN CHANGES. From birth until puberty the ovary contains a number of immature eggs. Each egg is surrounded by a number of smaller *follicle cells*. At the beginning of the first menstrual cycle, and at every one thereafter, some of the follicles begin to mature. Usually only one reaches maturity in each cycle, the others degenerating. The maturation of the follicle consists of a rather rapid growth in size and the accumulation of fluid within its cavity. At this stage the mature follicle looks like the representation in Fig. 135.

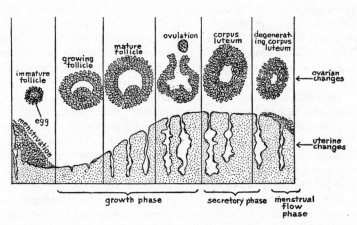

Fig. 135—Ovarian and uterine changes during the menstrual cycle. See text for complete description.

The mature follicle is now bulging out from the surface of the ovary. Some 10 days after the beginning of its development (or 10 days after the cessation of the menstrual flow), the follicle bursts and the ovum is extruded into the body cavity. This process is called *ovulation.* The cells of the ruptured follicle now undergo modifications and form a solid, yellow mass of cells—the *corpus luteum* (yellow body).

If no fertilization of the egg occurs at this time, the corpus luteum grows for the next 12–14 days but then degenerates. If sperm cells are introduced into the vagina at about the time of ovulation, they travel (by means of a whip-like motion of their "tails") through the uterus into the Fallopian tubes. This is usually the site of fertilization. If the egg is fertilized, it slowly passes down the oviduct into the uterus and beds itself in the uterine wall. Once fertilization has occurred, the corpus luteum remains and grows for almost the entire duration of pregnancy.

UTERINE CHANGES. Cyclical changes in the lining (*endometrium*) of the uterus accompany ovarian changes during a menstrual cycle. During the period of maturation of the follicle, the uterine lining grows much thicker because of multiplication of its cells (the *growth phase*). The mucous glands in it also grow larger and more blood vessels grow into it.

After ovulation occurs, there is an accentuation of these changes. The lining becomes even thicker; the glands and blood vessels proliferate even more. In addition the glands now elaborate a viscous, mucous secretion (the *secretory phase*). If fertilization has occurred meanwhile, the uterine lining remains in this state for the entire pregnancy period. If not, the top layers of the endometrium degenerate and are sloughed off. This entails some bleeding (the *menstrual flow phase*). The breakdown process is known as *menstruation*. The cells and blood pass to the exterior, the whole process lasting some four days. At the end of this time the uterine lining has returned to its initial state and is ready to repeat the cycle.

VAGINAL CHANGES. In some mammals (the mouse and rat, for example) marked cellular changes take place in the lining of the vagina during the estrous cycle. By making a smear of some surface cells and observing it under the microscope, it is possible to tell at what stage of the cycle the animal is. The human vagina also shows changes but no completely reliable method has been found which will permit determination of the phase of the cycle.

We should note that the lengths of the different phases of the menstrual cycle—10 days for the growth phase, 14 for the secretory phase, 4 for the menstrual flow phase—are averages based on the observations of cycles in a large number of women. It does not mean that every woman has a cycle of these proportions or even that her cycle runs 28 days. There is actually a great deal of individual variation, even variation in successive cycles in the same woman.

Effects of Removal of the Ovaries. *Spaying* or removal of the ovaries causes effects analogous to castration in the male. If it is performed before sexual maturity has been reached, spaying results in the failure of the secondary sex structures to mature and a tendency for the secondary sex characteristics (high-pitched voice, female distribution of hair and fat deposits) to become mannish.

Removal of the ovaries after puberty causes the cessation of the estrous or menstrual cycle, degeneration of the secondary sex structures, and increased adiposity. Spaying at any time will result in sterility, of course.

The Ovarian Hormones. The endocrine effects of spaying can be prevented or reversed by injection of an ovarian extract. The sexual cycle can be reinstituted in a spayed female by the administration of such extracts.

The ovary must then be still another endocrine organ. Confirmation of this came from the isolation of two hormones from ovarian extracts. These hormones have been crystallized and even synthesized.

THE FOLLICULAR HORMONE. The hormone secreted by the growing follicle of the ovary has been given the name *estradiol*. This hormone can induce the growth, vascularization, and glandularization of the uterine lining when administered to the spayed female. When administration stops, menstruation occurs. Estradiol is carried by the blood to the uterus and causes the changes occurring during the growth phase.

Many other chemical compounds, somewhat like estradiol in chemical structure, have been found to possess "estrogenic" activity. They are not as a rule as potent as estradiol.

THE LUTEAL HORMONE. *Progesterone*, the hormone secreted by the corpus luteum, is responsible for the secretory activity of the uterine glands and for the maintenance of the pregnant uterus. The spayed female to whom only estradiol has been administered will show the growth phase of the sexual cycle but will not exhibit the secretory phase unless progesterone administration follows that of estradiol. Estradiol must be given first, however, probably sensitizing the uterine lining to progesterone.

Pituitary-Ovarian Interrelationships. Gonadotropic hormones of the anterior lobe of the pituitary exert a very definite control over the ovaries and their hormones. Removal of the anterior lobe results in degeneration of the ovaries and accessory sex structures and loss of the sex urge. Administration of gonadotropic hormones can prevent or reverse these changes.

The hormone similar to the one which promotes spermatogenesis in the male is called the *follicle-stimulating hormone* (FSH) in the female; that similar to the one which stimulates secretion of testosterone in the male is called the *luteinizing hormone* (LH) in the female. A third hormone, *luteotropin*, may also be involved. Injection of FSH into a female animal whose anterior pituitary has been removed prevents the ovaries from degenerating and promotes growth of the follicles and secretion of estradiol; injection of LH is believed to cause ovulation and to initiate secretion of progesterone by the corpus luteum. Luteotropin (now believed identical with lactogenic hormone) maintains this luteal secretory activity.

Estradiol and progesterone, on the other hand, can inhibit the secretion of gonadotropic hormones by the pituitary. Injection of estradiol seems to inhibit the secretion of FSH particularly, and injection of progesterone seems to inhibit secretion of LH.

Pregnancy. During the first half of pregnancy the corpus luteum is essential. It maintains the uterine lining in its secretory phase and is necessary for the nesting of the fertilized egg in the uterine wall. It also prevents menstruation. If the corpus luteum is removed during this time, abortion occurs—the uterine lining sloughs off and the embryo is discharged from the uterus. After the first half of pregnancy, the corpus luteum is not essential; in fact, it degenerates in the late months of pregnancy.

The placenta (the structure, formed by the combination of uterine and embryonic tissue, through which the embryo is nourished) in the second half of pregnancy secretes hormones (both progesterone and estrogen) that contribute to the maintenance of the pregnant condition. A gonadotropic hormone, produced in early pregnancy by one of the membranes that surround the embryo, supplements the hormones of the pituitary gland. This embryonic hormone is found in the urine of a pregnant woman and provides a basis for pregnancy tests: if urine from a woman is administered to a rabbit or frog and causes ovarian changes in the test animal (because of the gonadotropic hormone present), pregnancy is indicated.

Lactation. The growth of the breasts at puberty is caused by the liberation of estradiol into the blood. Their subsequent greater development in premenstrual periods and especially during pregnancy is due to the cooperative action of progesterone. The actual secretion of milk is inhibited rather than fostered by the ovarian hormones.

During pregnancy the anterior lobe of the pituitary secretes a *lactogenic hormone* which stimulates the production of milk by the mammary glands. It is quite clear that actual release of milk is brought about by the reflex effects upon the pituitary which are initiated by suckling. It is not completely certain that the lactogenic hormone is responsible both for production and for release of milk. There is some evidence that pitocin (see section on the posterior pituitary) may be the agent involved in the release of milk.

The Menopause and Menstrual Disorders. Sometime between the ages of 42 and 52 the female sexual cycle ends. The ovaries begin to atrophy and, subsequently, degenerative changes take place in the uterus, vagina, breasts, etc. Sterility then ensues. Quite frequently there are outward signs of changes in hormonal balance—hot flushes, sweating, and psychic symptoms. In some women this "change of life" is a difficult period. Attempts to bring about a more gradual change by the administration of ovarian hormones have been successful in some cases, but many failures have been reported.

Treatment of menstrual disorders in younger women is not invariably successful. Scanty, painful, excessive, or absent menstrual flow is not uncommon. The difficulty in treatment probably lies in the fact that administration of hormones does not faithfully imitate the cyclical changes in hormone levels that occur normally.

The Sequence of Events in the Female Sex Cycle. At the onset of puberty the FSH of the pituitary stimulates the growth of ovarian follicles and secretion of estradiol. Estradiol in turn promotes the development of secondary sex structures and characteristics. It also causes the growth phase of the uterine lining. In each menstrual cycle when the concentration of estradiol in the blood rises to a high enough level, FSH is inhibited and the pituitary is stimulated to secrete LH. LH causes ovulation to occur and initiates growth of the corpus luteum and its secretion of progesterone. Luteotropin maintains the luteal activity. Progesterone turns the sensitized endometrium into a mucus-secreting tissue.

When the level of progesterone reaches a certain height, secretion of LH is inhibited. If no egg is fertilized, the corpus luteum degenerates and the concentrations of estradiol and progesterone fall rather sharply. This brings on menstruation. If an egg is fertilized, the corpus luteum remains throughout most of pregnancy and inhibits the usual menstrual cycles (there are occasional exceptions to this). In the later stages of pregnancy, after degeneration of the corpus luteum, the placenta secretes estrogen and progesterone. Meanwhile, estradiol and progesterone are stimulating the development of the mammary glands and, later, lactogenic hormone stimulates milk production.

When pregnancy reaches its term, the levels of progesterone and estradiol again drop sharply, and labor begins. After birth, some hormone of the pituitary stimulates the release of milk.

It is possible that the menopause is also caused by a sharp fall in estrogen and progesterone levels at this later time.

With the serious concern about the "population explosion," it is pertinent to say a few words about *birth-control* or *contraceptive* pills. These are becoming used more and more widely, and, apparently, more effectively. Such pills contain a progesterone-like compound, and produce their contraceptive action by inhibiting the release of LH (and, possibly, other pituitary hormones); the net result is the prevention of ovulation.

CHAPTER XIII

Nutrition

WE ARE DELUGED daily with inducements to eat this, not that, eat what we want but take this afterwards, and so on. Many of us are understandably less than certain as to the definition and elements of a proper diet. We cannot expect to plumb the science of nutrition very deeply in these few pages. What we may get from them is some concept of a balanced and adequate diet and some reason for including the various important constituents.

Fifty years ago nutrition experts were thinking mainly in terms of a diet furnishing sufficient calories (units of heat) and thought it did not matter too greatly what foodstuffs supplied the caloric needs. Some years later vitamins were considered of primary importance. Recently much has been said and written about the dangers of excess weight, and we are concerned with such things as the effect of high cholesterol and of saturated fats in the diet, and the advantages of high protein diets. All of these trends, though including useful information, represent emphasis upon one aspect of diet at the expense of others. A sounder basis on which to construct a good diet is to grant each important group of nutrients its proper place and proportion. The number of calories that the diet will supply must also be taken into consideration.

THE SIX CLASSES OF NUTRIENTS

We recognize six important classes of nutrients—carbohydrates, fats, proteins, water, minerals, and vitamins.

Carbohydrates. Starches and sugars constitute the larger part of most of our diets and they rightly should. Carbohydrates are more easily and more quickly digested than fats or proteins and are our primary source of energy. In times of stress the carbohydrate reserves of the body (seldom very large) are the first to be called upon and depleted. Although other considerations come first when we are thinking in terms of health, it should not be overlooked that foods rich in carbohydrate are generally less expensive than protein- or fat-rich foods. In many respects, then, more carbohydrates should be eaten than other nutrients.

Good sources of starch are the grains (corn, wheat, rice, etc.) and the products derived from them (bread, cereals, etc.) as well as vegetables like potatoes and fruits like bananas. Sugars are found especially in fruits, berries, beets and some other vegetables, cane sugar itself, and "sweets."

Fats. Although a richer source of energy than carbohydrates (weight for weight, fat provides more than twice as many calories as carbohydrate), fats are digested more slowly and with more difficulty than other foodstuffs. Too much fat in a meal can slow digestion of other foodstuffs by coating them. In addition, fat specifically inhibits gastric motility and secretion.

But fats are essential as secondary sources of energy and can be stored in many body regions for future use. To a certain extent fats or related substances are also necessary as parts of the cellular and body framework. Several of the fatty acids have been reported essential for growth in some mammals, and quite probably they are necessary for growth and maintenance in man, too. Fats are also important as the carriers of certain vitamins (the fat-soluble group).

Dairy products (butter, milk, etc.) are rich in fats. A certain amount of fat can be obtained from vegetables and from animal foods (meat, poultry, fish, lard, etc.). Nuts are also good sources.

Proteins. Not ordinarily necessary as a fuel substance, proteins can, when oxidized, liberate as much energy as carbohydrates. They are of primary importance as the stuff of which protoplasm is made, for growth and repair of tissues.

In this respect not all proteins in foods are of the same quality and of the same value to the body. The differences in value among proteins depend upon the amino acids of which they consist. Proteins, as we have noted, are composed of amino acids. Although there are only some twenty-odd amino acids, a multiplicity of proteins can be formed from them. Some proteins have all the known amino acids in their make-up, others have not. Two proteins having the same kinds of amino acids in their molecules can differ greatly from one another by virtue of the amount of each amino acid contained and the arrangement of the amino acid groups within the molecules.

From the nutritional viewpoint the number of different amino acids, and specifically which amino acids, determine the value of a protein in the diet. In the early part of this century feeding experiments showed that mice receiving *zein*, the protein of corn, as the only source of protein in the diet were very much stunted in growth (Fig. 136). *Gelatin*, if the only protein in the diet, causes similar effects. Knowing that some amino acids were not present in these proteins, the investigators now added the missing amino acids to the diet of the stunted animals. Growth was reinstituted immediately.

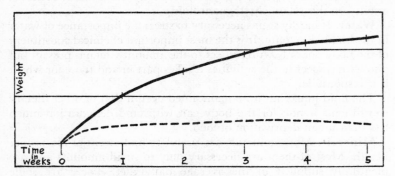

Fig. 136—The increase in weight of mice on a diet containing incomplete proteins (— — —) contrasted with that of mice on a well-balanced diet (———).

Experiments of this kind have revealed that there are nine or ten amino acids which must be present in the diet for growth and maintenance of tissue. These are the *essential* amino acids, those which cannot be synthesized in the body. All other amino acids can be formed by the body cells.

Proteins are classified, for dietary purposes, with respect to their content of essential amino acids. Those that contain the essential amino acids are called *complete* proteins; those that do not, *incomplete* proteins. Using this classification as their criterion, scientists have been able to show that the best sources of protein are milk and eggs. Offhand we should expect that these would be the most adequate because the food material of eggs is the source of nourishment for embryos until they hatch and that of milk is the immediate food for mammalian infants after birth.

Other animal proteins, such as in liver, meat, and fish, are next most valuable, and then come the vegetable proteins. Although mentioned last, vegetables should not be looked upon as poor sources of protein. An adequate protein intake can be maintained on a vegetarian diet, but greater amounts and varieties of such proteins must be eaten to supply the necessary quantities of essential amino acids.

Aside from their value as tissue builders, proteins are important as the material of which enzymes and some hormones are constructed.

In addition to the absence of growth and maintenance, protein insufficiency may show up in *nutritional edema*. A severe lack of dietary protein results in depletion of the plasma proteins and consequent lowering of the osmotic pressure of the blood. Not as much water can be held in the blood under these conditions, and a great deal of it leaves the blood stream. It accumulates in the tissue spaces and causes a swelling, especially of the lower regions of the body (effect of gravity on this relatively stagnant fluid).

Water. It hardly seems necessary to stress the importance of water in the bodily economy. It is the most important chemical constituent of the body not only with respect to the amount which is present but also with respect to the activities it takes part in and those for which it is responsible.

The fluid intake must be maintained even if that of other dietary constituents is not, for the body can withstand dehydration much less than it can deprivation of food.

Minerals. Many minerals are useful to and essential for proper health. Most of them are necessary only in small amounts and are plentifully supplied in the average daily diet. There are some minerals that do have to be given more attention, however.

Sodium, potassium, and *calcium* salts are, as we know, necessary in the proper proportions to preserve a suitable environment for the body cells in general and are of especial importance in the preservation of irritability of muscle and nerve.

Chlorine is the mineral most often associated with sodium, potassium, and calcium to form the essential salts of the blood and body fluids. It is also a constituent of the hydrochloric acid in gastric juice.

Calcium has some specific functions of its own which make it doubly important. It is, of course, an essential element in bone and thus is necessary for bone growth. It is essential also for the coagulation of blood, the coagulation of milk by rennin, the beating of the heart, and transmission of impulses across the synapses in certain parts of the nervous system. Since it is present in only small amounts in most foods, care should be taken to get the daily minimum requirement in the diet. This is especially true of growing children but it applies to all of us. Milk is probably the best source of calcium. Other good sources are cheese and a variety of green vegetables and vegetable greens.

Iron is another very important mineral to which special dietary attention should be paid. Hemoglobin and certain intracellular enzymes will not be formed in the proper amounts if iron is lacking. Liver, oysters, greens, kidneys, eggs, potatoes, and beef are good sources of iron.

Phosphorus is an important constituent of bone. Phosphates are vital for many metabolic activities and as buffers in body fluids. Foods like wheat, milk, meat, beans, and nuts are rich in phosphorus.

Sulphur is an important constituent of some amino acids and enzymes. It is usually ingested in proteins of which it is a part. *Iodine* is necessary for the formation of the thyroid hormone. In regions where the soil and water contain adequate amounts of it, the ordinary diet will contain sufficient quantities. Otherwise, iodized salt should be used. *Copper* is needed in very small amounts as a catalyst in the formation of hemoglobin. Its dietary supply is almost always adequate. Magnesium, manganese, molybdenum, cobalt, and zinc are also required in trace amounts. The first three of these are used as *coenzymes*, factors necessary for the completion of some enzymic reactions. Magnesium, additionally, seems a necessary ion in body fluids. Cobalt is a part of the molecule of vitamin B_{12}, and zinc is probably a part of the insulin molecule.

Vitamins. Certain diseases such as beri-beri, scurvy, and pellagra have been known for many years. It was not until the 1890's, however, that men began to suspect their cause. Feeding animals on purified proteins, carbohydrates, and fats, they found that in the course of time the animals developed symptoms very like those of these diseases; and further experiment established that the above ailments were in fact *deficiency diseases*, due to the lack of certain essential dietary substances in addition to the three principal nutrients. Nowadays, quite a number of these accessory substances—named *vitamins*—are known, and we have learned enough about their chemistry to be able to crystallize and synthesize many of them so that they are available as pure compounds.

In almost no case are we quite sure of a vitamin's mechanism of action. Some vitamins appear to function as parts of essential enzyme systems within the body. The fact that vitamins are needed in only very small amounts is, perhaps, presumptive evidence that they act as catalysts in the body.

As most vitamins are distributed fairly widely in foods, a balanced diet should insure an ample supply of them. When, for economic reasons or lack of information, a good diet is not provided, then deficiency diseases crop up. (It appears that an American diet, even a "good" one, may tend to be deficient in the B vitamins.)

Vitamins since their discovery have been divided into *fat-soluble* and *water-soluble* categories. The fat-soluble vitamins—vitamins A, D, E, and K—have in common the fact that all can be stored in fatty accumulations in cells, and hence can build up in the body. The vitamins that are soluble in water—the B vitamins and vitamin C—are, if taken in excess, more easily carried off in the urine, and hence are not stored in any appreciable amounts.

VITAMIN A. Yellow vegetables (carrots, sweet potatoes, etc.), some greens, butter, cheese, and cream are excellent sources of *vitamin A*. Lack of this vitamin causes night blindness, greatly increased susceptibility to infections, failure to gain weight, drying up of tear and cutaneous gland secretions with thickening of epithelial surfaces and, perhaps, degenerative changes in the nervous system.

Visual purple in the rods of the retina is bleached by light to another substance, visual yellow. Vitamin A is an integral part of the latter. Deficiency of the vitamin interferes with the regeneration of visual purple and brings on the inability to see normally in dim light. The infections resulting from lack of the vitamin are very often localized in the eyes and can lead to blindness if unchecked.

VITAMIN D. Absence or great lack of *vitamin D* results in rickets and decay of the teeth. Vitamin D is essential for the proper calcification of bone. In its absence bones become soft, weak, and deformed. In rickets the leg bones, for instance, are unable to support the body weight adequately and tend to become bowed.

Unlike most vitamins, vitamin D does not have a very wide distribution. The best sources are fish liver oils (especially halibut and cod liver oils), some fish, meat, and eggs. The vitamin is, however, formed by irradiation of a fat-like substance in the skin with ultraviolet rays. Exposure to the sunlight, then, enables vitamin D to be formed and stored in the body for use when needed. In winter when there is comparatively little sunlight in some places, it is especially important to supplement the diet of infants and growing children with some good source of vitamin D.

VITAMIN E. The "anti-sterility" vitamin is *vitamin E*. Its absence causes sterility in rats and its administration appears to favor fertility in some other mammals. There is no conclusive evidence for any deficiency symptoms in man due to lack of this vitamin; nor has it been found effective in curing human sterility. It may be necessary for proper muscular function. It is found especially in green vegetables (lettuce, peas, etc.) and in wheat germ oil.

VITAMIN K. The absence of vitamin K lengthens the coagulation time of blood and provokes a tendency to bleed easily. The vitamin is essential to the liver's manufacture of prothrombin which, in turn, is essential for blood clotting. The vitamin K concentration tends to be low in newborn infants, a fact which has been used to explain a number of cases of hemorrhagic disease of the newborn. Usually, nowadays, women are given vitamin K injections late in pregnancy to insure better levels in the fetus. This *anti-hemorrhagic* or *coagulation* vitamin is found especially in green vegetable leaves.

THE B VITAMINS. A number of compounds have been isolated which, although not closely related chemically, have in common two things: they are widely distributed in foods (but not in large amounts in any one food) and they serve as coenzymes (factors necessary for enzyme functioning) in a number of enzyme systems. Not all of the B vitamins have been conclusively demonstrated to be dietary essentials for man (each has been so demonstrated for other organisms) but it is rather probable that most, if not all, are important in human metabolism.

The absence of *thiamine* (vitamin B_1) results in the disease, *beriberi*. Severe thiamine deficiency is marked by progressive paralysis of peripheral nerves, muscular incoördination, degeneration of parts of the central nervous system, cardiac disability, and edema. If untreated, the disease is fatal. In countries where the staple food is polished rice (thiamine is present in the coats of rice grains and not in the grain itself), frequent cases appear. Thiamine deficiency is also accompanied by loss of appetite and poor digestion, which can lead to stunted growth. Slight thiamine deficiencies (sometimes occurring in supposedly good diets) may result in "nervousness and irritability." Lean meats, peas, beans, grains, and yeast are the best sources of this vitamin.

Severe *niacin* (or *nicotinic acid*—not the same as nicotine) deficiency causes *pellagra*. Symptoms include skin disorders, digestive disturbances, degeneration of nervous tissue, and mental aberrations. Insanity and death can occur. Niacin is most abundant in liver, lean meats, milk, yeast, eggs, and green vegetables. In past years, pellagra was common among the poor in Europe and southern United States whose diets were often deficient in the above-mentioned foods.

Riboflavin (*vitamin B_2*) is present especially in liver, eggs, leafy vegetables, yeast, fruits, and milk. Its deficiency can result in disturbances of skin and mucous membranes and of the eyes.

Other vitamins in the B "complex" include *pantothenic acid, pyridoxine, folic acid,* and *vitamin B_{12}*. The two former are known as parts of enzyme systems and the two latter as anemia preventatives. It is probable that well-balanced diets contain adequate amounts of these vitamins in most cases, but more study of dietary requirements is needed to substantiate this belief.

VITAMIN C. Scurvy is the deficiency disease resulting from lack of *vitamin C*, or *ascorbic acid*. In the past it has most often occurred during long sea voyages, or similar situations in which men have been deprived of fresh fruits and vegetables. Vitamin C is found especially in fresh vegetables (mostly green ones) and citrus fruits (oranges, grapefruit, limes), and tomatoes.

Scurvy is symptomatized by hemorrhages in mucous membranes, subcutaneous tissues and muscles (the gums are especially affected), painful bones and joints, weakness and emaciation. Vitamin C is essential for the normal maintenance of capillary walls; in its absence they become fragile and rupture easily.

A BALANCED DIET

It is important to get the proper amount of calories from your daily diet. You should eat enough food to furnish the energy needed for your particular mode of living. In this respect it is important not to waste protein by using it as an energy-producing foodstuff. Carbohydrates and fats are more easily used as fuels and, if they are in proper amounts in the diet, will spare protein for its more specific uses. It is difficult to assess any strict proportions to the three major foodstuffs, for their amounts should vary according to the conditions in the individual. For the average diet of a man doing moderate work, about 60 percent of the calories should be derived from carbohydrates, 25 from fat, and 15 from protein. These proportions should satisfy both fuel and building needs.

You will assure yourselves of a balanced diet if representatives of the following groups of foods are included on your daily menu: milk; water or liquid in some form; eggs; green vegetables; yellow vegetables; meat, fish, cheese, beans; potatoes, whole grain products; fruits (especially citrus); butter and other fats.

Adherence to such a diet will supply the vitamins, minerals, and proteins needed as well as sufficient calories and will allow for variety. Other items can be added which would not necessarily fall into any one of these categories, but they should not be included as substitutes, nor at the expense of one or more of the basic groups.

DIFFERENCES IN DIETS

There are so many different kinds of foods that a really balanced diet can be planned for everyone, even for those with fussy tastes.

Sometimes it is not only tastes that must be taken into consideration. It is quite clear, for instance, that men doing hard physical work need more calories than those leading sedentary lives. More protein, too, would be indicated for the former because their exertions will cause greater destruction of tissue which will need to be replaced.

Pregnant women need extra amounts of calcium and iron; the vitamin D content of the infant's diet requires special attention.

For many conditions there is a suitable diet, and various ones are prescribed for one ailment or another. Such prescriptions should be left in the hands of physicians and should not be self-inflicted. This holds true especially for reducing diets. There are good ways of losing weight without resorting to starvation diets, omitting certain essentials, or basing one's diet exclusively on one class of nutrients. In any case, it is far better to employ common sense and see a reliable physician than to risk illness.

CHAPTER XIV

Metabolism

THE total energy of the universe remains constant. It is neither being added to nor subtracted from at any moment. Do you wonder then how "activity" goes on? If you think of energy in terms of the "capacity for performing work," you can see that this state of affairs need not lead to a deadlock at all. Existent energy can perform work in many different ways and, since it cannot be destroyed, is always a potential source of more work, though perhaps of a different nature. Energy is constantly being converted from one form to another—chemical to mechanical, mechanical to electrical, electrical to thermal, chemical to electrical, and so on. And all these forms must come from pre-existent energy.

These energy relationships apply to living as well as non-living bodies. We know, for instance, that the source of our energy is the food we eat which, in turn, derives its energy from the sun directly or indirectly. Appropriate chemical action changes this food energy into forms available to our body cells.

METABOLISM AND BODY ENERGY

Each cell is a "laboratory" containing the chemical "equipment" needed to release energy from food by breaking it down to smaller, simpler substances. The chemical energy so released is converted into all the other forms in which it manifests itself in living activities and also is used to build up the complex protoplasm of living matter. *Metabolism* is, then, a composite of chemical reactions which tear down and release energy (*catabolism*) and those which build up and store energy (*anabolism*).

Total Heat Production by the Body. The lowest form of energy is *heat*. All of the other forms of energy can be converted into heat, but heat—so far as we know—cannot be reconverted to other forms. We can use heat but cannot change it into anything else.

At the end of the 18th century it was first recognized that the heat given off by the body was the result of combustion of substances within the body in the presence of oxygen. The basic reactions in a burning candle and an animal body were seen to be similar. Each used up oxygen in burning carbon compounds with the resultant liberation of carbon dioxide, water, and heat.

During the 19th century, scientists found quantitative evidence that the animal body liberated as much energy in one way or another as it received in the form of food. This was determined by placing men as well as other animals in chambers called *calorimeters* and measuring their heat output from a given amount of food. Calorimeters are chambers which are so well insulated that no heat can be lost from them. In the walls of the chamber are tubes through which water circulates. This water absorbs the heat liberated, and its temperature is measured as it enters and leaves the pipes. Knowing the difference in temperature and the amount of water in the pipes, you can calculate the amount of heat taken up by the water.

Comparing the heat produced by the body after food intake with the heat liberated by burning the same amount and kind of food outside the body, the heat levels were so nearly equal as to be considered the same (the slight difference is accounted for by the small errors inherent in the experimental method). Thus we can conclude that food oxidized completely by the body yields as much heat as it would when burned outside the body.

There are certain checks that have to be made. It was found that carbohydrates and fats yield the same amount of heat when burned in or outside the body. Proteins, however, yielded less in the body than outside. The reason for this was soon discovered. In the body, protein is not completely oxidized, while its burning outside goes to completion. But, if the incomplete products of its oxidation are burned separately and the heat liberated added to that liberated by its partial oxidation in the body, the sum is found to equal that produced when it is completely oxidized outside the body.

You may wonder how these scientists knew that the body oxidized only the food eaten and not other foodstuffs already present in the body. That could be a source of serious error. It can be checked by other analyses, however.

There is an unvarying proportion of nitrogen in proteins and the nitrogenous portion of the protein molecule is the part not oxidized in the body. It is instead excreted in the urine (urea is the main waste product of protein metabolism). By collecting all the urine excreted by the subject during the test period and analyzing its nitrogen content, the amount of protein that would have to be broken down to yield that much nitrogen can be calculated.

Knowing the amount of protein oxidized, we next calculate how much oxygen will be needed for it, and how much carbon dioxide produced. Our second analysis is to measure the oxygen consumption and carbon dioxide production of the subject during the test period. Taking these total values for all three foodstuffs, we subtract the amounts calculated for the oxidation of protein and are left with the oxygen and carbon dioxide values for the sum of carbohydrate and fat oxidations.

How can we determine how much of each has been oxidized? There is no distinctive end product for them since both are changed to carbon dioxide and water. A knowledge of the chemistry of the reactions involved has shown that in carbohydrate oxidation there is always as much carbon dioxide produced as oxygen consumed. The ratio of oxygen to carbon dioxide in this case is, then, 1:1. For fat, more oxygen is consumed than carbon dioxide produced, in the constant ratio of 10:7. If, after subtracting the values for protein as above, we are left with amounts of oxygen and carbon dioxide in one of these ratios, then only carbohydrate or fat has been oxidized. If the ratio were found to be 10:9, then two-thirds of the totals must refer to carbohydrate oxidation and one-third to fat. And from the amounts of oxygen and carbon dioxide we can then calculate how much carbohydrate and fat were oxidized. We can determine, therefore, the amount of each foodstuff that has been oxidized and check it against the amounts given to the subject.

To establish the facts about total heat production it was necessary to measure very directly the heat produced. But, as you can imagine, a calorimeter capable of housing a man comfortably is a large, cumbersome, and very expensive piece of apparatus. In most cases we now measure heat production indirectly, taking advantage of the constant relationship of oxygen consumption to heat production. Measuring oxygen consumption is a much easier, more rapid, and convenient method. The calculations from oxygen consumption to heat production have been standardized and are easily made.

The Basal Metabolic Rate. *Total heat production* is taken as an index of *total metabolism*. This can vary so much in the same individual at different times because of changing circumstances (difficult to measure quickly and simply) that it gives us no clear impression of the state of his metabolism. For this reason it is customary to test the *basal metabolic rate* (B.M.R.) of an individual.

The B.M.R. is the heat production of a person under standard conditions which reduce activity to a minimum. The usual method of measurement is the determination of oxygen consumption over a given period of time. The subject is tested early in the morning, when he has not eaten since dinner the night before, has not exercised strenuously during the preceding twenty-four hours, and has lain at rest for half an hour before the test in a room at comfortable temperature. In this way an attempt is made to get as complete muscular and mental relaxation and digestive tranquillity as is possible. Any heat produced by the body is then due to the basic metabolic processes of the cells and the activities of organs that are necessary for life.

We should expect a larger, heavier person to produce more heat than a smaller, lighter one. He does. When we calculate the heat production per unit of weight, though, we find that the heavier person generates less heat per unit than the lighter. Calculating the heat production per unit of surface area of the body, however, we find that we get a figure which is surprisingly constant for all individuals. And not only is this true for all human beings, but it applies to a great number of warm-blooded animals. A mouse and a man have approximately the same heat production per unit of surface area. This means, of course, that per unit of body weight the mouse has a much greater B.M.R. and a more active metabolism of its cells than has a man.

The smaller an animal is, the greater its surface area in proportion to its size. This means that the small animal has more surface proportionately from which heat can be lost to the environment. Since the body temperature of warm-blooded animals is kept at a constant level, a small animal must produce more heat per cellular unit to keep pace with its greater heat loss.

The average surface area is about 1.6 square meters for adult women and 1.8 for adult men. The basal heat production ranges from 1200 to 1800 Calories per day (a Calorie is the quantity of heat required to raise the temperature of one liter of water 1° centigrade). For a basal heat production of 1800 Calories and a surface area of 1.8 square meters the B.M.R. would be 1000 Cal./sq. m. It is customary to express the B.M.R. in per cent of normal (based on the averages taken on a large number of people). Thus, if the average for an individual of a certain age who has 1.8 sq. m. of surface area is 1000 Cal./sq. m., then a person of those qualifications whose heat production is 950 Cal./sq. m. would have a B.M.R. of − 5%. In practice, a B.M.R. within the limits of + and − 10% is considered to be normal.

Factors Influencing Heat Production. There are certain factors which influence a given individual's basic metabolic rate, and other factors which affect his total heat production or total metabolism.

INFLUENCES ON B.M.R. The B.M.R. is influenced by a number of factors. It decreases progressively with age. It is somewhat lower in women than in men. There are varying racial differences: Eskimos have a higher rate than whites, and some Oriental peoples have a lower rate than Occidentals. People who engage in hard physical work generally have a higher rate than those leading a sedentary life. Pregnant women show an increase after the sixth or seventh month of pregnancy. At this time the weight of the fetus appreciably increases the weight of the mother and the B.M.R. is the sum of the mother's and that of the fetus.

In some abnormal or pathological conditions the B.M.R. is lowered or raised. Hypothyroidism and starvation decrease it. Hyperthyroidism and fever increase it. For every additional degree of temperature above normal the B.M.R. rises some 5–7 per cent. We see in this another example of a rise in temperature speeding up chemical reactions—the metabolic reactions in the cells are accelerated during feverish states.

INFLUENCES ON TOTAL HEAT PRODUCTION. Engaging in any activity involving the slightest muscular effort raises the *total heat production*. In moderate exercise the increase may amount to a 25–60 per cent jump over the B.M.R. Strenuous exercise may cause as much as a 1500 per cent increase above the basal level.

Mental activity, strangely enough (the brain contributes about 10 per cent of the B.M.R.), involves almost no extra heat production. It has been said that "extra Calories needed for one hour of intense mental effort would be completely met by the eating of—one-half of one salted peanut."

During quiet sleep there is less heat produced than at any other time. Here is the true "basal metabolism," for relaxation of muscles is at its maximum. We cannot, however, use heat production during sleep as a standard index because the depth of sleep, and muscular relaxation along with it, varies considerably and cannot be controlled as the standard conditions for the B.M.R. test can.

Environmental temperature can affect the total heat production. When the surrounding temperature is uncomfortably low, we begin to shiver. The involuntary muscular contractions which constitute shivering will increase the total heat production of the body. If the temperature of the air is warmer than body temperature, heat production may or may not be changed.

The *specific dynamic action* of foods raises the total heat production. When foods are eaten, it is found that the heat production rises more than can be accounted for on the basis of their heat values. This is especially true of protein, less so for carbohydrate and fat. The effect lasts for 12 to 18 hours after the food is ingested. It is believed that some products formed in the metabolic breakdown of foodstuffs directly stimulate the metabolism of cells and extra heat is evolved.

THE DISPOSITION OF FOODSTUFFS
IN THE BODY

The burning of carbohydrate outside the body results in the formation of carbon dioxide, water, and the liberation of 4 Calories of heat per gram. The end products of fat oxidation are the same except that 9 Calories of heat are liberated from each gram. Protein oxidation results in the formation of some nitrogen-containing products as well as carbon dioxide and water and 5 Calories of heat per gram.

Let us see what happens to these in the body. For direct liberation of energy we will not have to consider water, minerals, and vitamins. They do not contribute appreciable numbers of calories directly. They do, of course, have much to do with the proper metabolism of the energy-yielding and protoplasm-producing foodstuffs.

The Liberation of Energy. When a gram of carbohydrate is oxidized completely in the body, the same end products result, and, as outside the body, 4 Calories of heat are liberated. Thus,

$$C_6H_{12}O_6 + 6O_2 \rightarrow 6CO_2 + 6H_2O + 4 \text{ Cal. of heat}$$
(glucose)

A gram of fat similarly oxidized will also yield the same products and amount of heat as it does outside the body:

$$2C_{57}H_{110}O_6 + 163O_2 \rightarrow 114CO_2 + 110H_2O + 9 \text{ Cal. of heat}$$
(a common fat)

Proteins when oxidized in the body are not completely burned. The nitrogenous parts of their molecules are first removed and the remainder (largely consisting of carbon, hydrogen, and oxygen) is then oxidized. Some of the end products of oxidation within the body differ from those formed when protein is burned outside the body, and only 4 Calories of heat result as compared with 5 outside.

The potential energy stored in the foodstuff molecules is liberated by oxidation as chemical energy which can be used as such or subsequently converted to mechanical or electrical energy. All forms of energy are eventually turned into heat.

Metabolism in Cells. Looking at the equations for the oxidation of glucose and fat, you might readily think that these substances are directly broken down to carbon dioxide and water. Such is not the case. Each equation represents an over-all summary of the many reactions involved in producing these end results. As previously indicated, in Chapter IX for example, the complete oxidation of glycogen (a carbohydrate) is accomplished by some twenty chemical reactions, each of which is controlled by a different enzyme.

Is this an unnecessarily complicated sequence of events? Not really, difficult though it has been for scientists to unravel the complex chemistry of the cell. Now that a number of the pieces are beginning to fall into place and a pattern is emerging, we can comprehend the many advantages and economies of this fundamental biochemistry.

Each cell in the body receives via the blood its basic nutrient materials—water, vitamins, minerals, glucose, fats and fat-like compounds, and amino acids—and also oxygen. In addition, the cell receives some regulatory chemicals (hormones, for example). Each cell thus has a full complement of the structures and enzymes necessary for its operation (see Chapter XV). When the nutrients enter a cell, they become—so to speak—part of a metabolic "pool" of materials to be used as the conditions within the cell dictate at a particular moment.

The diagrammatic sequence of reactions shown below appears to be fundamentally similar in all our cells (with slight exceptions) and in the cells of most living things. As such, it represents a striking example of a fundamental similarity in living material, no matter what its source.

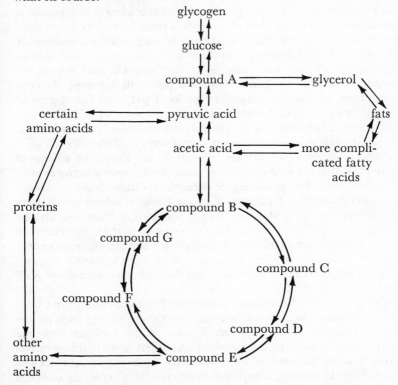

While more complex than the sequence of reactions shown in Chapter IX, the above diagram is still a simplified version of cell chemistry. Nevertheless, it aids in visualizing some of the following important aspects of cellular metabolism:

1) Starting with any one of the three major foodstuffs, a cell can synthesize either of the other two (carbohydrate to fat, fat to protein, etc.). There are certain qualifications to the preceding statement. Our cells cannot synthesize certain amino acids, and these therefore must be supplied in the diet (see Chapter XIII). For other amino acids there must be a source of nitrogen present; and since neither pyruvic acid nor compound E contains nitrogen, the nitrogen must be supplied from some compound not indicated in the diagram. Moreover, although all directions indicated in the diagram are possible, not all reactions occur with equal ease in the cell; for example, fats do not convert to carbohydrate or to protein as readily as proteins or carbohydrates convert to fat (this is one reason for difficulty in losing weight).

2) The reactions are reversible. The direction in which any reaction will proceed at a given moment will depend on the prevailing local conditions. For example, if the concentration of compound A is relatively high and that of glycerol is proportionately lower than the concentrations of glucose and pyruvic acid, more of compound A would tend to go into glycerol formation than into pyruvic acid or glucose formation. Also influencing the direction and rate of reactions would be the concentration of pertinent enzymes, the concentration of enzyme cofactors, the local pH, and the degree of competition for a particular compound. As you can see, the above set of reactions permits both synthesis and breakdown of compounds.

3) Any one reaction represents a relatively small chemical change. If you remember that the above diagram is a simplified scheme of what are actually many more reactions, this statement becomes even more obvious. This small degree of chemical change is advantageous in several important respects. For one thing, it allows much more flexibility in shifting the directions of reactions as conditions change from moment to moment. Another reason is that, especially in catabolism, a small chemical change is valuable because energy which is released in small amounts can be more efficiently trapped by the cell (that is, incorporated into the high-energy bonds of ATP —see Chapter IX).

4) The circle of reactions, compound B through compound G at the bottom of the above scheme, releases more energy than all the other reactions taken together. Known as the *Krebs* or *citric acid cycle* (since citric acid is formed in its earliest stage), this series of reactions as pictured above ordinarily proceeds in a clockwise direction. In essence, compound B reacts with a molecule of acetic

acid so that in the course of one rotation the acetic acid molecule is in gradual stages completely oxidized to carbon dioxide and water; compound B is re-formed, accepts another molecule of acetic acid, and the cycle begins again.

The crucial events during this cycle are the release, at certain points, of hydrogen atoms which are then transferred through a series of compounds (not shown) to oxygen, forming molecules of water. For every two hydrogen atoms so transferred, enough energy is captured to form three molecules of ATP from ADP. The Krebs cycle plus the hydrogen transfer system is the major source of energy for our cells. Since cells do not create large supplies of stored ATP, these reactions must be going on continuously in order to replenish ATP stores.

This is the best explanation we can give for our constant need of oxygen. Anything that prevents adequate oxygen supply to or use by the cells will soon bring all of the chemical machinery to a halt because of insufficient utilizable energy (which is primarily stored in the energy-rich bonds of ATP). For example, cyanide is a deadly poison because it inactivates a vital enzyme in the hydrogen transfer system, preventing the transfer of hydrogen to oxygen; all of the chemical reactions "back up," one after another, and soon stop.

We can point out, with reference to the above scheme, the importance of regular daily intake of fuel and accessory substances in the diet. Insufficient vitamin or mineral supplies can prevent certain reactions from occurring (for example, lack of thiamine seriously interferes with the reaction pyruvic acid to acetic acid; pyruvic acid levels rise considerably, since it cannot be properly utilized, with consequences outlined in Chapter XIII). Insufficient fuel material can obviously be detrimental. Cells do not "care," so to speak, what the source of the fuel is; if insufficient supplies arrive through the blood, cells will draw upon their stored or structural components (fats and protein) to satisfy their energy needs; in time, this will cause breakdown and increased loss of cells themselves.

CHAPTER XV

Growth

GROWTH in living things is a natural result of normal metabolism. It does not resemble growth in non-living things. A small snowball rolling down a snow-covered hillside may end up as a big snowball at the bottom of the hill. A microscopic crystal of a solid in solution may have other small crystals join it, thus becoming a crystal visible to the naked eye. In both of these examples growth is a matter of *accretion*—external addition.

In living things, the living organism selects materials from its environment, breaks them into "building-block" size and quality, and then *synthesizes* from them the materials that are characteristic of itself and essential for its survival.

GROWTH AND REPRODUCTION IN BODY CELLS

Whether a cell is an Amoeba, a bone cell, a gland cell, or any other cell which can grow and reproduce itself, the general procedure it follows is much the same in every case. (The only exceptions are sex cells, which we will discuss in the next section of this chapter.) As long as a cell receives the proper nutrient materials and as long as other factors maintain it as a normally functioning unit, the cell takes in nutrients and fashions them into its protoplasm. This, of course, makes it become larger.

Growth continues until a certain critical size is attained. Just what it is that makes a cell stop growing is not definitely known. A possible explanation is that in growth the volume of a cell increases at a faster rate than its surface area; and, since diffusion of nutrients, wastes, and gases occurs through the cell membrane at the surface of the cell, there may not be enough surface area to provide sufficient diffusion of substances into and out of the innermost points of the cellular protoplasm.

Whatever the reason, it seems to be at this stage of its existence that the cell divides. The two daughter cells certainly have more surface area than the parent cell for the same volume of protoplasm. Reproduction of cells has the advantage of apportioning the work that an organ, tissue, etc. must do among many units, thus ensuring a margin of safety in case of partial damage to or unusual strain upon that organ or tissue.

The process by which body cells divide, *mitosis*, involves a fascinating sequence of events (Fig. 137). The *nuclear contents* change from an amorphous mass of particles into discrete *chromosomes* which at first appear quite long and thin (the chromosomes obviously exist in the nucleus all the time but, in non-mitotic phases, are not visible under the light microscope). The *nuclear membrane* disappears. The chromosomes shorten and thicken and migrate to the center of the cell. Meanwhile, the *centrosome* has split and its two parts move to opposite poles of the cell. Fibers "grow" out from each part, producing an *aster* at each pole and a *spindle* that extends from pole to pole.

The chromosomes move to the midline and now appear as double units, *chromatids*. (We believe the doubling takes place quite a bit earlier; under sufficiently high magnification the double units can be seen before mitosis begins.) Each chromatid becomes attached to a special spindle fiber and is "pulled" to a pole of the cell. Since each member of a pair of chromatids moves to an opposite pole, there will now be the same number of chromosomes at each pole as there were in the parent nucleus originally. A nuclear membrane begins to form around each group of chromosomes, the fibers of the spindle disappear, and the *cytoplasm* begins to pinch in two along the equator

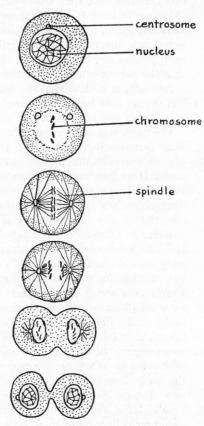

Fig. 137—Mitosis of a body cell (description in text).

of the cell. Finally the cytoplasm completes its division, the chromosomes form into a compact mass again, and two new cells have been formed from the one.

But what is the significance of these nuclear events? The cells of every species have their own characteristic number of chromosomes. (Man's cells have 46.) Each chromosome is composed of a number of submicroscopic bodies called *genes*. The genes are the bearers of the hereditary characters. The splitting of the chromosomes assures to each prospective daughter cell the same kind and number of genes that the parent cell had and, therefore, the same characteristics.

Not only is it clear that the nucleus controls the division of a cell but we are now beginning to see how some of the genetic "machinery" works and what its major significance is.

We have said above that, prior to mitotic division, each chromosome becomes two chromatids. Does this represent a simple splitting of each chromosome, including its component genes, into two equal parts? If so, how can the genes in each chromatid be exactly alike? We now have evidence (part of the big "breakthrough" in genetics during the 50's and 60's) that the process is better termed a *replication;* that is, an exact duplicate of each gene is made.

Refer to Chapter II and what was said about DNA and RNA. DNA in our genes is double-stranded, and the two strands are helically wound about each other. To begin the replication process, the two strands, for reasons still unknown, unwind and separate. Each strand now serves as a *template* upon which a new strand is constructed (from a pool of adenine bases, phosphate ions, and sugar molecules). Since one particular adenine base can link only and invariably with one other kind of adenine base (see Chapter II), an exact replica of the second strand is built in each case, and two molecules of DNA are formed which are exactly alike. When a similar process has been accomplished for many molecules of DNA, two chromatids exactly like the parent chromosome are created. When, later, these chromatids separate, each going to a different daughter cell, each of these cells will have exactly the same genetic constitution. Thus, we believe, hereditary characteristics are passed on from one generation of cells to the next.

How does the DNA in a cell express these hereditary traits? The story continues. Within each DNA strand the linear sequence of adenine bases represents a *genetic code* which, in essence, carries this information: each triad of bases (ABC, ABB, AAA, DBC, etc.) is a code for a particular kind of amino acid; the strand, therefore, carries the code for a particular sequence of amino acids or, in other words, for a particular protein molecule. The many DNA strands in each cell's nucleus bear the information, from one generation to the next, as to which protein molecules that cell can synthesize.

There is a complication. We know that most, if not all, protein synthesis occurs in the cytoplasm rather than the nucleus. How does this information get to the cytoplasm? The answer is that DNA remains in the nucleus but it also acts as a template for construction of RNA molecules. These molecules, known as *messenger RNA's*, go into the cytoplasm bearing the same base code as the DNA molecules that directed their synthesis. In some fashion they direct other RNA molecules (*soluble RNA*) in the cytoplasm to pick up appropriate amino acid molecules and transport them to special bodies within the cytoplasm, the *ribosomes*. In the ribosomes, *ribosomal RNA* acts as a template for the construction of protein molecules from the amino acids.

DNA information is used by the cell, in accordance with the process described above, to manufacture specific proteins. Since these structural and enzymic proteins of a cell are the compounds that distinguish it from all other cells, each cell is enabled to express itself in the same way as its genetic forebears; in other words, it will build exactly the same cellular parts as its parent cell and be capable of exactly the same kind of metabolic reactions. While all of the details of the procedures of the foregoing narrative are by no means known, to be able to sketch this much of an outline is a giant stride forward in biological knowledge.

MATURATION AND FERTILIZATION OF SEX CELLS

Immature sex cells, just as body cells, have 46 chromosomes each, or, more properly speaking, 23 *pairs* of chromosomes. The two chromosomes constituting each pair are called *homologous chromosomes*. They look alike when viewed under a microscope; and, even more, it is quite well documented that each consists of a series of genes that is closely related to the series of genes in the other chromosome. Suppose that on chromosome A of a pair, a particular point represents a gene for tallness; at that same location on chromosome B would also be a gene for body size (it might be for tallness or for shortness, depending upon the inheritance of the individual). At all other comparable points, chromosomes A and B would also have pairs of related genes (but for other traits).

Body cells, as the result of mitosis, have exactly the same chromosomal complement as the cells from which they were derived. The total influence of the gene pairs in their homologous chromosomes will be exactly the same as it was in their predecessors. The case is different, however, with sex cells, which as they mature come to have only half the number of chromosomes than is present in the body cells or in the immature sex cells. We shall now see how this happens.

Maturation of Sex Cells. The very immature precursors of the sex cells divide mitotically, just as do the body cells. When, however, they become ready for the maturation process proper, they undergo *meiosis*, a sequence of two very special cell divisions, with the second following the first quite rapidly, which in effect halves their number of chromosomes. The essential events of meiosis are quite similar in both sexes.

In meiotic division I, until the point at which the chromosomes congregate in the center of the cell, the progress is much like that occurring in mitosis. At this point in the process you will recall that each chromosome has already replicated so that it is actually present as two chromatids. In mitosis, each pair of chromatids then separate, one of each going to opposite poles of the cell; but in meiosis, the following occurs. Each set of homologous chromosomes comes together, making very close contact, so that there are actually four chromatids lying side by side. During this period of *synapsis* the chromosomal strands intertwine, and interchanges of material occur between them. Thus, some of the genes originally in chromosome A of a pair become part of chromosome B, and vice versa. Now, the two homologous chromosomes separate, one going to each pole; but *the chromatids do not separate at this time*. Each daughter nucleus of this division will receive, therefore, only 23 chromosomes; but each of these consists of two chromatids.

Meiotic division II will soon take place. The point of paramount importance in this division is that *no replication occurs*. Each of the daughter cells from meiosis I now undergoes a sequence of changes exactly like those of mitosis. Since, however, no replication has occurred, the two chromatids of each chromosome separate and move to opposite poles.

The four cells produced by these meiotic divisions, as compared with the one cell from which they were derived, have only 23 chromosomes (one of each pair of original homologous chromosomes), and each chromosome will tend to have a somewhat different composition of genes than the original cell. Meiosis results, then, in sex cells with only half of the original chromosome number but with new combinations of genes which can introduce variety in the new organisms resulting from sex cell unions.

All of the above applies equally to the two sexes but there are some differences we should note in the maturation of sperms and ova. Of the 23 pairs of chromosomes in our cells, one pair is designated as the sex chromosomes. In females, this pair look alike and are called the X chromosomes. In males, there is one X chromosome which is matched with a very dissimilar chromosome, the Y chromosome. The ova resulting from meiosis will, therefore, always have one X chromosome. In the case of the sperms, however, half will contain an X and half a Y chromosome, since only one of a homologous pair go to each mature sex cell.

There are further differences. Each immature sperm cell undergoes meiosis and, as we have said, four cells result. Each of these cells undergoes further maturation, and most of its cytoplasm eventually disappears. The nucleus remains as the *head*, the centrosome the *neck*, and the remaining cytoplasm the *tail* of the sperm. Meiosis in the female, on the other hand, produces only one mature ovum for each immature cell. In meiosis I and meiosis II, the nuclear divisions occur as we have outlined, but the cytoplasm divides very unequally, producing one quite large cell and one very small cell. The small cell degenerates each time, leaving but one mature egg cell, which remains unchanged in shape.

Fertilization. At the time of copulation, many sperms swim towards an ovum. And then, as soon as one sperm penetrates the egg cell, a *fertilization membrane* is formed about the latter and all other sperm cells are prevented access to the ovum. Of that one sperm cell, only the head and neck actually enter the egg, the tail being discarded. The sperm head, or nucleus, and the egg nucleus meet and fuse. Once this essential event of fertilization is completed, the fertilized egg or *zygote* is ready to develop into a new individual. If the sperm cell that entered the egg possessed an X chromosome, the new individual will be a female, since the egg could only have an X chromosome; if the sperm had a Y chromosome, the new individual will be "XY," a male.

The significance of meiosis should now be quite clear. Synapsis provides for variation of characteristics in the new organism although, of course, it will still be basically similar to its parents. The reduction by half of the chromosome number in each sex cell now enables the zygote to have the usual number of chromosomes for the species. If reduction had not occurred, the fertilized egg would have had twice the normal number of chromosomes and the next generation twice that, and so on.

REPAIR AND REGENERATION OF TISSUE

The processes of *repair* and *regeneration* of tissues are again examples of growth of cells. In general, we think of repair as minor restoration of destroyed tissue, and of regeneration as the restoration of some larger part of an organism. Actually, the two processes are very similar and depend not so much on the size of the affected region as on the character of the cells composing it.

The Process of Regeneration. The less specialized a tissue is, the greater its powers of regeneration and recuperation from injury. Many invertebrates whose cells are much less specialized than man's are capable of seemingly amazing regeneration of tissue and organs. Some worms when cut in half can grow into two new worms; a lobster can replace a lost claw. Even some vertebrates show such powers. The glass snake (really a limbless lizard) has a very brittle tail which easily breaks. When it does, the tail can be completely re-formed in time.

The more complex an organism is, the more specialized are its tissues and organs and the less easily they can be replaced. In man certain mature tissues are so specialized that they cannot reproduce themselves or regenerate when destroyed. We have noted that nerve cells are of this kind. If the cell body of a neuron is destroyed, that neuron is lost forever—it will not be replaced. The processes of the cell can regenerate, but not the cell body. Mature red blood cells, which have no nuclei, cannot regenerate.

Most connective and supporting tissues are of less specialized character and can successfully regenerate. In fact, they generally take the place of destroyed tissues that are more specialized. Scar tissue is connective tissue. Glandular tissue also regenerates easily, a fact which often leads to annoying problems in some cases of hyperfunction of endocrine glands.

Abnormal Tissue. Sometimes tissues which are not useful appear in parts of the body. Such abnormal growths are known as *tumors*, and can appear at any place in the body. Some tumors are relatively harmless and are called *benign* or *innocent* tumors; others are dangerous to life and are known as *malignant* tumors. Benign tumors are generally enclosed in a capsule of tissue which prevents their spreading throughout the tissues in general. Malignant tumors, of which the various types of *cancer* are examples, are not enclosed in tissue capsules. Their cells tend to infiltrate through tissues and they may travel to various parts of the body.

The question of the origin of tumor cells is an unsettled one. One of the more likely hypotheses is that they are embryonic cells, cells which have never reached maturity or become specialized and which were not used in the formation of the parts of the adult body. When set into activity by some irritating stimulus (the stimulus itself is not known), these cells begin to grow and multiply.

THE NORMAL GROWTH OF THE BODY

Body growth is the sum of the changes in its various parts, and is not something separate. There are, of course, limitations imposed on the extent of growth of the body which are not imposed on tissues growing outside of the body in a nutritive medium.

The Processes of Growth. Increase in weight is not always a true index of body growth, for deposition of fat can and often does occur without any increase in stature of the body. Most often bone growth is taken as the index, for this it is that determines the eventual height, breadth, and width of the organism.

There are two different methods of bone growth in vertebrates. One is by the deposition of calcium salts in a connective tissue membrane. This is the method by which the jawbone and the top of the skull are formed. Most bones of the body are first modeled in cartilage which is later replaced by bone. This is the essential method by which the long bones grow—and the body along with them.

In a long bone—like an arm or leg bone—the cartilage in the middle of the shaft is first calcified. A bone-forming membrane grows about the outside of the bone and bone-forming cells begin to deposit calcium salts around the shaft. Meanwhile the interior of the bone is still composed of calcified cartilage. At this time bone-destroying cells invade the interior and tunnel through the cartilage and calcium deposits. Bone-forming cells follow in their wake and deposit true bone in the walls of the cavities formed by the bone-destroying cells. This procedure is followed up and down the shaft and also in the ends of the bone. Growth of the bone continues, however, for the bone of the shaft is separated from the bone in either end by a plate of cartilage. Growth hereafter amounts to a pushing of the ends of the bone away from each other by the inclusion of new bone tissue at these growth regions. Growth of long bones finally stops when the cartilaginous plates are calcified.

Growth of soft tissues also occurs by a multiplication of the number of cells in the tissue. It should be recognized that at all times there are two antagonistic processes proceeding simultaneously in the tissues. On the one hand, cells are continually reproducing (except in places like the nervous system) and tending to increase the size of the tissue; on the other hand, cells are continually dying or being destroyed and being removed from the tissue. During active growth in the young, growth overbalances destruction. After growth stops and for most of our lifetime, growth and destruction are proceeding at approximately equal rates. In old age the equilibrium is shifted in the other direction, destruction being in the ascendancy. The latter accounts for the tendency of old people to shrink both in height and as regards some tissues and organs.

This mobility of tissues applies even to such apparently stable tissues as bone. Bone-forming and bone-destroying cells are continually at work and a "solid" bone is built up and torn down many times during its lifetime.

The Control of Growth. The factors controlling growth are known only in a quite general way. The intimate mechanisms by which a particular organ is limited to a certain size are unsolved mysteries.

Healthy growth is regulated both directly and indirectly. The intake of oxygen and proper foods is a primary factor. But ingestion is of no value if the processes of digestion, absorption, and distribution of essential materials do not coöperate to deliver the right kinds and amounts of substances to the cells.

Hormonal control is another very important factor in the regulation of body growth. We have seen that the anterior lobe of the pituitary gland secretes a growth hormone which regulates the growth of all the tissues. Abnormal amounts of this hormone cause not only changes in bone growth but also changes in growth of the various viscera. We know that the thyroid hormone influences growth. Its influence is probably an indirect one based on its regulation of the oxidative reactions in the cells.

It was thought at first that the pituitary growth hormone might be the thyrotropic hormone and thus would influence growth by causing thyroid hormone to be secreted. This does not appear likely since administration of thyroglobulin to a pituitary dwarf does not result in increased growth.

The sex hormones apparently can influence growth, too. A castrated or spayed animal often grows larger. Where this regulation fits into the hormonal pattern is obscure.

As regards bone growth, all of these hormones plus the parathyroid hormone and vitamin D are involved. With so many factors concerned, the interrelationships are bound to be complex. The complexity only increases when we realize that the hormones must work through the metabolism of the cell and we still have very much to learn about the ways in which hormones influence cellular reactions.

CHAPTER XVI

Body Temperature

THE EXTENT and rate of activity of the great majority of animals can be greatly influenced by the temperature of their environment. These are the "cold-blooded" animals whose body temperature fluctuates with and is just about the same as the environmental temperature. If the temperature is cold, their activity is sluggish; if hot, their activity is accelerated. Whether they "like" it or not, that is their lot.

Only birds and mammals—the "warm-blooded" animals—have mechanisms to control their body temperature. Man maintains his body temperature at a constant level (about 98.6° F.) when he is in good health whether the weather man reports "below zero weather" or "100° in the shade." Because of this constancy of body temperature, man is to that extent independent of his environment. His cells can proceed in their tasks with their accustomed vigor, for, whatever the temperature outside the body, their temperature is constant. Under certain rare conditions this works to the disadvantage of the "warm-blooded" organism. Should the internal temperature drop some 20° or rise as much as 15°, the cells could not withstand the change for long. To most cold-blooded animals such changes would mean only a shift in their metabolic rate. But these changes in birds and mammals occur only when their temperature-regulating mechanisms are seriously askew. The possible disadvantage is many times outweighed by the almost constant advantage.

HEAT PRODUCTION AND HEAT LOSS

As with so many physiological constants, the constancy of body temperature is maintained by the interplay of antagonistic processes. Heat is continually being produced in the body and must continually be lost.

How the Body Produces Heat. Heat production is the sign of a metabolizing unit, and it ultimately must be traced back to the cells of the organism. So long as a cell lives, chemical reactions proceed within it and production of heat is an inevitable consequence. Any factor which influences the metabolism of a cell will influence its heat production.

The only adequate mechanism available to us in the control of heat production is a change in activity of skeletal muscle. There are no mechanisms which are capable of reducing or increasing the metabolism of a sufficient number of other kinds of body cells to influence the body temperature appreciably. But the skeletal muscles are the greatest source of body heat and their activity can quickly be adapted to changing temperature requirements by reflex or voluntary control.

How the Body Loses Heat. The loss of heat from the body is, in the final analysis, the result of a number of physical processes. A small amount of heat is lost by warming the air we inhale. An even smaller amount is lost in the excretion of urine and feces.

By far the greatest amount of heat loss occurs through the skin. Here there are four different processes by which it can occur— *radiation, convection, conduction,* and *evaporation.*

Radiation is the emission of energy from a body as rays or waves. Any body that is warmer than its environment throws off waves of heat. (Hold a thermometer—not a clinical one—near a lighted electric bulb and note the temperature rise.) The environmental temperature is generally below body temperature so that heat waves radiate from the skin through the medium surrounding us. Radiation accounts for about 55% of heat loss.

Convection is the process of transmission of heat by currents of matter. Warm air is lighter than cool air and tends to rise. Thus the warmed air surrounding the body rises, cooler air rushes in to take its place, and currents are set up. The cooler air is warmed in turn and the process repeats itself. About 15% of heat loss is accomplished by convection currents. You can observe cigarette smoke being carried upward by the convection currents set up by a lighted electric light bulb. Convection from the skin is greatly influenced by air movements, a breeze accelerating heat loss.

Conduction is the process of heat transference when two bodies at different temperature are in contact with one another. Ordinarily conduction is of minor importance in heat loss since air is a very poor conductor of heat. When the body is in contact with a cooler body such as a cake of ice, heat is lost to the latter.

Evaporation is the process of heat loss which inspires the oft-repeated, "It's not the heat, but the humidity!" As water changes from a liquid to a vapor (evaporates), it absorbs heat. Thus, the evaporation of water on the skin surface helps the body to lose heat. It is not only sweat which is evaporated but also water which escapes from the skin capillaries and diffuses to the surface. If the air is well-nigh saturated with water vapor (if the humidity is high), evaporation becomes very limited or impossible. Since at high external temperatures evaporation is the only effective method by which the body can lose heat, a hot (120° F.) humid atmosphere cannot be endured for more than a few minutes. If the atmosphere is dry, a temperature of well over 200° F. can be withstood with no increase in body temperature.

Evaporation of water occurs in the lungs as well as on the skin. In the dog, which has no sweat glands except on the pads of its paws, it occurs from the surface of the tongue. Panting is a dog's mechanism for losing heat when very hot.

THE REGULATION OF BODY TEMPERATURE

The mechanisms which regulate the body temperature are for the most part nervous reflexes beginning in the *temperature receptors* of the skin. Nerve impulses from these receptors pass into the central nervous system and up to the *temperature-regulating centers* in the hypothalamus. From these centers impulses are sent out to the arterioles of the skin, to the sweat glands of the skin, to the skeletal muscles, to the smooth muscles of the skin, or to combinations of these. These hypothalamic-induced changes are fine examples of coördination between somatic and visceral spheres as controlled by higher levels of the nervous system.

The Responses to Low Environmental Temperature. When the environmental temperature falls well below the temperature of the skin, the body will tend to lose heat faster than it can produce it. The cold receptors in the skin are stimulated by the drop in external temperature and impulses are sent to the *heat-raising center* in the hypothalamus. From this center impulses are relayed to the smooth muscle in the arterioles of the skin, causing it to contract. This constricts the arterioles and allows less blood to flow through the skin. In this way the processes of radiation and conduction are reduced in effectiveness since less of the warm blood is giving up heat in this region. Fewer impulses are sent to the sweat glands, less sweat is secreted, and evaporation is reduced (it is probably not effective at low temperature anyway). If the external temperature is not too low, these mechanisms will be adequate to maintain a constant body temperature by reducing heat loss.

If the temperature of the environment drops even lower, the reduction in heat loss will not be adequate and an increase in heat production will have to supplement it. The heat-raising center then sends impulses to the skeletal muscles and increases their activity. The increased contractions result in greater production of heat by the muscles. If this does not prove sufficient, more impulses travel to the muscles and greater involuntary contractions result—shivering and chattering of the teeth.

In animals with feathers or a heavy coat of hair, impulses go to the smooth muscles of the skin which control the erection of the hairs or feathers. The hairs or feathers are thereby fluffed up and imprison a blanket of air which acts as an insulator. This, of course, is an accessory mechanism, the contractions of the skeletal muscle being much more effective. In man this mechanism still exists but is quite ineffective since the hair on the body is not thick enough to hold much of a layer of air. It does give rise to the phenomenon of "goose-pimples."

We can also aid these processes voluntarily by indulging in vigorous activity, wearing heavier clothes, eating more protein-rich foods (to increase specific dynamic action—see chapter on metabolism), or simply by moving to a warmer environment.

The Responses to High Environmental Temperature. When the environmental temperature rises above the temperature of the skin, an opposite series of events takes place. The heat receptors in the skin are stimulated and send impulses to the *heat-lowering center* in the hypothalamus. Impulses are now sent to inhibit the vasoconstrictor center so that smooth muscle of the cutaneous arterioles relaxes. The arterioles dilate, more blood flows through the skin capillaries, and heat is given up by radiation and convection. If the temperature is high enough, these processes will no longer be able to work. Stimulation of the sweat glands, greater secretion of sweat, and greater evaporation now occur.

If it is hot enough outside the body, heat production must be cut down. The action of the skeletal muscles is reflexly reduced and less heat is produced. In hot weather we generally are less active voluntarily and tend to eat "lighter" foods, cutting down on proteins. Exposing as much of the body's surface as possible also helps by increasing the surface area over which evaporation can take place.

It is interesting to note that the temperature-regulating centers can be activated by the temperature of the blood flowing near them as well as by nerve impulses. Thus, a fall in blood temperature activates the heat-raising center; a rise, the heat-lowering center. The typical effects which result from their stimulation will result even if the external temperature does not warrant such actions.

DISTURBANCES IN BODY TEMPERATURE

The average normal body temperature as measured in the mouth is 98.6° F. Rectal temperature is about one degree higher. Some individuals normally have a temperature a few tenths of a degree higher or lower. In all of us, though, there is a daily cycle of temperature variation. The peak of the day's temperature is reached late in the afternoon or in the early evening, the low point being in the early morning hours. There may be as much as a degree difference between high and low points. Those who work at night may show, after some time, a reversal of the high and low points.

During muscular exertion there is a raised body temperature which persists for some time after the activity stops. There are also abnormal conditions, though, in which body temperature is shifted up or down for longer periods.

Effect in Glandular Disorders. In hypothyroidism and in some pituitary disorders (those in which the production of thyroid hormone is curtailed by a deficiency of thyrotropic hormone), body temperature is subnormal. The fall in body temperature is due to a decreased heat production, more heat being lost than produced. This results from the decreased oxidative powers of the tissues. In hyperthyroidism the reverse is true for the opposite reasons.

Effect in Heatstroke and Sunstroke. Rises in body temperature are much more common than depressions, and are apt to have more serious consequences. Too great an exposure to a moist, hot atmosphere can bring on *heatstroke*. In this condition the mechanisms regulating heat loss are either unable to cope with the increased environmental temperature or, in attempting to do so, become exhausted. Body temperature rises and, if not lowered, may bring on death due to irreparable damage to the central nervous system.

The term *sunstroke* applies to a special form of heatstroke. Besides the inadequacy of the mechanisms controlling heat loss there is an absorption of radiant energy from the sun and there are local rises in temperature above the general body temperature in those regions unprotected from the sun's rays. The brain especially may be heated too much.

To avoid heatstroke and sunstroke it is best to eat lightly, drink a lot of water, be as inactive as possible, and give evaporation as much opportunity to work as is possible. Protection of the head and neck against the direct rays of the sun is advisable.

Effect in Fever. In *fever* the body temperature is maintained for some time at a higher level. The rise in temperature in fever is, to some extent, due to a vicious cycle of events. Fevers are usually associated with an infection or infectious disease. The infectious "germ" liberates a toxic substance which, travelling in the blood, stimulates the heat-raising mechanisms of the body. Thus, there is constriction of the blood vessels of the skin (the pale skin in early stages of fever) and reduced heat loss. This starts the body temperature on a climb and, as it rises, the increased temperature speeds up the metabolism of cells and more heat is produced. In the early stages the chills which a patient commonly experiences are the result of the constriction of the skin blood vessels and the consequent fall in temperature of the skin. This stimulates the cold receptors in the skin.

After the temperature has risen to a certain height, the heat-lowering center is stimulated. The cutaneous blood vessels are reflexly dilated, blood rushes to the skin (now flushed), and the patient feels very hot. But, heat loss can come into play now and the mechanisms for heat production and heat loss counterbalance one another again. The temperature remains raised, however, as long as the toxic substance retains a critical concentration in the blood. So, although heat loss balances production, the "thermostat" of the body remains set at a higher level. When the toxic substance is removed from the blood, the fever drops gradually or sharply and temperature returns to normal.

Fever is not an unmitigated evil. If it goes as high as 108-110°, it will usually be fatal, it is true. In most cases, however, fever appears to be an important aid in combatting disease. Just how it helps is not clearly known, but we do know that fevers artificially induced are of practical value in treating some diseases. Fever also serves as a warning of approaching danger, and attention can thus be focused on the cause of the pathological disturbance.

CHAPTER XVII

Movement

A GREAT MANY VARIETIES of movement exist in the animal world. These may seem to result from almost as many different kinds of mechanisms. There are, nevertheless, but three main varieties of movement possible, each of which may be modified in certain manners. The three general types of movement are *amoeboid*, *ciliary*, and *muscular movement*.

AMOEBOID MOVEMENT

The simplest animals move about in their surroundings by streaming movements of their protoplasm. We have seen that Amoeba almost constantly changes its shape by projecting pseudopods now in this direction, now in that (Fig. 4). Such an animal cannot retain a stable shape.

This kind of movement is extremely slow and limited as to variability. It serves Amoeba, though, as a method of locomotion and as a method of engulfing and "swallowing" its food. This primitive type of movement not only occurs in one-celled organisms but is carried over to some of the body cells of multicellular animals.

The *neutrophils*, the most numerous of the white blood cells in the higher animals, retain amoeboid movement as a means of locomotion and of *phagocytosis* (the engulfing of foreign particles or bacteria by means of pseudopod activity). Fixed phagocytes also retain at least the latter property. That is, although they are anchored to other cells at some point, they can extend pseudopods and snare cells or cellular debris passing near them.

CILIARY MOVEMENT

Certain one-celled animals that have a fixed shape are observed to have hair-like processes or *cilia* extending from their cell surfaces. Movement of the cilia can propel these animals about in the water in which they live. Some one-celled animals instead of being covered with cilia have one or several sturdier and longer hair-like processes localized at one end or both ends of the cell. These processes are called *flagella* (singular, *flagellum*). Whip-like lashings of flagella serve to propel these animals from place to place.

The movement of cilia or flagella is oscillatory in nature. It involves a rapid beat in one direction and then a gradual return to the resting position. It is known that a little swelling at the base of each cilium or flagellum controls the beating of these processes. How this control operates has not been discovered.

Many-celled animals have some ciliated or flagellated cells. Most of these are incapable of locomotion but the sperm cells are examples of ones that are motile. The "tails" of sperm cells are flagella and by their lashing movements enable sperm to swim about. Of the non-motile ciliated cells in man, those lining the trachea and bronchioles are in continual activity. The rapid movement of their cilia is in a direction away from the lungs. The action of these cilia carries dirt and other small foreign particles in that direction. Their action is very efficient in preventing clogging or irritation of the delicate alveoli of the lung.

The movements of the cilia here are wave-like (Fig. 138), reminiscent of the ripples caused by a breeze in a grassy field. The ciliary beats are wonderfully coördinated, apparently by chemical means.

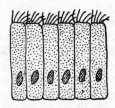

FIG. 138—Ciliary action. Note the wave-like movements of the cilia.

There are other important ciliated cells in man. The "hair" cells, the receptors of the cochlea, of the utricle, saccule, and semicircular canals are activated by the bending of their cilia.

MUSCULAR MOVEMENT

Most of the movements made by animals are based on the contractions of muscles. The lowly sponge has cells that are specialized for contraction purposes. These effector cells are directly stimulated by environmental changes and respond by contracting. Not until nervous elements had evolved, however, were very efficient muscular responses possible. The earliest muscular responses were slow and uncoördinated, but later in evolution they became more rapid and increasingly better coördinated as reflex connections and control improved.

Internal Movement. The movements of our viscera, controlled by the autonomic nervous system and chemical substances in the blood, resemble the earlier types of muscular movement in being relatively slow, but they are usually well coördinated.

Movements of the viscera play very important parts in the activities of our essential internal organs. The contractions of the heart muscle impart movement to the blood. Contractions of the smooth muscle in the digestive tract serve to carry food along the tract and to break it down mechanically, enabling the digestive enzymes to fulfill their roles more efficiently.

Contractions of the diaphragm (it should be remembered that the diaphragm is composed of skeletal muscle) are most important in increasing the volume of the thoracic cavity. The smooth muscle contractions of the blood vessels regulate the speed of flow and distribution of blood. Peristaltic waves in the ureters aid the movement of urine flow from kidneys to the bladder. Uterine contractions propel the fetus through the birth canal.

Most of these movements go unnoticed by us day after day. Yet, if it were not for them, the movements we are more familiar with would not be possible.

External Movement. Contractions of some of the "external" muscles are responsible for some of our internal processes rather directly. For instance, contractions of the limb musculature are important factors in the flow of venous blood and of lymph; again, contractions of the intercostal muscles (along with that of the diaphragm) regulate the volume of the chest cavity.

The movements that catch our eye are usually those involved in locomotion of an animal or dexterous manipulation of its parts. The laborious movement of a snail, the soaring of a hawk, the lithe leap of a panther, the swift strike of a snake, the fingering of a trained violinist are but a few of the varied and complicated movements of which animals are capable.

Contraction of skeletal muscle is very rapid, and some movements occur faster than the eye can follow them. Sleight of hand makes use of this phenomenon. The beating of a humming-bird's wings as it hovers over a flower is a fine example of rapid, precise movement. "External" movements enable most animals to track down food, catch it and eat it, fight or flee, focus their sound- and sight-perceiving organs, etc. How are these movements made possible in man?

Skeletal Muscle Movements in Man. We have already discussed the energy basis and the nervous control of muscular contraction. We have not seen how movements of the body's parts are effected.

Muscles are attached to parts of the skeleton or the skin by *tendons*. Most muscles are attached to two different bones. When they are, one end of the muscle is attached to a bone which remains immovable when the muscle contracts. This point of attachment is the *origin* of the muscle (see Fig. 139). Since this is a more fixed attachment than the other, the muscle pulls toward this point when it contracts. The other attachment is called the *insertion*. Contraction of the muscle pulls the bone to which it is attached here towards the origin.

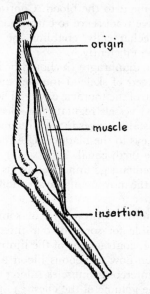

FIG. 139—The attachments of muscle to bone.

The external muscles of the eye (those which move the eyeball) have their origins on the bone of the orbit of the eye and their insertions in the connective tissue covering the eyeball. There are six muscles for each eye, each of which brings about a different movement of the eyeball. Either eye can be moved up and down, towards the nose and towards the side of the head and can be rotated. Since both eyes generally move coördinately, it is to be expected that a complicated but delicate controlling mechanism is required to regulate their movements.

The facial muscles are attached to the bones of the front of the skull at their origins and to the skin of the face at their insertions. Some have both origin and insertion on the skin. These are capable of pulling parts of the skin of the face in various directions and are, therefore, responsible for the various facial expressions.

Some other muscles of the body also have their insertions in the skin. The sheet of muscle running from the shoulder blade to the skin of the back is such a muscle. It is of more value in animals like the horse and cow than it is in man, for this is the muscle responsible for the quivering of the skin that you have probably seen when a fly lands on the back of these animals.

CONSTRUCTION OF JOINTS. As just mentioned above, most muscles are attached to bone at both ends. Thus, when they contract, a bone is moved. The movements that a bone can make depend upon the kind of *joint* or *articulation* it forms with another bone. The surfaces of bones at which they articulate are covered over with a layer of smooth hyaline cartilage. When one bone moves against another, this smooth covering reduces the friction considerably. Between the two bones is a space, the *joint cavity*, which is lined with a layer of epithelial cells. These cells secrete a watery fluid which serves to lubricate the moving parts of the joint. If these cells are irritated or inflamed, a greater than normal secretion may result and fluid may accumulate in the joint cavity ("water on the knee", for instance). Passing through the cavity are *ligaments*, the dense connective tissue strands which connect bone to bone.

The articulations that bones make with one another in the skeleton (Fig. 74) are of three kinds—*immovable joints, partially movable joints,* and *freely movable joints.*

Some bones are fused together so firmly that no movements are possible. The lines at which they join one another may still be visible and look somewhat like the seams made when pieces of cloth are sewed together; hence their being called *sutures.* Joints of this kind are found between the bones of the *skull* and between the three fused bones that make up the *innominate bone* of the pelvic girdle. The fusion of the skull bones tightly seals the cranial cavity and protects the brain. The solidity of the pelvic girdle produces the firm foundation needed in this region to support the weight of the upper part of the body.

Partially movable joints are especially found *between the vertebrae* of the backbone. Such joints allow one bone to glide over the surface of another but not to move freely upon one another. The twisting and bending movements of the trunk, especially when the trunk is not held straight, are made possible by the sliding of the vertebrae upon one another. If the vertebrae should by any chance become fused, we should either have to hold outselves stiff at all times or risk the chance of cracking the vertebrae. The small bones in the wrist and ankle (*carpals* and *tarsals*) also articulate in this fashion.

The joints that allow bones comparative freedom of movement can be classified in three subgroups. One kind allows movement along only one axis of rotation. A second permits movement in two axes of rotation. The third group allows most freedom of movement—movement in all three axes of rotation. The best way to study the joints is to try the movements on yourself.

JOINTS WITH ONE AXIS OF ROTATION. A joint with only one axis of rotation is called a *hinge joint*. The joint between the *femur* and *tibia*, the knee joint, is of this type. It allows for flexion and extension of the lower leg. The articulation between *humerus* and *ulna* in the arm is a similar one, allowing for flexion and extension of the lower arm at the elbow. Between the *first and second*, and *second and third phalanges* of the fingers and toes are other hinge joints.

JOINTS WITH TWO AXES OF ROTATION. A good example of a joint that permits rotation along two axes is the articulation of the *occipital bone* of the skull with the *atlas*, the first vertebra of the neck, on which the skull rests. This joint allows the movement of the head towards the chest and the back (one axis) and towards either shoulder (a second axis). Some of us can bend our toes and also spread them. In such people the joints between the *first phalanges* and *metatarsals* are in this category; others can only flex them and so have only a functional hinge joint in this region.

JOINTS WITH THREE AXES OF ROTATION. Articulations that allow movement in many directions are of different kinds. Some restrict action somewhat more than others and have been called *pivot joints*. One example of such a joint is that between the *humerus* and *radius* of the arm which makes possible the turning of the hand to the palm-up or palm-down position. Another is the joint formed by the *atlas* and *axis* (the second vertebra in the neck) which permits the pivotal movement of the head.

The joints which restrict action least of all are those between *scapula* and *humerus* (shoulder joint), and *pelvic girdle* and *femur* (hip joint). These are the *ball-and-socket joints* and allow movement of arms and legs in almost every possible direction.

Other joints also permit considerable freedom of movement. Those between the *tibia* and the *tarsals*, between the *ulna* and *radius* and the *carpals*, and between the *phalanges* of the fingers and thumbs and the *metacarpals* allow up-and-down, side-to-side, and rotary movements.

While the joints permit movement of the bones, it is the contraction of the muscles, of course, that is the driving power of such movement. Several muscles may be involved in the performance of any one movement—some contracting and some relaxing. The interplay between cooperating and antagonistic muscles is responsible for the fine gradations and niceties of movement that are characteristic of the actions of man and of many of the higher animals.

CHAPTER XVIII

Exercise

IN PRECEDING CHAPTERS we have mentioned the effects of exercise on many of the organs and activities of the various systems. Let us try to get a more complete picture of what happens inside the body when we exercise.

WHAT HAPPENS IN MODERATE EXERCISE

With the beginning of moderate exercise (housework, walking at moderate speed, etc.), the skeletal muscles become more active than before. A series of events occurs which results in a greater flow of blood carrying an increased supply of oxygen and fuel to the active muscles. As muscle activity increases, muscle metabolism does likewise. The increased metabolism means greater heat production and an increased temperature of the muscles themselves. The warming of the muscles lowers their viscosity and increases the efficiency of the work they perform. Body temperature probably will not rise much, if at all, except, perhaps, for a very short period at the onset of activity. The warmed blood leaving the muscles will shortly reach the heat-lowering center in the hypothalamus. Reflex dilation of skin vessels will allow more heat loss by radiation, balancing the increased heat production.

The increased muscle metabolism will also mean a greater output of carbon dioxide—resulting from increased oxidation of glucose. Increased amounts of carbon dioxide will diffuse into the smaller blood vessels of the muscles and, once there, will directly cause the smooth muscle fibers in the walls of these vessels to relax. Their consequent dilation will allow more blood to flow more quickly through the skeletal muscles.

The increased amount of carbon dioxide in the blood will not only exert local action but will, in its travels, help to coördinate the general responses of the circulatory and respiratory systems to the demands placed upon them. The increased carbon dioxide concentration in the blood flowing through the medulla of the brain directly stimulates the vasoconstrictor and inspiratory centers. The latter responds by an increase in the frequency of the impulses it rhythmically discharges. The greater number of impulses which eventually reach the diaphragm and intercostal muscles (via the phrenic and intercostal nerves respectively) induce stronger than usual contractions. Breathing thus becomes deeper.

Stimulation of the vasoconstrictor center sends impulses along vasoconstrictor nerves to the arterioles of the abdominal cavity. Constriction of the many arterioles in this region significantly increases the peripheral resistance and the general arterial blood pressure rises. Constriction of these blood vessels also serves to shunt blood from the abdominal organs to the skeletal muscles (whose vessels are dilated).

Other factors are cooperating to increase the return of blood to the heart: the force of the heart beat, the cardiac output, and the blood pressure. The increased number and force of skeletal muscle contractions squeeze down upon the veins more vigorously and thus help to "pump" blood back to the heart more quickly. The respiratory "pump" also aids in this. Deeper breathing means greater fluctuations of the pressures within the thoracic and abdominal cavities. The alternating expansions and compressions of the large veins in these cavities will be increased in force and more blood will be forced onward to the heart.

The increased return of blood to the heart stretches the heart muscles, increasing its force of contraction and, thereby, its output per beat. Impulses from the active muscles ascend to the cardio-acceleratory center, and, via the cardio-acceleratory center and the accelerator nerves, the heart rate is quickened. The faster heart rate plus the stronger contractions of the cardiac muscle increase the cardiac output per minute and this, in turn, aids in producing the rise in blood pressure. (See also Chapter IV.)

The increase in depth of breathing meanwhile tends to increase the rate of breathing. The greater stretch of the lung walls at each inspiration stimulates receptors in the wall more strongly; more impulses pass up through afferent fibers of the vagus nerve to the expiratory center, which then inhibits the inspiratory center more quickly than during restful breathing. Cutting inspiration short accelerates the respiratory cycle. Impulses from active muscles also aid in increasing breathing rate and depth.

Faster and deeper breathing ventilates the lungs more thoroughly. A greater amount of carbon dioxide is thus removed in the expired air, which prevents its concentration from rising too high in the blood (too much carbon dioxide can increase the acidity of the blood to a dangerous extent). The blood will contain no more oxygen than before, because, as you will recall, the blood is almost saturated with it during restful breathing. Since the circulation time of the blood is decreased, however, more oxygen does enter the blood each minute than before exercise began.

The mechanisms we have just reviewed ensure more blood getting to the skeletal muscles faster and at a greater pressure. Because of the more rapid circulation, more oxygen is brought to the muscles per minute and more carbon dioxide removed. What of the glucose supply?

The active muscles, of course, oxidize more glucose and do it more rapidly than before because of the increased temperature in them. This tends to deplete the blood sugar concentration. Since the sugar in the blood is in equilibrium with the glycogen in the liver, a fall in blood sugar concentration causes more glycogen to break down into glucose which is released into the blood. As the muscles drain more glucose from the blood, more is poured into it from the liver. There is an adequate mechanism, then, for supplying fuel to the muscle.

In moderate exercise the oxygen supply can keep pace with the oxygen used and no oxygen deficit results. The only residual effects will be a depletion of the carbohydrate reserves and a need for more protein to be used in rebuilding the cells that broke down in activity.

WHAT HAPPENS IN STRENUOUS EXERCISE

As we prepare to take strenuous exercise, there usually is a mental and emotional "warming up." The memories and emotions caused by previous experiences, especially if the exercise involves competition of one sort or another, stir up the nervous system to an increased "tone." This helps to ready the body for the demands soon to be placed upon it. The subjective feelings may induce autonomic effects, particularly those mediated by the sympathetic division, and a quickened pulse, faster breathing, and dilation of the pupils are not uncommon at times like this. The keying up of the mind and body aid in making the transition from inactivity to activity a more gradual one and one less apt to inflict a sudden strain upon our capacities.

The many changes described above for moderate exercise take place in strenuous exercise, too. You might imagine there would be even more, but where differences occur, they are mainly differences in degree rather than in kind. The heart rate is faster, blood pressure higher, respiration faster and deeper, and circulation time more rapid than in moderate exercise.

The heat production, too, is more greatly increased in strenuous exercise. In this condition, though, the body temperature is not maintained at its usual level. The heat production becomes too great for the heat loss mechanisms to counterbalance it, even though sweating may be profuse. Body temperature rises and is then stabilized at a new, higher level for the duration of the exercise and some time afterwards.

Adrenaline may be released from the adrenal medulla and aid in the respiratory and circulatory changes. It would also favor the release of glucose from liver glycogen and delay fatigue of skeletal muscles by increasing the oxidation of muscle glycogen.

The greatest limiting factor for the maintenance of severe exertion is the oxygen supply. Even though the spleen is stimulated to contract and discharge red blood cells into the blood (which increases the oxygen capacity of the blood), the intake of oxygen cannot meet the muscular demands for it. Consequently lactic acid accumulates in muscle and in blood. Without sufficient oxygen to reconvert it to glycogen, the concentration gradually increases and fatigue sets in. There is a limit to the size of the oxygen deficit that an individual can incur and, when this limit is reached, the exercise must stop.

After the completion of the exercise respiration continues to be more rapid and deep than usual until the deficit is paid off.

MUSCULAR EFFICIENCY IN EXERCISE

There are certain ways of doing things that are more efficient than others, ways that waste the least amount of energy possible. We can define the *efficiency* of any machine or organism doing work as the *proportion of useful work done to the total energy used* in the operation.

As you might expect, neither muscle nor machine is ever 100 per cent efficient. Muscle efficiency compares very favorably, however, to even the best of man-made machines. Steam engines have a range of efficiency from $7\frac{1}{2}$ to 19%, gas engines from 14 to 28%, and Diesel engines from 29 to 35%. The human body (especially its muscles, of course) is from 0 to 25% efficient.

The usual and best all-round method for measuring efficiency is to have the subject breathe in air from the atmosphere and to expire it into a portable bag during the time he is doing work. A set of valves in the tubing connecting the mouthpiece with the bag allows for this method of breathing and collection. After the test period, the gas volume is measured and its contents are analyzed for the respiratory gases. It can then be calculated that a certain amount of oxygen was consumed. It is known that oxidation involving a unit of oxygen can perform a definite amount of work. The oxygen consumed can thus be converted into units of work. Dividing this value into the work done, which is measured directly, we arrive at the efficiency.

What factors modify or influence the efficiency of a muscular act? There are five important ones—the initial stretch of the muscles, temperature, the viscosity of the muscles, the speed of performance, and fatigue.

We have already noted that stretching a muscle before it contracts enables it to contract more forcibly. A stretched muscle can, therefore, perform more work than one only normally relaxed. We can prove this point rather simply with an isolated muscle preparation. Stimulating such a muscle loaded with progressively heavier weights, we record the successive heights of contraction. We find that the heights decrease as the load increases in weight (Fig. 140). But, when we measure the work done (work here being equivalent to the weight lifted times the distance lifted), we discover that more work was done in lifting moderately heavy weights than in lifting

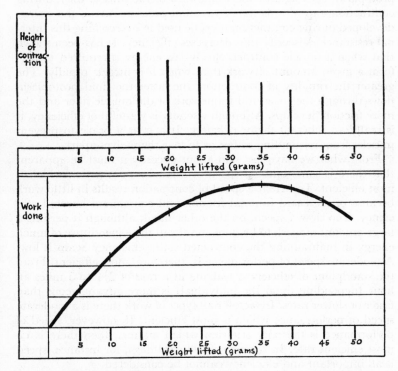

FIG. 140—The heights to which a muscle contracts when weighted with progressively heavier loads, and the work done by such contractions.

lighter or heavier ones. Thus, moderately loading a muscle is the most efficient way of getting the most work done. When not stretched enough, the muscle is not very efficient; when stretched too much (beyond the limits of its elasticity), its efficiency is impaired. The windup a baseball pitcher makes before he throws may serve to stretch muscles and make them more efficient.

A rise in temperature speeds metabolic processes. Since muscular contraction depends upon chemical reactions, it is quickened in all phases by an increased temperature. All phases of the contraction process are accelerated—the latent period shortens, both the rapidity and effectiveness of contraction are increased, the relaxation period is especially shortened, and the recovery period is also decreased in duration. The benefits of "warming up" for athletic events are mainly due to the increased temperature in the muscles.

By viscosity is meant internal friction, the friction resulting when molecules rub against one another. The viscous fluid part of muscle protoplasm rubs against the framework of the muscle fiber during contraction and retards the contraction process. Part of the energy developed during contraction must be used in overcoming this internal resistance. Viscosity thus decreases efficiency. It has been shown that when a muscle contracts slowly less energy is required to perform a given amount of work than when it contracts rapidly. The greater the rapidity of contraction, the faster the fluid protoplasm flows through the structural framework of the muscle fiber and the more friction develops. Although viscosity is wasteful of efficiency, it is really an inherent factor of safety. It acts as a brake to prevent muscles from responding so fast as to tear themselves apart.

From what we have just said about viscosity it must be apparent that there is some optimal speed of muscular contraction which is most efficient. Too great a speed of contraction results in little work because of increased internal friction and consequent lowered efficiency. Too slow a speed, on the other hand, although it permits a large amount of work to be done, results in the expenditure of much energy in maintaining the contracted state; efficiency again is low. A moderate speed of performance is, therefore, most efficient. From the standpoint of efficiency, walking at a rate of $2\frac{1}{4}$ to 3 miles an hour (depending upon the individual) is more advantageous than faster or slower rates. In fact, for all types of work there is a moderate speed of performance which is most efficient. If, however, speed of performance is the only criterion which matters, then there is no most efficient rate. In running a 100-yard dash, for instance, speed is all important and efficiency cannot be considered.

It is rather obvious that the more fatigued a muscle is, the less efficient it will be. This is largely a matter of how much of an oxygen deficit can be built up by an individual. It depends not only on the character of his muscles but also on the development of his circulatory and respiratory mechanisms.

From almost every standpoint we are led to the conclusion that moderation in activity is a good principle to follow. Unless you are trying to set a new speed record, moderate activity is more efficient, for it wastes less energy and gets more work done. It is now being recognized that driving a man at his work to the point of exhaustion is not practical with regard to the health of the individual nor with respect to getting more and better work done.

THE EFFECTS OF TRAINING

You know from your own experience and observation that a trained individual is generally more efficient in the performance of his specialty than an untrained one. How does training influence efficiency?

In training for muscular performance an individual builds up his muscles to a larger bulk. This is accomplished by an increase in the size of the individual fibers rather than by an increase in the number of fibers. The larger muscles are capable of doing more work.

Many of the benefits of physical training are due to the changes brought about in the circulatory and respiratory systems. The heart of a trained individual is somewhat larger than that of an untrained one. The trained heart can beat more forcibly than the untrained and generally beats at a slower rate for the same amount of activity. This is a more efficient way of increasing the cardiac output than by depending to a greater degree on an increased rate. Respiratory effects are somewhat similar—the trained individual breathes more deeply and less rapidly than the untrained. The increase in vital capacity that results makes for a greater and more economical ventilation of the lungs.

The greater efficiency of circulatory and respiratory systems enables oxygen to be transported to active muscles more rapidly and wastes to be removed more quickly. The increased efficiency means that for a given amount of work a smaller oxygen deficit will be incurred—more lactic acid will be oxidized and reconverted to glycogen during activity than in the untrained subject. It also means that a greater oxygen deficit can be incurred, so that the trained person can work harder and longer without fatiguing. He will also be able to recover more quickly from the effects of exertion than the untrained person.

Much of the increased efficiency is due to the increase in coördination and sureness of performance that training develops. These effects depend upon the central nervous system. Repetition of acts makes them more and more reflex in nature (conditioned reflexes are implied here) and that in itself improves their coördination. The untrained subject will stumble, both mentally and physically, more often than the trained. The increased confidence that better performance brings with it, plus the increased coördination, will result in economical and efficient activity.

Though not all of us have the desire to emulate the prowess of the trained athlete, we can, knowing that it is largely a matter of training, increase our own efficiency for the perhaps less-strenuous tasks we have to do. Moderate and consistent exercise, aside from making us feel better, can help our bodies to become more adequate for the demands placed upon them.

CHAPTER XIX

Fatigue, Rest, and Sleep

THE INTERRELATED phenomena of fatigue and rest are of great interest and importance. Man has pondered over them ever since ancient times, yet certain questions still remain enigmatic. We can partially understand how a particular organ or system should fatigue. But why should we require rest even after all the nutrients necessary for recovery of the parts of the body have been supplied? Why can't we go without sleep for more than a few days? Why do some individuals need more sleep than others? What brings on sleep? To some of these questions we have only vague answers while for others we have at least partial answers.

FATIGUE

Almost any part of an animal organism will fatigue if its activity is prolonged. How long it will take for fatigue to occur will depend on the special characteristics of the tissues involved, how well they are supplied with oxygen and necessary nutrients by the blood, how quickly the waste products of their metabolism are removed, how much of a store of fuel substances they have, and the physiochemical state of their immediate environment. In other words, the maintenance of activity and delay of fatigue are dependent upon the physiological fitness of the tissues themselves and of the body in general.

Fatigue has a very definite value for the tissues and for us. It prevents us from continuing activity to the point of excessive breakdown of tissue, tissue which may or may not be replaceable. We find, therefore, that the more valuable tissues either fatigue very quickly from repeated activity or possess inherent mechanisms of various sorts which largely prevent fatigue from occurring over a wide range of circumstances.

In general, the tissues that have high metabolic rates fatigue most quickly. Thus, the central nervous system fatigues very rapidly when made to work excessively. Nerve, muscle, and the outlying portions of the autonomic nervous system fatigue more slowly if at all.

We have most information about fatigue of skeletal muscle. There it definitely seems to be caused by the accumulation of metabolic waste products such as lactic acid. Too high a concentration of lactic acid depresses the irritability and contractility of muscle and may abolish both. With a decrease in the concentration, muscle becomes irritable and contractile once more. We know, too, that lactic acid accumulates because of an insufficiency of oxygen. If the oxygen supply keeps pace with the production of lactic acid there is no building up of lactic acid concentration. Part of the acid formed is oxidized and the resultant energy is used to convert the remainder to glycogen.

How an increased lactic acid or other waste product concentration depresses or abolishes contractile activity is, at present, an unanswered question. We just do not know enough of the cellular metabolism in muscle to give a good reason. This same incompleteness of knowledge prevents us from understanding fatigue in other organs and tissues.

It may be that lactic acid released from active muscles is carried in the blood to other organs and brings on fatigue of them, too. Cardiac muscle is also depressed by too great an increase in lactic acid concentration. Of course, cardiac muscle produces lactic acid in its own metabolic activity and, when skeletal muscle is more active, the heart is also. Enough lactic acid may, therefore, be produced locally in the heart muscle to account for depression. But lactic acid and other metabolic acids (of which there are many) may affect the irritability of central nervous tissue sufficiently to fatigue it.

The heart, as we know, is not easily subject to fatigue because of its long refractory period. The latter gives it enough of a respite between contractions to forestall the rapid onset of fatigue by permitting the constructive metabolic processes to balance the destructive ones. Nerve is relatively indefatigable because of its refractory period. Even though it is brief, the refractory period allows enough time for processes of repair and recovery to maintain nerve in an irritable state.

We have noted that the synaptic regions of neurons have no refractory period. Continued elicitation of reflex or voluntary acts can, therefore, relatively easily fatigue those junctions. What brings on fatigue at these sites has not been established.

Other non-irritable tissues can fatigue. We usually think of these as being exhausted by too great usage. For instance, a gland can be made to stop secreting by stimulating it to a prolonged period of activity. The red bone marrow may stop producing red blood cells when overworked. In cases like these, the cause of exhaustion is partly due to reduced or completely depleted supplies for the elaboration of the particular product that the tissue produces. There may be, and probably are, other metabolic effects that contribute to the condition.

What produces the feeling of weariness after strenuous activity is another unsolved problem. The impact of the change in bodily conditions upon the nervous system undoubtedly is an important factor. Emotional and purely mental processes can decidedly influence the condition for better or for worse.

REST AND SLEEP

When we are tired, we have an urge to sleep or, at least, rest. There is definite survival value in rest and sleep. Without them we cannot go on for very long. Animals have been known to die after fourteen or more days of sleeplessness. Examination of the brains of these animals revealed shrinkage and other changes in neurons of the cerebral cortex.

How long human beings can remain awake without suffering fatal effects is not known. Self-inflicted wakefulness for nearly five days has been carried out by some scientists. They found it extremely difficult to remain awake after the first few days, the only possible means being to keep some muscles active. There were evidences of increasing neuromuscular fatigue, as we should expect. Tempers became sharp, and subjects were annoyed and irritated by trifling incidents. Otherwise there did not appear to be any ill effects.

Short periods of rest definitely allow for the recuperation of fatigued tissues. But why is it necessary that we sleep as long as most of us find it necessary to do? If it is merely for the sake of replenishing vigor and recovering from the breakdown processes that go on during wakefulness, we should expect to rise from sleep very much refreshed and able to work at maximal capacity. Yet experiments have shown that maximal performance of skilled tasks does not occur just after rising but much later in the day (in the afternoon for a person sleeping at night and rising fairly early in the morning).

Another perplexing aspect is that sleep does not necessarily follow only after fatigue. We can fall asleep when not at all fatigued. Is there any value in such sleep? In an attempt to gain a better understanding of the problems that the sleep process brings to light, let us examine some of the things that occur during sleep and some of the theories proposed as explanations.

Changes During Sleep. During sleep many of the body's activities are reduced to their lowest levels. The heart rate slows, the blood pressure drops, and respiration becomes slower and more irregular. The metabolic rate is lower than at any other time principally because muscle activity is also at its lowest level. Along with this there is usually a slight fall in body temperature and some depression of the heat-regulating mechanisms.

The thresholds for receptors are raised and stronger stimuli are needed to arouse sensations and most reflexes. Some of the enteroceptive reflexes, such as the circulatory ones, are actually elicited more easily.

Tear and salivary secretions are decreased, but sweat secretion is increased considerably. The secretion of gastric juice is not changed greatly. Stomach contractions and digestion continue normally.

The depth of sleep varies considerably, generally being deepest toward the end of the first hour. It lightens after that—quickly at first, gradually later—until waking time. In deep sleep no dreams occur and movements are at a minimum. Dreams occur most often just before waking and, if they are exciting (nightmares, etc.), may result in changes opposite to those usually occurring in sleep—fast heart rate, high blood pressure, accelerated respiration, inhibition of gastric motility, etc.

Theories of Sleep. Since the time of the ancient Greeks men have speculated as to the nature of sleep. Some of the proposed theories are fantastic, others are based on incomplete evidence. Some are plausible, but only one is a comprehensive attempt to arrange as many of the known facts as possible into a scheme that gives promise of future confirmation.

According to one theory, sleep was due to fatigue of the vasoconstrictor center, vasodilation of the skin vessels resulting. This diverted blood from the brain, and the decrease in cerebral blood flow initiated sleep. Subsequently, however, it was shown that blood flow to the brain is not decreased in sleep.

A group of theories have centered about the production of chemical substances which induced sleep. Some believed fatigue products like lactic acid were responsible. The accumulation of these substances during the activity of the day gradually built up their concentration in the blood to the point at which they induced loss of consciousness an 1 sleep. But serious objections to such theories have been raised—sleep can occur without preceding fatigue or may not occur even though considerable fatigue has developed.

It has been known that lesions in the hypothalamus of man often result in excessive sleep in patients so affected. Stimulation of a region of the hypothalamus was tried and claims reported that sleep was induced in experimental animals by this procedure. Later work showed that, although there was a center in the hypothalamus concerned with sleep and wakefulness, it was not a *sleep center*. That is, stimulation of this center did not cause sleep. Destruction of the center brought on bouts of prolonged sleep. The center is more correctly, then, a *waking center*. We shall shortly see the possible significance of this center.

The eminent Russian physiologist, Pavlov, as the result of his work on conditioned reflexes, formulated the theory that sleep is the result of an inhibitory conditioned reflex. Repeated monotonous stimulation set up such a reflex, and the inhibition of activity of a part of the cerebral cortex spread to the rest of the cerebral cortex and to the rest of the brain. Although there are points in favor of this theory, it does not account for the important fact that sleep can and does occur in the absence of the cerebral cortex. A dog deprived of its cerebral cortex will sleep most of the day, in fact.

Certainly the cerebral cortex is involved, for sleep involves the loss of consciousness and, therefore, of cortical activity. It is also definite that the brain stem is involved. Dr. Kleitman of the University of Chicago has made the most comprehensive attempt to show the interrelationships of the mass of data collected on sleep and wakefulness.

We know now that it is more accurate to say that a center in the *reticular formation* of the brain stem is the true waking center. The reticular formation receives collateral branches from all of the ascending sensory pathways. The many sensory impulses flooding this region cause it to discharge impulses upward to the thalamus. Unlike the situation in which activity of a specific sensory pathway causes the thalamus to discharge to a specific sensory area in the cerebral cortex, impulses from the reticular formation cause the thalamus to discharge diffusely to all cortical areas. When a sufficient number of this kind of thalamic impulses reach cortical levels, the neurons of the cortex are activated—causing the individual to exhibit wakeful, conscious behavior. Any marked reduction in this special flow of upward impulses or any marked tendency towards monotony of stimulation will usher in a condition of sleep.

An objective index of sleeping vs. waking states is the EEG of the cerebral cortex. Fig. 130 is a representation of the wakeful EEG. In a sleeping man or animal, the waves in the EEG become slower and larger than those in Fig. 130 (actually, a number of different patterns can be seen which quite accurately relate to stages or depths of the sleeping state). Experimentally it can be shown that stimulation of the reticular activating system in a sleeping animal can quickly convert the EEG from a sleeping to a wakeful pattern, and that this is soon followed by the typical waking activities of the animal. Furthermore, if the brain stem of an experimental animal is severed in the midbrain region, the cortical EEG remains permanently in a sleep-like pattern.

Of the many ascending impulses that reach the reticular formation, those from proprioceptors of muscles and tendons seem most effective in keeping us aroused and wakeful. Impulses from other types of receptors, if insistent enough, also keep us wakeful but, by and large, the best way to remain awake is to foster muscular activity. There seems to be no authentic documentation of anyone being able to sleep while standing unsupported.

It is also known that sensory impulse patterns of a very homogeneous nature (resulting from monotonous or boring circumstances) are conducive to sleep. Thus, not only is it necessary for a sufficient number of impulses to bombard the reticular formation but, for keeping alert and awake, it is best that there be heterogeneous sensory stimulation.

There is an evolutionary aspect to Kleitman's hypothesizing. He claims that sleep, rather than wakefulness, may be the "natural" state. If we think back to the animals lower than man, we note that most of them sleep a good part of each day. They do not, however, have one long period of sleep and remain awake for the rest of the day. Instead they have shorter and numerous periods of sleep scattered throughout the day. In an animal like the rabbit, periods of wakefulness are devoted to satisfying basic needs and desires such as hunger, thirst, excretion of wastes, sexual instincts, and so on. Apparently a rabbit is kept awake only by very urgent sensations or emotions. The type of wakefulness produced in this manner Kleitman calls "wakefulness of necessity."

As the cerebral cortex develops to a greater extent in somewhat higher mammals, another type of wakefulness is introduced—"wakefulness of choice." Such animals take a greater interest in their environment and indulge in other forms of activity than satisfying their basic desires. They learn to play, for instance, among other things. Rats and mice, dogs and cats are examples of such animals. Although they still sleep several times during a day, the proportion of wakefulness to sleep increases.

In still higher animals—monkeys, apes, and finally man—wakefulness of choice becomes increasingly important. The development of the mental processes gives them the opportunity to do many more things than satisfying desires and needs. In man this culminates in spending most of the day awake and having one main sleeping period.

The diurnal sleep rhythm in man is established as the result of conditioning. Children are taught, as they grow older, to sleep at night. They are put to bed at a certain time; the room is darkened and made quiet. With repetition, the approach of the hour of usual retirement induces a feeling of sleepiness. A conditioned reflex is established.

As confirmation of this evolutionary viewpoint we find that a dog without cerebral cortices reverts to a more primitive state with respect to sleep. It sleeps most of the day, only waking when it needs to urinate or is hungry, etc. Also, the human infant (whose cerebral cortex does not function very well at birth) sleeps the greater portion of the day and has many sleep periods which have no relation to day or night. Through conditioning the infant is taught to sleep more and more at night. The diurnal sleep rhythm is gradually developed.

Kleitman's hypothesis seems to have much in its favor and should lead to further experimentation. In time, then, we may learn the complete answer to a problem that has bewildered man for so many centuries.

CHAPTER XX

Coordination of Bodily Functions

IF THERE were no mechanisms for the interaction and coördination of activities, an organism would be at most an extremely loose union of almost independent parts and probably could not exist. One aspect of evolution has been the ever-increasing efficiency of coördinating agencies in the life processes of an animal. The higher animals are, therefore, more closely knit organisms, better equipped for survival as individuals and presumably able to get more out of life than their predecessors.

There have been many instances in preceding chapters in which we have noted the coördinating influences of the nervous system, the endocrine glands, and chemicals other than hormones. There is, in fact, no system or activity of our bodies that is not affected by at least one, and probably more, of these coördinating agencies.

The interplay of various factors modifies the rate at which the food we eat is digested, the speed with which it is made directly useful to the body, the efficiency with which its wastes are removed. The body is a delicate mechanism made up of many physiological balances and counterbalances; the active equilibrium of its many parts must be maintained for effective functioning.

Cells must have their proper supply of nutrients and be able to make use of them. So, out of the many substances found in the body, just the right environment must be created and maintained.

COORDINATION AND BALANCE OF FOODSTUFF METABOLISM

The general metabolic rate will, of course, influence the metabolism of the individual foodstuffs. Conversely, the metabolism of the foodstuffs will influence the general metabolic rate—how much of the foodstuffs is being burned at any given moment will determine to a large extent at what level the metabolic rate will stand. In other words, nutrition of the individual and the extent of his activity play important roles in the regulation of metabolism. Internal factors also play important roles. For example, the thyroid hormone controls the oxidation rate of all of the body's cells, and this hormone in turn is controlled by the anterior pituitary's thyrotropic hormone.

Carbohydrate Balance. Once carbohydrates have been digested to simple sugars and absorbed as such, a number of checks and balances contrive to maintain a constant level of sugar in the blood. Carbohydrate is not stored in the body as sugar but rather as glycogen, to which sugar is readily converted and vice versa. The main reserves of this compound sugar are found in the liver and in muscles. Starting from the liver, glycogen is broken down to glucose which is released into the blood. Glucose travels to muscle where it may be reconverted to glycogen or used somewhat more directly. Breakdown of glycogen or of sugar in muscle may produce lactic acid. Some of the lactic acid may be reconverted to pyruvic acid and oxidized, but most of it is poured into the blood. When it reaches the liver, lactic acid is changed over to glycogen. The cycle is then ready to begin anew. The control of how much sugar is released from the liver, returned to the liver, stored as glycogen, or oxidized by the tissues is the function of a variety of endocrine and nervous factors. As a result of this control the level of blood sugar is kept approximately constant.

Insulin, the pancreatic hormone, very possibly maintains at proper levels the store of glycogen in the liver and in muscle, and also aids in the oxidation of glucose in the normal animal. Insulin deficiency results in a high blood sugar level due to three possible causes—an abnormally increased formation of liver glycogen and conversion to glucose, a decreased storing of glucose as muscle glycogen, or a decreased oxidation of sugar by the tissues.

Removal of the pituitary's anterior lobe relieves the symptoms of diabetic animals and enables them to survive for long periods without administration of insulin. On the other hand, injection of large amounts of anterior lobe extract can induce a severe diabetic condition in previously normal animals. Both of these effects can be explained by granting that the anterior lobe itself and/or its influence on other glands (via ACTH and TSH—see Chapter XI) yields a hormone or hormones which oppose(s) the actions of insulin. Thus, while insulin works to lower blood sugar levels, other major hormones tend to raise this level. A diabetic animal, because of the absence of insulin, is suffering from severe overproduction of sugar in the body under the influence of the other hormones still present; if one or more of the latter are removed from the scene (as by anterior lobe excision), the diabetic state should be improved. It is noteworthy that adrenalectomy also ameliorates diabetic symptoms; the adreno-cortical hormone, cortisone, opposes the action of insulin in ways comparable to that of pituitary influences.

The presence of excess pituitary hormones in an otherwise normal animal raises the blood sugar level. As you will recall, a rise in blood glucose normally stimulates increased insulin secretion in the pancreas. Thus, if the pituitary excess is maintained, the islet tissue of the pancreas is continually forced to secrete greater than normal amounts of insulin; eventually, the islet tissue breaks down under the stress, and the animal becomes permanently diabetic.

The adrenal cortex and anterior pituitary most probably counter-act insulin influences by causing the overproduction of glucose and also the reduced tissue utilization of this substance. Thyroid hormone opposes insulin function, as does adrenaline (the latter by promoting breakdown of liver and muscle glycogen). The influences of these latter two hormones are, however, not as profound as those men-tioned above.

Whether there is any direct influence of the nervous system on cellular metabolism, per se, is a moot question. There is, however, ample evidence of indirect influence via nervous control of the adrenal medulla and the pituitary gland.

Protein and Fat Balance. The major hormones are not only important in regulating carbohydrate balance; without doubt they are just as important in regulating fat and protein mobilization, levels, and utilization. This system of checks and balances is, how-ever, not yet as well understood as that for carbohydrates.

COORDINATION OF SALT AND WATER BALANCE

In discussing the balance of any of the chemical constituents of the body, it is rather obvious that a great deal depends on how much of that constituent is ingested and how much leaves the body. Intake is, of course, largely a voluntary act, so that there is no strict control over it. In times of stress our bodies do indicate a need for certain items. For example, the sensation of thirst is aroused when the body has too little water. The degree of intake, however, is too often dic-taged by emotional satisfaction rather than by basic requirements. In terms of unconscious, automatic controls, output can be regulated with more precision than can intake.

Hunger pangs also are a warning that more food is needed. The pangs themselves do not give us an urge to eat specific things, but there are authentic reports that a specific deficiency can give rise to a craving for a specific foodstuff. For instance, there are cases of craving for fat and for salt when those nutrients are deficient in the body. Feeding experiments on rats have shown that these animals select from an array of foods set before them those that are most suited to their bodily condition at the moment. We should not, however, place too great a reliance on this mechanism as a safety factor in man. Intelligent planning of a well-balanced diet is still a wise procedure, since we are too often ruled by appetite rather than by hunger.

Water Balance. Our sources of body water are the liquids we drink, the water present in the "solid" foods we eat, and the water released by cellular chemical reactions. Water is lost from the body especially in the urine, but also in the feces, expired air, and sweat. These latter losses are regulated, for the most part, by environmental factors beyond the control of the body. In a hot environment large amounts of water and salt can be lost in sweat. (This may be so severe as to induce *heat cramps* in the muscles. Drinking salt water is the best treatment or prevention of this condition.)

For over-all maintenance of as constant as possible a level of body water we rely upon the work of the kidneys. In general, the amount of water loss in the urine will vary directly with the blood water concentration: if the latter is high, there is copious urine excretion, and vice versa. There is, of course, a lower limiting value as some water must be excreted each day to accompany the solids dissolved in the blood.

The volume of urine excreted depends upon two major factors: the blood pressure in the glomerular capillaries, and the extent of reabsorption of water in the renal tubules. Any rise in arterial blood pressure will usually be reflected in a higher glomerular pressure and, therefore, a greater volume of filtrate in the nephrons; other conditions remaining static, this would result in increased urine volume.

Under most circumstances, however, the degree to which water is reabsorbed is the more important influence on urine volume. The greater the concentration of unreabsorbable dissolved substances within the nephrons, the less water will be reabsorbed. (This is because the higher osmotic pressure within the nephron prevents passive osmosis of water into the blood.) The greater the concentration of dissolved substances in blood, the more water will be reabsorbed; in this case, the increased osmotic pressure of blood signals forth greater release of antidiuretic hormone from the posterior pituitary, and consequently there is greater reabsorption of water.

The thyroid and sex hormones also influence water balance but their mechanisms of action are not well understood.

Salt Balance. This must really be considered hand in hand with water balance, for any significant change in salt concentration will, because of altered osmotic relationships, promptly cause shifts in water distribution. The two major influences on salts as such are aldosterone and parathyroid hormone. Aldosterone, the adreno-cortical hormone, vitally regulates sodium and potassium levels throughout the body by regulating reabsorption of these ions in the kidneys. Parathyroid hormone controls calcium and phosphate level in body fluids primarily by regulating the equilibrium of calcium salts between bone and blood and by regulating excretion of phosphate ions in the urine. Vitamin D also aids in maintaining these levels by promoting proper absorption of calcium and phosphate by the intestinal mucosa.

COORDINATION OF THE ACTIVITIES OF THE BODY

Although we have yet to complete our understanding of the exact mechanisms by which all acts of coördination and integration are accomplished, some of the main outlines in this field are well established. When rapid adjustment to a change in internal or external circumstances is imperative, nerve impulses race over reflex arcs and a relatively prompt response ensues. Adjustments of this kind involve the acceleration of some processes, the inhibition of others. When only a relatively slow adjustment need be made, chemical mechanisms are brought into play. These are most often changes in metabolic state and will take more time to complete.

We cannot make any hard-and-fast rule about this, though, for almost never is one activity solely influenced by nervous or chemical factors. There is usually a fine correlation between these two, other factors entering as well. For instance, when food is ingested a chemical stimulus initiates the reflex response which starts it on its journey through the digestive tract. Along the way nervous, chemical, and mechanical factors are responsible for its being broken down, digested, and transported. Peristalsis is under reflex control but is usually initiated by a mechanical stimulus. Secretion of digestive juices is under the control of both nerve impulses and hormones.

Another prominent example is the coördination of endocrine secretions themselves. The pituitary gland (anterior lobe) plays a prominent part in bringing this about by its secretion of "tropic" hormones. These hormones regulate the amount of secretion of the thyroid, adrenal cortex, and gonadal hormones. Apparently coordination of these secretions results from their relative levels in the blood (see Chapter XI). Delicate balance is maintained and hormonal levels are continually shifted to meet new demands.

Even in the case of endocrine secretions, nervous influences help in coördination. Certain glands are definitely subject to nervous control. The adrenal medulla secretes adrenaline only in response to nerve impulses reaching it over sympathetic nerve fibers. The posterior lobe of the pituitary is under the control of the nerve tract coming to it from the hypothalamus. Many anterior pituitary functions are nervously initiated.

Indirect control of endocrine secretions is vested partly in the autonomic nervous system, too. Vasoconstrictor and vasodilator fibers run to the blood vessels in the glands. These vasomotor nerves help to control the amount of blood reaching the gland and the secretion of hormones depends upon substances brought to the gland cells by the blood.

Conversely, the nervous system itself does not function without the help of chemical coördinators. Throughout the central and peripheral divisions of the nervous system, chemical substances released at nerve endings are responsible for transmitting nerve impulses to the next neuron or effector unit. We have also seen that carbon dioxide directly stimulates centers in the brain (vasomotor, respiratory centers).

The integrating influence of chemical and nervous factors cannot be overestimated. In discussing the effects that go on in the body during exercise, we have seen that what might seem a bewildering number of activities are directed to a definite goal and, despite their diversity, achieve that goal.

The large number of physiological constants that we have discussed—the number of red blood cells, the blood sugar level, the body temperature, etc.—can only remain stable by the preservation of equal rates of activity in the constructive and destructive processes at work "behind the scenes." The maintenance of equality in rates of activity is the function of the coördinating agents that synchronize these processes. Yet these same agents must be flexible and allow one or another process to outstrip its antagonist if that is in the interest of the body at a particular moment.

From confusion and anarchy of parts and processes the coördinators of the body produce a unified organism capable of meeting and overcoming most of the natural challenges of life.

CHAPTER XXI

Protection against Disease

WHEN we hear of the many ways in which something can go wrong with the "machinery" of our bodies, we are perhaps amazed that so many people are healthy. You may ask, "How can so delicately attuned a machine as man resist periodic, if not fatal, breakdown?" It is true that the body contains many delicate parts and that normal function often appears to be separated from malfunction by a hairbreadth. At the same time we should realize that the body has amazing capacities for resisting breakdown or counteracting the invasion of a disease-bearing organism. We shall be particularly interested in this latter process.

THE FIRST LINE OF DEFENSE

An infectious organism finds it relatively difficult to enter the body. Over most of the body surface the *skin* affords a protective barrier of great impenetrability. Its outer portion is composed of stratified epithelium whose outer layers contain only dead cells. As cells die they are continually being pushed upward by the multiplication of the living cells beneath them and the top ones are shed. These dead cells form a rather horny tissue which effectively excludes bacteria unless broken at some point.

If the organisms enter the oral or nasal cavities, they must penetrate the mucous membranes lining those cavities to get into the underlying tissues. Many of them are trapped in the mucous secretions which cover the surface of the membranes. Should they travel down into the pharynx and then into the trachea, not only the membranes and mucus bar their way but also the waving cilia which tend to sweep them toward the outside again. Or should they enter the esophagus and abdominal parts of the digestive tract, they are plunged into the very acid stomach contents. The acid is deadly poison for most bacteria. Even if they survive the acid, very few are able to penetrate the mucous membranes further down the digestive tract. Those that reach the lower regions of the tract are eliminated in the feces.

THE INNER DEFENSES

When the outer defenses are breached and bacteria invade the underlying tissues, they must surmount other lines of defense if they are to live and multiply.

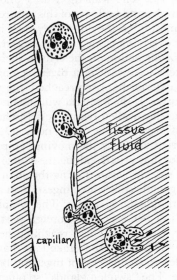

FIG. 141—A neutrophil "crawling" into the tissue spaces and ingesting bacteria.

When bacteria are able to get below the skin, they must travel through other tissue before they can enter the blood stream. Generally they are unable to progress this far, for processes are set into motion which tend to localize the infection. As if drawn by invisible strings, *neutrophils* (also some monocytes) are very quickly attracted to the infected area. Squeezing between the cells of the capillary walls (Fig. 141), these white blood cells progress by amoeboid motion into the tissue spaces and begin to ingest the bacteria.

They are aided in their efforts by the production of *inflammation* in the region. The capillaries in the infected area dilate. The dilation is due to toxic substances liberated by the bacteria or to chemical substances having vasodilator action liberated from tissue cells killed by the bacterial poisons. The capillary dilation allows more than usual amounts of plasma to filter out into the tissue spaces. The plasma, of course, contains all the essential elements for clotting except thrombokinase, and the latter is liberated from the destroyed tissue cells. The fluid clots and a ring of coagulated material surrounds the invaded region. Some time later connective tissue grows around the area which becomes completely walled in. Until this happens, the danger of a spread of infection is always present.

Within the inflamed region a veritable fight to the death is being waged by the neutrophils and bacteria. Many on both sides are killed. The dead bacteria, dead leucocytes, disintegrated tissue cells, and fluid constitute *pus*. The walled-off area and its contents are called an *abscess*. Pimples and boils are of this nature. If the body cells win the fight (and most often they do), they then hew a path to the outside through the overlying tissue. This is in part accomplished by exerting their phagocytic action on the cells in their path, in part by digestion of those cells by means of a digestive enzyme which they produce. When the exterior has been reached, the pus is discharged.

Lymphatic Defenses. If the bacteria win the first round of battle, they may invade the thin-walled lymph vessels which are extremely numerous in almost every region of the body. Once in the lymph vessels they are carried along by the moving lymph.

You will remember that situated along the course of the lymph vessels are many *lymph nodes* or *glands*. Lining the channels in the lymph nodes are large phagocytic cells which ingest in an amoeboid fashion bacteria passing through the channels. The lymph nodes are very effective "strainers" of bacteria or of foreign particles of any kind and may effectively bottle up bacteria reaching them.

Rather frequently their task is so tremendous that the nodes themselves become swollen in the process of ingesting bacteria. They are then rather sensitive. The "swollen glands" so often characteristic of a "sore throat" are swollen lymph glands.

The *tonsils* and *adenoids* are lymphoid tissues situated in the pharyngeal region. In a great many of us they lose their fight against infection, become highly infected and inflamed themselves, instead of protecting us, as normally happens. Then they have to be removed to prevent the spread of their bacterial contents to other more vital regions of the body.

Phagocytosis in the Blood. Bacteria that do enter the blood may suffer the same kind of fate that awaits most of them in the superficial regions of the body. The neutrophils in the blood stream are no less voracious than when outside it. They engulf bacteria as they meet them.

There are other large phagocytic cells which line the blood sinuses in the liver and spleen. For the most part these cells are fixed in position and cannot wander about. They still retain some amoeboid properties, however. As bacteria float near them in the blood, they stretch out pseudopods and ensnare the invaders (Fig. 142).

Other Blood Defenses. If all of the preceding defenses against the spread of bacteria have not eliminated them, there are agents in the blood that may do so. It is known that the introduction of any "foreign" protein (one not characteristic of the animal) into the blood causes the production of a substance which destroys that protein. The protein introduced is called an *antigen* and the substance that destroys it an *antibody*. One of the most remarkable aspects of this phenomenon is that the antibody is specific for the antigen introduced and will not attack any other foreign protein.

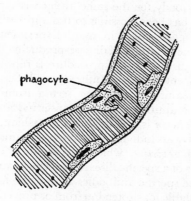

FIG. 142—Phagocytic cells lining a blood sinus. A cell is shown ingesting a bacterium in amoeboid fashion.

The introduction of any cells or their protein products, not peculiar to a particular species, into the blood of this species calls into play this antigen-antibody reaction. Recent evidence indicates that the thymus gland is the site of origin of antibodies, and that it contains certain cells—*plasma cells*—which house the antibodies at birth. Multiplication of the plasma cells and their migration to other parts of the body accounts for the widespread distribution of antibodies later in life. In some experimental animals, surgical removal of the thymus shortly after birth prevents them thereafter from resisting disease by antibody action.

The first time particular bacteria or their toxic products invade the blood an antibody may not be produced quickly enough to prevent disease from occurring. But, if the person recovers from the disease, it shows that the antibody has finally overcome the antigen. What is more, a second infection with the same bacteria may result in no repetition of the disease. The antibody has remained in the blood since the first time and the person is said to have acquired *immunity*. Such immunity may last a lifetime for certain diseases. For others it may last a number of years and for still others may only persist a very short time.

Of course, acquiring immunity by uncontrolled contact with disease-producing organisms is neither satisfactory nor desirable. But modern preventive medicine is evolving methods by which we can reduce the intensity or forestall the onset of an increasing number of diseases. In other words, with respect to certain diseases, it is now possible to impart immunity safely to a person for a period of one or more years.

Because the antibody for the same antigen is very similar in different animals, it has been possible to use antibodies elaborated by other animals to good effect in man. Experimental animals, injected with weakened cultures of disease-producing bacteria, develop mild cases of the disease. If the procedure is repeated a few times, a significant concentration of antibody will be present in such animals' bloodstreams. By injecting serum from this blood into human beings, the antibody can be transferred and immunity obtained. *Tetanus antitoxin* is obtained in this fashion.

More frequently, an individual is made immune by injections of small amounts of a *vaccine*, which is a solution containing killed bacteria or viruses of a specific disease. Vaccines cause the individual himself to produce specific antibodies against the foreign organisms. Vaccines are available for protection from or prevention of a number of infectious diseases, including *smallpox, diphtheria, typhoid fever, whooping cough, tetanus, cholera, yellow fever,* and *poliomyelitis*.

CHEMICAL TREATMENT OF DISEASE

For many years much research and effort has been devoted to the discovery and development of chemical substances which, when administered, would in some way prevent proliferation of infectious organisms without harming the body. The search was accelerated during World War II and has continued unabated since. There are now many chemical substances for the relief of various infectious diseases.

Sulfa Drugs. One class of such substances is exemplified by the *sulfa drugs*. These compounds slow down or prevent proliferation of certain disease organisms in the body by interfering with their metabolism. *Sulfanilamide* was the first of these drugs; other derivatives— including *sulfadiazene, sulfamerazine,* and *sulfathiazol*—are now widely used.

Antibiotics. The *antibiotics* are a group of substances produced by living organisms (certain molds and fungi have been the main sources) that are capable of destroying other organisms. *Penicillin*, the first antibiotic, has been followed by *streptomycin, aureomycin, chloromycetin, terramycin, erythromycin*, and *tetracycline*, among others. Each has certain advantages in combatting one or another disease organism.

Goals and Cautions concerning Chemical Treatment. Ideally, we would like to find a substance that specifically "knocks out" a particular disease organism without producing an ill effect in the human body. Sulfa drugs work rather specifically against the bacteria causing meningitis, and penicillin is particularly effective against organisms causing tetanus and diphtheria; but both also have widespread effectiveness against many other disease-producing organisms. The choice of a particular sulfa product or antibotic is determined by its over-all potency and by its relative freedom from side-effects on the body. Development of new substances is directed toward increasing potency and eliminating side-actions.

While chemical treatment has had on the whole a marvelous degree of success in the control of infectious diseases for which there are no other specific remedies, some reservations must be kept in mind. The ideal has not been completely realized. Some sulfa drugs are known to produce anemia, so that their excessive use may, in addition to controlling infection, bring on adverse consequences. Massive doses of antibiotics have been known to cause growth of molds in the body of the recipient. It has also been observed that certain infectious organisms develop strains resistant to a particular chemical and are no longer conquered by its use. It is wise, therefore, in order to achieve as uncomplicated and effective relief as possible, to use chemical treatment only in times of real need.

ALLERGY

Some of us are for some obscure reason overly sensitive to certain substances or conditions in our environment. Eating certain foods causes some of us to break out in rashes; others of us get hay fever, rose fever, asthma, or some such disturbance from the pollen or other parts of certain plants; still others are peculiarly sensitive to heat, cold, light, or other physical agents. In all of these cases the persons affected are said to be *allergic* to the substance or condition in question.

Allergies, antigen-antibody reactions, and the phenomena associated with transfusion of dissimilar blood into an individual all produce effects which have similarities to one another. They are all examples of bodily reactions to foreign substances or conditions. However, while antigen-antibody reactions and blood transfusion phenomena are common to all human beings, specific allergic reactions occur only in some individuals. For example, a certain protein in a particular food is harmless for the vast majority of people, yet it evidently gets into the blood of some people without first being digested and tends to bring on allergic symptoms in these individuals.

Probably most allergies are due to the reaction of the body to a foreign protein. But other *chemical* substances can be responsible as well. However, sensitivity to *physical* factors, such as dust, etc., although classed as allergy, may be due to different mechanisms of reaction in the body.

Many allergic reactions may result from the liberation of *histamine* or a like substance in the body. Histamine is known to dilate small blood vessels and make them more permeable. This could be responsible for such phenomena as skin eruptions and runny noses. Theoretically any substance that would inactivate histamine would prevent these symptoms (this is not a *cure* for the allergy, but merely symptomatic relief). A group of chemicals, the *anti-histamines*, does afford some people relief from allergic symptoms. That all persons are not relieved by such treatment indicates our incomplete knowledge of the basis of allergic reactions.

GENERAL DEFENSE AGAINST DISEASE

It is apparent that the more resistant the body is to disease, the more successful its bouts with foreign invaders will be. While many defenses will and do proceed despite hardships wrought upon them by lack of coöperation from the individual, some are weakened to such an extent by the general state of the body that their actions are feeble at best. A cold, for instance, is most effectively combatted by a body in good condition. Too little sleep or the wrong kind of food can increase the likelihood of catching a cold and can prolong its duration.

Things can sometimes go wrong in the body in spite of our efforts to prevent them simply because the human organism is such a complicated structure. But as we can see by the number of healthy individuals around us, much more often than not there are equally complicated and delicate protective devices that the body has to offer.

There is no doubt that we can aid the body's drive for self-preservation. A knowledge of how that drive manifests itself, particularly in fighting disease, has enabled medicine in many cases to know what to do when the body's defenses have been inadequate. Vaccination is only one of many methods used in aiding the body to defend itself. That knowledge should also enable us to keep our bodies in as resistant a condition as possible. We can know, for instance, that we should get proper rest, proper food, proper exercise; that we should not be careless about breaks in the skin, about sore throats, about dirt, about exposing ourselves to disease unnecessarily, and about the aches and pains that give us warning of something being wrong.

The body is inherently healthy in most cases and has its methods of remaining so. Healthy living will aid the body in its efforts.

CHAPTER XXII

The Health of the Body

THE NORMAL FUNCTIONING of any organism is the result of each of its parts doing the job for which it is responsible. More than that, each part must function as a cog in a larger unit, the organism itself. Before the arrival of man in the world, only those species and individuals which did function normally and vigorously had much chance for survival. The "laws" of life were ruthless in this respect—the weak and the misfits were given little opportunity to perpetuate themselves.

Those animals which survive today are, then, the more durable stock, those whose constitutions have been most suited to survival in the world they live in. Very few animals have a chance to live to a ripe old age, but while they are alive, their bodies are capable of responding in a healthy way to most of the demands that the environment may make.

Man is unique among animals in that he has the ability to change his natural environment. Much that has resulted from this ability has placed added handicaps in the way of living successfully and healthfully. Many people are crowded into unfit habitats, live in unsanitary conditions, receive improper nourishment, get too little sunlight, breathe in dirt and harmful gases, live too tensely and hurriedly. This is not meant to imply a plea for a "back to nature" movement. We cannot go backward, nor should we. Cities and factories are now part of our environment, evidence of our struggle to live long and well. This does not mean that we must put up with dirt, disease, and many other factors that contribute to improper functioning of our bodies. Medical science has made many wonderful advances, but it alone cannot create a healthy people. We have the power—the knowledge and the means—to prevent many types of malfunction and disease before they occur. We hope that in the near future men will give to others and to themselves the opportunities for the happiness that can result from healthy bodies.

CONSERVATION AND DISTRIBUTION OF ENERGY BY THE BODY

The body has a surprisingly large number of factors of safety. These factors make for a great saving in the energy costs of living and for the preservation of life. For instance, we have two kidneys but can get along with one. Under normal conditions, then, not all of the renal units are in use at any one time. Some are active now, some later. The alternation of use of the kidney tubules saves wear and tear on any one.

Most of our endocrine organs have more glandular tissue than is needed to maintain normal amounts of the hormones they secrete. If part of a gland is removed or destroyed, the rest of its tissue reacts by multiplying at a greater rate and, in time, will replace the tissue lost.

Except for the digestion of fat, we have more than one enzyme which is capable of breaking down ingested food into products that can be absorbed and used by the body. Thus, if the peptic activity of the stomach is impaired, the pancreatic and intestinal enzymes can adequately digest proteins. The abundance of enzymes normally active insures a greater division of labor among the gland cells secreting digestive enzymes.

There are many examples that might be mentioned, but the above will perhaps serve to illustrate. Other general activities insure an equitable distribution and sufficient production of usable energy. The metabolism of cells is so controlled and coördinated that, in general, just the amount of energy needed by the body is produced. This is not true in quantitative terms, of course, for we have seen that the efficiency of the body is only 25 per cent maximally; but, generally, all of the energy that can be used is used. The extra energy produced is converted to heat and not "wasted," since it is used in maintaining body temperature. The proper body temperature in turn allows the proper chemical reactions to proceed. Only those regions required to be especially active at a given moment are very active; other regions merely keep maintenance reactions going.

There is an elaborate mechanism for the delivery of energy-producing substances to regions in which they are needed. We have seen that the active region itself provides the impetus for a greater blood supply to itself. The body as a whole, through the nervous system, then sees to it that other regions tone down their demands.

There is a constant shuttling of metabolic essentials to and from cells as their needs vary. Energy is produced where and when needed; some is stored for future use (the foodstuff reserves) and the remainder is of use in the maintenance of body heat and metabolism.

STRENGTH AND WEAKNESS

A species or an organism is strong insofar as it can survive in its environment and weak insofar as it cannot. Though insects for the most part may be considered weak, their rate of breeding more than compensates for their other inadequacies. Some animals have a highly developed sense of smell, but lack the power to fight enemies successfully; others have great strength, but may lack the ability to run fast enough to escape danger. All animals that have managed to survive would seem, then, to have a measure of weakness and a measure of strength, the latter being predominant.

The highly developed brain of man is his unique claim to superiority in an evolutionary sense. Without the special characteristics furnished him by his nervous system, man would not be better suited for survival than many other animals; but with his highly coördinated nervous system, his brain, and his ability to think in terms of suiting his environment to himself, man has great potential strength. Particularly because of the endowments of his cerebral cortices, man is able to translate the constant stream of sensory information that he receives into more complex concepts than are possible for other animals. There is little doubt that this highly developed nervous superstructure results in greater subtleties and nuances of control of various activities of the body, and it also makes possible foresight and planning for the future to a degree not observable in other living things. Man's strength and capacity for survival are seen in his ability to conquer the land, the sea, and the air with his brain and hands.

The danger of injury to the nervous system, however, is man's greatest weakness; damage especially to the higher levels of the brain might well turn out to be catastrophic for the individual, as these organs of greatest specialization cannot be replaced if destroyed. However, the brain is well protected from physical injury by the skull, its blood supply is especially protected by the carotid sinus mechanism, and it receives essential materials preferentially in times of need. This fragile and all-important organ does not fail us without a struggle.

THE ORGANISM AS A WHOLE

In discussing the activities of the body we have selected this system or that process and dealt with each as a more or less isolated phenomenon. This has been necessary, of course, since it is a virtual impossibility to understand a complicated organism without knowing the details of the activities of its parts. However, nothing could be farther from the truth than a belief that any part or activity of the organism is independent of the rest.

We find that if we start to discuss the functions of any one system of the body we are inevitably forced to bring in all the other systems of the body. Each system is quite intimately related to and dependent upon all others. A man is not merely a union of organs, systems, and activities; he is a highly integrated individual whose every part or process is normally working toward the maintenance of his life and individuality.

When he receives a stimulus from his external or internal environment, the resulting response is not a simple, localized one. He responds as an organism and a variety of things occur in his many parts. Sometimes we are conscious of these many effects when the stimulus is sufficiently strong or surprising. At other times we are not aware that a realignment of forces has taken place in our "innards."

The day-to-day existence of an individual depends a great deal on the unconscious forces at work within him. They control his "destiny" at almost every point along the way, enabling him to do this but not that, coloring his mental attitude, helping to give rise to and influencing his emotions. If his metabolism or digestion or circulation is not normal, for instance, his will and desires and reasoning capacities cannot have free play. Yet much as the individual is dependent for existence and fullness of life upon his internal functions and capacities, they in turn are much influenced by the higher levels of activity that have been superimposed upon them during the long course of evolution and during the shorter span of his own life. In other words, one without the other is not capable of creating the organism we know as man.

In this sense "mind" and "body" are but two aspects of the same thing. One cannot exist without the other. The health of the body is the health of the mind and vice versa. Each has its proper place in the making of a healthy, normal individual.

THE ORGANISM AS A WHOLE

Throughout the activities of the body we have surveyed this system a concurrence and good will with part in a state of unresolved difference as another person.

APPENDIX

The Metric System

1 kilometer	= 1000 meters	= ⅝ of a mile (approx.)
1 meter (m.)	= 100 centimeters	= 39.36 inches
	= 1000 millimeters (mm.)	
1 centimeter (cm.)	= 10 millimeters	= 0.39 inches
1 liter (l.)	= 1000 milliliters (ml.)	= 1 quart (approx.)
	= 1000 cubic centimeters (cc.)	
1 cubic centimeter	= 1000 cubic millimeters	
1 kilogram (kg.)	= 1000 grams	= 2.2 pounds (approx.)
1 gram (g.)	= 1000 milligrams (mg.)	

Temperature

	Fahrenheit	Centigrade
Freezing point of water	32°	0°
Boiling point of water	212°	100°

To convert from Fahrenheit into Centigrade:
(Degrees Fahrenheit -32) $\times$ $^5/_9$ = Degrees Centigrade.

To convert from Centigrade into Fahrenheit:
(Degrees Centigrade $\times$ $^9/_5$) $+ 32$ = Degrees Fahrenheit.

INDEX

INDEX

Abdominal cavity, 4, 34–37
Absorption, 14, 118–20, 127–29
Acetylcholine, 140, 178
Acids, 18; in blood, 129–31, 226
Acromegaly, 230
ACTH, 229, 297
Action current, 145, 147
Active transport, 25, 120
Actomyosin, 145
Addison's disease, 223
Adenine base, 21–22, 262
Adenoids, 44, 81, 304
Adenosine, 147, 148
ADP, 147, 148, 259
Adrenal glands, 9, 37, 128, 212,
  221–25, 229, 284, 298, 300
Adrenaline, 221–23, 284, 298
Agglutinin, 52
Air, 88–90
Air-sacs, 6, 26, 84–85
Albumin, 46
Alcohol, 119, 129
Aldosterone, 224–25, 300
Alkalis, 18; in blood, 130–31
Allergy, 307–8
All-or-none response, 159, 169
Alveoli, 84, 85, 90–94, 276
Amino acids, 20, 104, 107, 119, 128,
  225, 227, 244–46, 257–58, 262-63;
  essential, 245
Ammonia, 128
Amoeba, 12–14, 27, 38, 83, 100, 122,
  137, 150, 232, 260, 275
Amoeboid movement, 13, 45, 275
Anatomy, defined, 1; microscopic, 33
Anemia, 42–44, 214, 249, 307
Anesthesia, 170
Antibiotics, 88, 306–7
Antibodies, 51–52, 81, 305–7
Antigen, 51–52, 305–7
Anus, 5, 116

Aorta, 53–54, 73, 74, 98
Aphasia, 211
Appendicitis, 121
Arms, 134, 135
Arteries, 5, 6, 52–54, 66–77
Arterioles, 66–68, 72–75 passim, 125,
  271–72, 282
Arteriosclerosis, 75, 131
Articulation of bones, 279–80
Artificial respiration, 88
Asphyxia, 169–70
Asthma, 223, 307
ATP, 147–48, 258–59
Auricles, 52–55, 58–60
Axons, 32, 33, 152–53, 164–65, 175–77,
  184

Backbone, 132
Bacteria, 88, 107, 116, 120, 302–7
Balance, chemical, 296–300
Bases, 18; in blood, 130–31
Basophils, 44
Bile, 105–6, 109–10
Bile pigments, 41, 105, 116, 121, 123
Biochemistry, defined, 82
Biology, defined, 1
Birth-control pills, 241–42
Bladder, 7, 37, 123–30 passim
Blood, 5–6, 38–52, 71–79, 90–95, 226,
  246, 300, 303–6
  acidity, 129–31, 226
  circulation time, 77–78, 283
  coagulation, 47–50, 246, 248
  and excretion, 123, 125, 126–29
  flow, 65, 76–79, 281, 292
  red cells, 6, 24, 40–44, 50, 266, 284,
    290–91
  and respiration, 90–94
  sugar in, 46–47, 225–27, 297–98
  types, 51–52, 307
  viscosity, 72